AMONG
FRIENDS

AMONG FRIENDS

L.R. Wright

Doubleday Canada Limited, Toronto, Ontario, Canada

DOUBLEDAY & COMPANY, INC.

GARDEN CITY, NEW YORK

1984

Library of Congress Cataloging in Publication Data
Wright, Laurali, 1939–
    Among friends.
    I. Title.
PR9199.3.W68A8   1984   813'.54
ISBN 0-385-18403-4
Library of Congress Catalog Card Number 82–45607

For John,
with love

ACKNOWLEDGMENTS

The author wishes to express her appreciation to Marti Wright and Dr. Peter Grantham for their helpful advice;

> and her gratitude
> to Johnna's Nicky,
> for comfort, companionship, and love
> during the writing of this book.

Grateful acknowledgment is made to anne mckay for permission to publish her poem.

. . . and i ran down the stair
holding my poem
like a star

        but no one was waiting
        no one was there

            anne mckay

LEONA

CHAPTER 1

It began as such an ordinary day.

When it was over she lay open-eyed in bed with borrowed pills dissolving inside her, irrevocably converted to the principle of mortality. Life seemed brief and dear indeed, at the end of that day. She was infinitely more vulnerable than she had imagined.

When it was over she lay on her back in her bed and knew that she would die, and for the first time thought about the when of it.

Which was a hell of a note, she thought, when a person was a mere thirty-three years old.

It had been an ordinary working day, in the middle of an ordinary November. It was cold and bleak in Calgary, although there was as yet no snow, and as she walked briskly to work Leona tried to summon August, tried to propel herself back into a hot day from her British Columbia childhood, scuffling barefoot down a dirt trail next to a strawberry field, tiny bursts of dust like small silent explosions issuing between her toes, strawberry bushes elderly with dust bordering the trail.

She walked quickly through incipient winter with swinging arms and challenging strides, her heavy black cape flapping in the wind, and when she entered the lobby of the Calgary *Star* building summer daydreams had faded and her ears ached and the tips of her fingers were numb.

She was a small, thin, quick-moving person with large dark eyes. She tried not to think much about the way she looked. She wasn't particularly offended by her appearance, but it disappointed her. There wasn't much there one way or another, she figured. She wasn't beautiful, and wasn't ugly. People didn't mind looking at her, but they wouldn't cross the street to do it.

In the women's washroom she clanged open the door to her locker and thrust her cape inside, to hang on one of the hooks. She took off her boots and put on the flat black shoes she wore around the newsroom in winter. From around the corner where the mirrors were she heard Gloria-Rose Merriwether, the newsroom receptionist, chattering like a starling to Bridget Walmsley, who wrote for the *Star*'s Lifestyles section. Leona didn't feel like joining them, so she stood by her locker and ran her fingers through her thick hair, which was brown with glints of red in it. She wore it short like a cap, got it trimmed every four weeks and used the blow-dryer after washing it every morning.

Her mouth was small and thin-lipped, her nose bony, and she thought her cheekbones ought to have been high and defined, but they weren't. Her cheeks were full, without even a dimple to make them interesting. A round-cheeked face upon a thin body didn't make any sense, she thought. But she liked her long-fingered hands, and enjoyed painting her nails, taking a long time about it, once a week or so.

On her desk she found two glossy photographs awaiting cutlines. She logged into the video display terminal she shared with Vern Palmer, whose desk was next to hers but who hadn't yet come in, and got to work.

Writing cutlines exasperated her. A photograph should either stand on its own, she thought, with perhaps just one identifying underline, or else it should accompany a story, in which case the reporter who wrote the story should also write the damn cutlines. She had expressed this opinion on many occasions, without any discernible effect. It was one of life's more tedious irritations that the city desk required its reporters to hastily compose, at eight o'clock in the morning, a few lines of lyrical, uplifting or humorous prose about photographs they had just that minute laid eyes upon.

One of the pictures was a file shot of a Chinook arch, a panoramic arc of clear sky above the mountains to the west whose appearance heralded a sudden and dramatic upsurge in temperature—a sweet sting of spring in the numbing cold of winter. Leona's cutlines tried to sound excited about the fact that one was bound to appear eventually. The other photograph showed a couple of giraffes at the zoo. "Giraffes at the zoo," Leona wanted to write, redundantly, but she confined herself to meaningless wistful burblings about a distant summer. She dealt with the pictures quickly and returned them to the city desk, where cries of mock gratitude caused her to grin despite herself.

As she sat down again, her phone rang.

"Newsroom," she said. "Leona Hadden."

"It's Marion," said a high, clear, composed voice. "Call me when you're ready to go down for coffee."

"I just got here," Leona protested. "It's only you editorial writers who go down for coffee all day long. Out here we've got work to do. Cutlines and things. Important stuff." She had a voice deeper than seemed credible in one so small and thin, and was frequently addressed as mister on the telephone, even when she had carefully articulated her first name.

"I've got some extremely interesting news," said Marion. "At least, it's interesting to me."

"Don't tell me," said Leona quickly. "Let me guess. Wait. I'm thinking." She scrunched her forehead and stared at her desk. "I know. Spot ate the mailman."

"Spot is the soul of gentleness, as you well know. Besides, the mailman doesn't come past the lobby."

"One more, okay? You're getting married."

Marion's laughter pealed through the phone. "Don't be ridiculous. It's no use. You'll have to wait. Call me when you can go downstairs," she said, and hung up.

Leona leaned back and lit a cigarette and contemplated her tidy desk. Her calendar was blank. She pulled out the notebook in which she kept a list of stories to do when nothing else was going on, and flipped through the pages. But she wasn't in the mood to write a feature story. She decided to make some phone calls, see if she could dig up something newsy from somebody.

"Leona, hey hey, you've already been at the goddamn machine."
Vern hooked his coat onto the rack that stood between two sets of
desks. "Don't tell me. Cutlines." He eyed her disapprovingly. He was
tall and balding, with an unlined face and a small paunch. There was
an air about him of innocent disreputableness. "I keep telling you.
Never get here on time." His full name, as it appeared in his byline,
was Vernon Titus Palmer. He said he used his middle name because it
inspired trust and confidence among his contacts.

"Tomorrow," Leona said to him, "be warned; any cutlines that get
dumped here, you're going to do them. It's your turn."

The assistant city editor approached them, clipboard in hand. "Well,
fellas? Whaddya got?"

"Jesus, Menzies, I just got here," said Vern, slumping into his chair.
"What day is it, anyway?"

"You're late," said the assistant city editor. "Again."

"I've got nothing," said Leona cheerfully. "Zilch. But I'll think of
something and let you know."

"If you haven't thought of something within an hour," said the
assistant city editor, "I'll give you—let's see." He checked the list on
his clipboard. "Flora McDonald's at the Canadian Club, how's that
grab you?"

Bruce Menzies was big and blond and Scandinavian-looking despite
his name, and Leona often had fantasies about him. But he was married, and she liked his wife. He gave her one of his deceptively gentle
smiles.

"Jesus," mumbled Vern, thumbing frantically through a dog-eared
stenographer's notebook. "Flora McDonald."

"Thanks anyhow," said Leona. "I'll come up with something."

"For today or tomorrow?"

"Oh God, Bruce," said Leona, exasperated. "I wrote two stories
yesterday and three more from last night's school board meeting, and
you know damn well you'll never get them all in today."

"That's true," said Bruce. "Who gives a shit."

She looked at him sharply, but gentleness continued to shine upon
his face. She decided he was still on the wagon.

He turned to Vern. "What about you?"

"Planning commission meeting," said Vern, beaming, tapping his notebook. "I knew there had to be something. It's Wednesday. Planning commission. Lots of good stuff. For tomorrow."

"I've got it all worked out, Leona."

They had managed to get a table by the window. After looking around for a couple of months, Marion had finally found a house she wanted to buy. This, it seemed, was her news.

She pushed their Styrofoam cups aside and put down a stained piece of paper covered with scrawled figures. Marion was exceptionally neat in her personal appearance, but every other outward aspect of her life was continually in messy chaos. Leona regarded Marion's jumble of an office, her food-spattered kitchen, her living room, strewn with dog hair, with a mixture of distaste and envy. Leona had days when she, too, wanted to be messy. She would deliberately let laundry overflow the hamper, and dirty dishes stack up in the sink, while her desk at work piled high and higher with unread newspapers and partially filled notebooks and empty cigarette packages. But it never lasted long. She would suddenly cry out, fling up her arms, and wade in to put things in order with murderous efficiency. When it was done, she took satisfaction in the newly restored peace around her and at the same time decried her need for it. Marion, on the other hand, lived serenely, surrounded by disorder which never seemed to get any worse.

"Apparently," said Marion, "I'll be able to get a mortgage of about sixty thousand dollars. That works out to about nine hundred dollars a month, divided by three is three hundred dollars. So you see, the three renters will pay for it." She looked over her shoulder. "Sorry, my dears," she said firmly to the two women approaching, coffee cups in hand, "but this is a private conversation."

"I didn't think those were allowed in here," said Bridget Walmsley, but she took Gloria-Rose by the elbow and they moved away.

"Wait a minute," said Leona, her eyes fixed on Marion. "The renters? What renters?"

"Three renters. One on the top floor, two on the second floor. The main floor is mine. And without mortgage payments to worry about," Marion went on quietly, leaning toward Leona, "I ought to be able to quit the paper and support myself freelancing." She sat back. "That's it. That's my news."

Leona felt a sharp ache. It was so real, so physical, that she put a hand on herself where her rib cage ended and pressed experimentally. The ache went away. "You can't do this, Marion," she said, conversationally.

"Of course I can," said Marion.

"Good Christ, Marion, people don't even dare to drop in on you without calling first, and half the time you tell them not to come. And here you are planning to throw open the doors of your brand-new house to a bunch of strangers."

"It isn't a brand-new house. It's quite an old one, actually. And I never tell *you* not to come."

Before she met Marion, Leona would have mistrusted the friendship of a beautiful woman. Marion Tyler, who was four years older than Leona, had blond hair, green eyes, pale skin that neither tanned nor freckled, and a voluptuous body. She was also tall. But Leona had sensed almost as soon as they met, five years earlier, that Marion tried to ignore her beauty; that it was something she had never grown used to, and which she herself mistrusted. The only aspect of her appearance to which she paid any attention was her weight. She weighed herself every day and whenever she exceeded by four pounds what she thought was right for her, she subjected herself to a rigorous diet of scotch and popcorn.

"Obviously I don't like the idea of sharing my house," said Marion. "But it's a financial necessity."

"Also I don't like the other part," said Leona. "About your freelancing. I don't like that at all, Marion." She was making slits in her empty Styrofoam coffee cup, using her long pink fingernails. "I'm stunned, I've got to tell you. You never even hinted you were thinking about quitting your job."

"I wasn't thinking about it. Not until I saw this house. Good heavens, Leona." Exasperated, Marion laid her hands flat on the table. "I thought that you, of all people—good heavens, you've rushed into this, and rushed into that; you've worked for I don't know how many papers—"

"Five. If you count the weekly in B.C."

"Do you realize I've worked only for the *Star?* For fifteen years? Good heavens, you've got to agree it's time I did something else."

"But it's so *impulsive*, Marion," Leona burst out. "It's not *like* you. You usually think everything out so calmly."

"I'm perfectly calm," said Marion. "And I have everything very carefully thought out." She reached over and took the tattered cup from Leona's hands. "Don't disappoint me, Leona."

Tears spurted into Leona's eyes and she lowered her head. "Who the hell am I going to have coffee with?"

Marion sighed. "You're considerably more emotional about this than I had expected."

Leona threw back her head and angrily blinked away her tears. "Christ, I don't know what's the matter with me. Pay no attention." She was puzzled and embarrassed by her turbulent dismay. I am too young, she told herself grimly, to be so flummoxed by change. Or perhaps, she added uncertainly, too old.

She studied Marion across the table. Marion was composed, her hands linked on top of the piece of paper on which she had done her calculations, and her green gaze was steady, but Leona knew that the impersonal but comforting security of a steady job was not, for Marion, something easily abandoned. She took Marion's hand and squeezed it. "I think it's great," she said. "I think it's bloody marvelous. I don't understand it—but if it's what you want, then good for you."

Marion smiled, and Leona saw her relief. She recognized that her approval had been important to Marion, and wondered uneasily what injury their friendship would have suffered if that approval had been withheld. She had once thought that friendship was a simple thing, immune to the inadvertent bruisings which inflict themselves upon a love affair; and perhaps this was true of casual friendships. It certainly wasn't true of important ones, she thought, watching Marion fold the paper with the figures on it and put it away in her purse.

"Now all I have to do," said Marion, "is get the down payment."

Leona stared at her. "You don't have the down payment?"

"Not yet. I've got some of it, and I'm going to break down and borrow some from my parents, but that still leaves me five thousand dollars short."

Leona groaned melodramatically and put her face in her hands.

"May I interrupt, ladies?"

From the corner of her eye Leona looked up at the city editor.

"Do you have to, Ziggy?" said Marion. "I'm about to solicit my friend's advice on a financial matter." She smiled at him, but he shook his head.

"Regrettably," he said, "I have a job for your friend." His name was Richard Glyn-Thomas, but everybody called him Ziggy. Nobody knew why. He was a quiet man, his clothes quietly natty, his thinning hair carefully combed, his face always looking freshly shaven; a gray and sturdy man.

"It's a house fire," he said to Leona. "They think they've got it out, but Dave and Gordon are out at the airport on something else and I'd like you to go take a look."

"You're sending her to a *fire?*" said Marion.

"You've got to be kidding," said Leona. "Why me? My God, Ziggy, haven't you got anybody else up there?"

"It's a busy day, Leona," said Ziggy. "I'm afraid you're it."

"Yeah, but a *fire,* for God's sake." She pushed her chair away from the table. The three of them began walking back to the newsroom.

"Just check it out," he said. "Bring back some notes for Dave and Gordon. And if there's no story, there's no story. I'll send Phil with you."

Marion returned to her office and Leona went irritably into the washroom to get her cape, feeling put-upon. Still, she thought, opening her locker, it could have been worse. The one thing she had always dreaded, and so far avoided, was being sent off to cover a construction accident or a highway smash-up—anything that would require her to look at bleeding, moaning, possibly dying, people. Getting dispatched to an already extinguished house fire, she thought, struggling into her cape, might be mildly damaging to her pride as a senior reporter, but at least it wasn't going to make her throw up or in some other way embarrass herself.

She was at the door when she saw that she hadn't put on her boots; but the photographer would be waiting. She hesitated, then flung open the door and went into the newsroom.

"Okay, here I am," she said to Phil, and they hurried down the back stairs to the lane where his car was illegally parked. She wondered if he actually paid the tickets which appeared with monotonous regularity on his window. Maybe the *Star* paid them, out of petty cash.

"Where are we going, anyway?" she asked in the car. "My God, I forgot to get the address."

"No problem," said Phil, pulling out onto First Street. "I got it."

Her feet beneath the heavy cape looked odd in her small black shoes. My feet are going to freeze, thought Leona.

They saw the smoke from a couple of blocks away, drifting lazily into the gray sky. "Looks like they've pretty well got it out, all right," said Phil. "What the hell are we supposed to do here anyway?"

"You're supposed to take pictures," said Leona, grinning at him, "and I'm supposed to talk to people."

"Yeah, but it's a house fire, for Christ's sake, a whole damn block didn't burn down."

He wheeled around a corner and headed up the street toward the smoke, toward a fire truck and a police car. He parked in front of a house two doors away from the fire and reached into the back seat for his camera.

"Okay, let's go," he said, and they got out of the car.

Leona left her shoulder bag on the seat and took her notebook and a pencil. The only pens she had in her desk were ball-points, and sometimes they didn't work properly outside on a cold day.

They walked up the sidewalk toward the house, which they couldn't see clearly yet because of the tall lilac hedge beside it. The leaves were gone, but the bushes were so tall and thick it was still impossible to see through them. As they approached the end of the hedge the front yard came clearly into view, and the house behind it, still smoking. It had once been white, but the back of it was black now. The house was still standing and it looked quite strong, but there must be a lot of damage inside, Leona thought. Her eyes flicked back and forth across the front of the building. She didn't know what she was looking for. There was no sign of life except for the wisps of smoke trailing up into the sky. A fire hose was stretched across the lawn but the firemen were huddled in a group at the front of their truck, talking and looking at the house. They would be leaving any minute, Leona thought.

A policeman stood on the sidewalk where it met at right angles the walk leading to the front porch of the smoking house. Leona went up to him. He looked cold, standing there with his hands behind his back.

He must have left his heavy coat somewhere, and his gloves; that uniform by itself certainly wasn't warm enough today.

"What happened?" Leona asked.

"There was a fire," said the policeman. There was no expression on his face, and he hadn't sounded particularly sarcastic.

"What caused it?"

"Why do you want to know?"

"I'm a reporter. From the *Star.*"

"You got nothing better to do than cover fires?"

Leona saw that he was angry, and she was nonplussed. "I usually cover education," she said lamely.

The policeman looked straight ahead.

"Do you know what caused it?"

He didn't answer.

Jesus, thought Leona. She thought it might be a good idea if she got angry, too, but decided to wait a minute or two.

"Was anybody hurt?" she asked.

He continued to look straight ahead.

Leona's scalp began to prickle. She looked quickly over her shoulder. Phil was across the street, taking pictures from a half-crouched position. Leona could see nobody else up or down the block on either side of the street. It was as though all the other houses were empty, deserted. Phil straightened up and wandered over to where Leona and the policeman stood. He nodded to them and crossed behind them to the front lawn of the house. The policeman didn't try to stop him.

"What's going on?" said Leona. Her voice came out in a husky, irritated bellow. "If you won't tell me, at least tell me who will."

The policeman looked at her. "You got any kids?"

Leona became aware that her feet and legs were numb with cold. She could hear the wind rattling the fleshless lilac hedge. It was slightly difficult to move her mouth to speak. "No," she said, looking up at him. "I don't have any kids."

The policeman stared straight ahead again. He wasn't young. His chin was beginning to sag, and pouches were developing beneath his eyes.

"It was a kid playing with matches," he said. "Happens a lot. This kid was about four. Set his bed on fire."

Leona turned her head slowly to the right. Her eyes went straight to the thing in the middle of the front yard, the charred mass with twisted iron legs which she hadn't looked at before. It had registered in the edges of her vision as she studied the house, but she hadn't looked at it. Why? she thought. Why didn't I look at it? I'm supposed to be a reporter. She was no longer aware of being cold, or of holding a notebook and a pencil. It lay upon the brown grass in the front yard, incongruous and abandoned, the remains of a child's cot.

"Yeah," said the policeman. "That's his bed."

Leona turned back to him. "He wasn't in the house alone, was he? He couldn't have been. He was too young."

"He wasn't alone. But his bedroom door was locked. From the outside. His mother was in the basement suite, with the guy who rents it from her."

Leona looked at his profile with great care. She waited for him to say something more, refused to think or draw conclusions until he had given her more information.

"How do you like them apples?" said the policeman.

Leona pushed at her mouth with her hand, then took her hand away to ask, "Is he dead?" Her voice was perfectly even.

"Yeah, he's dead."

"Where's his mother?"

He pointed at the police car, parked twenty feet away. Leona walked toward it and when she got just behind it, she stopped. There were two cops in the front seat. She didn't know why they were just sitting there. They ought to be driving somewhere, she thought. There ought to be some urgency here.

In the back seat was a woman with red-blond hair. She had rested her head against the glass of the window and wasn't moving at all. Leona couldn't see her face, just the mass of red-blond hair, untidy, uncombed, long, and dirty. Leona looked at it intently, wondering what the face looked like, what the woman was thinking. Does she know he's dead? Was he dead when she got to him? Did she smell smoke first, or did she first hear him scream? Did he pound at the door of his bedroom, screaming? And when she heard him or smelled the smoke, did she have the key to his room handy, or did she have to scrabble around in a drawer for it? Or did she get a hatchet and chop the door down?

Or maybe the guy in the basement suite did that. He was in the police car, too; Leona was sure it was he, a shadowy form huddled in the opposite corner of the back seat.

She saw that Phil was still taking pictures of the bed.

How does it feel, wondered Leona, to have a kid, and then to have him burn to death in your own house? She thought of the woman in the police car with something approaching awe; her curiosity was intense.

She also wanted to vomit, but she knew that would pass.

She went to Phil and said, "Come on. Let's get out of here."

When they got into the car she started scrawling notes for the police reporters who would write the story.

She also wrote notes for herself, for the cutlines.

Shaken, she told Marion about the fire at lunch.

In the afternoon she cleaned out her files, and when the photos of the blackened cot were ready she wrote the cutlines.

She left work a little early and strolled around the Bay, looking for something to buy. The Hudson's Bay Company was just a department store now, but it had started life more than three hundred years ago as a trading company, and Leona liked that; it was roots, of a kind, in a part of Canada which didn't have many of those. She shopped aimlessly, and found nothing she wanted except a paperback book. When she had bought that she was suddenly hungry, and decided to have an early dinner before going home. She hadn't eaten much at lunchtime.

The restaurant wasn't crowded and she didn't have to wait for a table. She took the paperback from its bag to read while she waited for her food to come. But her mind suddenly felt like snow in the wind, filled with bits of thoughts that needed ordering. She held the book, and smoked, and tried to concentrate on something; the book, or her job, or Marion's house, or going home for Christmas—but this proved impossible.

Her beef-dip sandwich was set before her and she put the book away. She would eat and let her overactive mind flicker itself into exhaustion.

She became aware of the sounds of the restaurant. The people at the next table were speaking together in a foreign language. Not French, she thought, I'd recognize French. Not Italian, not Spanish; what, then? They were speaking quite loudly, didn't care who heard them, knew they couldn't be understood, and when the waitress came they shifted into English, just like that. What power I'd have, thought Leona, if I could speak their language; what power, to be wrongly assumed ignorant. When I leave I'll give them a long, inscrutable look. Maybe they'll think I've understood them, at least maybe they'll have a second of wondering, of trying to remember what they've revealed about themselves in their foreign language, just a second in which, horrified, their hearts will skip a beat.

Her own heart stumbled, and she smiled; how closely her mind and body worked together. And she took a sip of coffee. And she realized then that something was not right.

At first she was confused. She thought some emergency had occurred in the restaurant. She looked around, alarmed, and saw only people eating and laughing and talking, and waitresses bustling back and forth between the tables and the kitchen. She hung desperate in the moment, trying to stay right there, and late that night, painstakingly examining her day, she thought of this as her last moment of innocence.

And then her heart struck the inside of her chest hard, once, twice, again and again, gathering speed, smiting her blindly as though pursued and frantic, in its terror attacking her.

Oh Christ oh God, she thought, I'm having a heart attack.

It pounded inside her chest, panicked and out of control, trying to batter its way out; the blood would be shooting through her veins in a torrent, her ribs would be broken, her heart would burst.

Oh my God, she thought, and pushed her chair away from the table.

The waitress hurried over and beamed a smile upon her. "Will that be all?"

Oh Jesus, thought Leona. It doesn't show.

The waitress scribbled a total on the bill and laid it face down on the table. "Have a good evening," she said.

The beat of her heart was faster and louder, increasing in intensity, but there was no pain. That must come next, thought Leona, and she stood up. I can still stand, she thought. Oh God, she thought, just let me get out of here. She imagined herself falling onto the floor, writhing in pain before the hungry eyes of astonished and disapproving patrons of the restaurant. She imagined them all staring down at her as she became one of those people struck down by misfortune in a public place. She didn't want to be one of those people. She wanted to have her heart attack in privacy, hanging on to the hand of a friend . . . it was Peter's hand she wanted to hang on to, she realized, which didn't make any sense at all; she hadn't thought of him in months.

She walked unsteadily to the cashier, her heart roaring and pounding, but still there was no pain. She paid her bill and pushed through the crowd now waiting to get in. Must get to a phone, she thought, which was ridiculous, because even if she reached him he was three thousand miles away . . . You're on your own, kiddo, she told herself, and thought she might explode.

She was glad of her cape, which she hadn't bothered to take off because this was an awkward procedure; now she didn't have to put it on again. She went out into the cold, speaking in her mind to her heart.

What is it, exercise? I'll exercise. Cigarettes? I'll give them up. Birth control pills? No more pills, I promise you, heart, who needs sex anyway, and no more caffeine, either, what more can I do? Just tell me, I'll do it.

There was still no pain. But her heart in her chest was thunderous, murderous, calling her name.

It wasn't getting any worse. It wasn't getting any better, but it wasn't getting any worse.

She walked around and around the block, waiting to fall in the street, struck down by her heart. She thought she ought to call her doctor, or maybe an ambulance, but this would be humiliating, and might also alarm her heart still further, so she didn't do it.

As she walked, gradually the tumult in her chest subsided, and finally her heart resumed its normal steady rhythm, and eventually she began walking through the cold darkness toward home.

As she plodded cautiously, she became increasingly anxious for the comforting familiarity of her apartment. But when finally she could see her building, the relief she had expected to feel didn't materialize. A sudden hotness swept through her. She approached the glass doors like one wading through heavy water. Her legs felt bowed from the weight they had to carry and her shoulders were hunched, pulled down by the massive burden of her heart, injured and swollen. What would she do with it in there, in the empty silent rooms that were her home? How would she protect herself? And how would she sleep—how would she ever, ever, sleep?

She pushed through the doors, unlocked the inner door and walked into the lobby. It was shockingly silent, except for the improbable gurgling of the small waterfall which fed a circular concrete pond over by the elevator.

I'm doing all this, she thought as she pressed the elevator button and waited for the car to ascend from the basement parking garage. I'm functioning. I still work.

She stared fixedly at the elevator doors. When they opened she was staring at the only other tenant in the building whom she knew well enough to talk to. For a moment Leona was completely confounded. She stared at Emily Murdoch in amazement and relief, until the elevator doors began to close, and Emily quickly pushed the button to keep them open.

Emily opened her mouth to speak but didn't. She stood there, her hand on the button, and smiled, and finally Leona shuffled into the elevator and leaned against the wall.

"Seven, isn't it?" said Emily.

"Yes, thank you." Leona tried to think of something to do when she got into her apartment. She couldn't even imagine taking off her cape. Maybe in the middle of taking it off, with both hands above her head, her chest undefended, her heart would go berserk again. She clasped her hands tightly and heard herself make a curious gulping sound.

Emily turned to look at her. "Are you all right, Miss Hadden?"

"Please call me Leona," she gasped, hanging on to her hands.

The elevator stopped and the doors opened. Leona pushed herself upright and looked out into the empty hall. Oh Jesus, oh God, she thought.

"Why don't you come up and have coffee with me?" said Emily.

"I don't drink coffee. I can't drink it. It's the caffeine," said Leona. The elevator doors began to close.

"Tea, then. The kind with no caffeine."

Leona blinked. Tears, twice in one day, she thought. Shit. "Okay," she said humbly. "That would be nice." She lowered her head and looked patiently at the floor until the elevator stopped again.

"It's this way," said Emily in the hall, touching Leona's elbow. Leona followed her, docile, and waited while Emily unlocked the door and reached in to turn on the lights.

"Do you want to take off your cape?" said Emily.

"No, thank you."

Emily led her into the living room, and turned on a floor lamp. "Sit here, on the sofa. Now, will you have tea, or would you prefer hot chocolate?"

"Tea would be very nice," said Leona, sitting down. She put her feet together and her hands in her lap.

Emily's apartment was precisely the same as Leona's, except for the view, which was much better, but it felt different, mostly because of the plants. There were dozens of them, and as she waited for Emily to return, Leona thought a warm fragrance was exuding from them, even though none of them seemed to have any flowers.

Emily came in with a tea tray and put it on the table in front of the sofa.

"I had a distressing experience," said Leona, watching steam rise from the spout of the brown enameled teapot.

"Yes, you look distressed," said Emily. "We'd better let it steep for a few minutes." She sat in an easy chair. "It's blackberry tea. I hope you like it."

"This is very kind of you, Mrs. Murdoch." Cautiously, Leona let the strap of her handbag fall from her shoulder, and pushed the bag farther back on the sofa.

"Please call me Emily," said Emily, with a smile.

They weren't quite strangers, but the pleasant acquaintanceship they shared was due more to the fact that they both knew Marion, who was Emily's niece, than to their living in the same building. Leona didn't even know the names of most of the other people who lived there.

"I don't suppose," said Leona, "that you happen to have any sleeping pills." She felt herself flush.

Emily poured the tea. "No, I'm afraid I don't," she said. "But I might have something that will do just as well." She handed Leona a cup of tea which did indeed smell like blackberries, and left the room.

Leona sipped and stared hopelessly at a glossy plant whose leaves trailed from the top of a bookcase almost to the floor.

Emily came back with a small bottle. "These aren't sleeping pills, but if you don't usually take medicines they ought to do the job for you." She sat, still holding the bottle of pills. "They're for travel sickness." She hesitated, looking closely but politely at Leona. "Do you take any kind of medicine, for anything at all?"

"No."

Emily handed her the bottle.

She's just about the same age as my mother, thought Leona, accepting the pills. She wanted to kneel beside Emily's chair and rest her head in the softness of her lap and feel a hand stroke her hair.

"Thank you," said Leona, and her hand closed gratefully around the bottle of pills.

She peered at the label, as she traveled on the elevator down to her own floor, and sure enough, it warned about drowsiness. This is going to do it, heart, this stuff I've got in my hand, she said silently; this is potent stuff I've got here, you aren't going to know what hit you, you're going to be asleep so fast.

In her apartment she turned on all the lights and wandered from room to room. The place felt cold and dusty, as though she'd been away from it for a long time. There was little comfort in the familiar things it contained.

She thought about her friends, people she liked who had sprawled on her sofa and crammed themselves awkwardly around her small dining area table and filled the air with the smoke from their cigarettes and the raucousness of their arguings and with their laughter and affection. She thought about them helplessly, unable to call upon them from the lip of the chasm which had opened at her feet, deep and black, with such terrifying suddenness. It was as though her voice had gone, and they were too far away to see whatever urgent signalings she might hurl across the abyss which separated them.

She put a small hand on her heart, carefully, and then took her pulse, which felt perfectly normal. But what the hell do I know about pulses, thought Leona.

She was impatient to take a pill, maybe two just to be on the safe side, but it was still only seven o'clock and she doubted that travel pills could provide twelve hours of unconsciousness.

She poured herself a glass of milk and sat in front of the television set to try to watch something, theorizing that television would concentrate her attention outside herself more successfully than a book, because television had such a lot of noise coming from it.

She would have liked to call her parents, just to feel loved, but they'd be sure to hear something peculiar in her voice and would probably get worried. They were six hundred miles away, and she didn't want to worry them.

She thought no more about phoning Peter. That had been a ludicrous idea in the first place.

She wanted to phone Marion and almost did, but stopped herself without quite knowing why, except that it had something to do with getting through things alone.

She smoked only two cigarettes, carefully, trying not to inhale.

Finally she took off her cape slowly and warily, and that was fine, and then she got undressed and took two pills and crawled into bed.

It occurred to her, as she lay quietly, looking up at the ceiling, that she had no interest whatsoever in dying.

It also occurred to her that nobody actually lives alone; that there is always a palpable something keeping you company. At the moment, for Leona, it was fear.

CHAPTER 2

During the next weeks Leona was aware, in a way she had never been before, of her heart's presence in her chest.

It leaped within her when she was startled, and had done so before, but now when this happened she was for a moment panic-stricken; it would take, she thought, so little to send it off again. But sullenly each time it subsided, and cautiously each time she took up her life again.

Sometimes she felt her heart tense and heavy in its protective cage of bone, and she thought it might have enlarged itself beyond comfort, into claustrophobia. Sometimes her awareness of its beating alone was enough to cause apprehension.

The days and weeks passed, however, and her preoccupation with it was the only evidence that her heart's appalling treachery had ever occurred.

She had decided to cancel her trip home for Christmas, but never got around to telling Air Canada, and by mid-December, her heart still stubbornly normal, she began to think she could manage to see her parents without bursting into tears.

The visit was uneventful, yet momentous. She ate her mother's Christmas cake, helped her father decorate the tree, went for walks in the small town in which she had grown up, called some old friends, visited relatives. She remembered that in other years she'd actually been bored, after Christmas Day had passed, and had looked forward to getting back to Calgary, and to work. Not this year, though. This year she was unrelentingly joyous, full of gratitude, because her heart, that neglected, unappreciated organ, behaved with perfect courtesy. It beat quiescently, obediently, and troubled her not at all, and she finally accepted that it had recovered. It just got a little glitch in it, she thought fondly; that's all, just a little temporary glitch.

She continued, back at work, to believe in its restoration, and when the time of Marion's move drew near, Leona offered to help. She had been distracted during Marion's preparations to leave the paper and take possession of her new house, and forgave herself for it, but was eager now to take some part in her friend's adventure.

The day in January that Marion moved was very cold but clear, except that ice fog breathed from the earth, obscuring the outlines of things, filling the air with white; the sun, struggling to penetrate it, had lost much of its light and all of its warmth by the time it got down to ground level. Leona, gazing from her apartment window, thought it looked like another planet out there. The coldness was a thing of unquestionable malevolence. It would strike skin numb, and make breathing painful. She thought there was a lot to be said for the colorless rain which had fallen on southwestern British Columbia at Christmas.

The heater in her Honda had broken, and although the car wasn't cold at first, because it was kept in the garage beneath the apartment building, it rapidly became so as she squeaked along the snow-packed streets to pick up Vern, who didn't have a car.

When she pulled up in a slow skid in front of the apartment building where he lived, Vern shot out of the lobby and slid across the sidewalk, hands outstretched to grab at the Honda.

"Where the hell's your hat?" said Leona, as he wrenched open the door and squeezed in beside her. "And your goddamn gloves?"

"Oh my God, turn up the heat," said Vern. "I think my gloves are in my pocket. Get this crate moving, will you?"

"I gotta have some coffee," said Vern, when Marion opened her apartment door. He pushed past her into the warmth of the kitchen.

"Jesus, he's an idiot," said Leona irritably. "He's going to be freezing the whole time. He's not going to be any help at all."

"Never mind, Bruce is here," said Marion. "Come on in, my dear, and have coffee before we begin."

In the kitchen, Emily was sitting at the table holding a cup of black coffee.

"And who's this lady, Marion?" said Vern, looking at Emily with bright eyes. "Am I to have the honor of meeting your mother?"

"Good heavens, no," said Marion. "This is my aunt, Emily Murdoch. Emily, this is Vern Palmer. He works at the *Star*. Get out of the way, Vern; let me pour some coffee."

Leona looked around for Marion's parents, whom she had expected would be there, but saw no sign of them.

"This place has never been so clean," she said approvingly. "Where's your dog?"

"He's in a kennel for the day, of course."

She had had the dog for six months. Leona had been astonished to meet him—he was a large dog—and astonished, too, when Marion told her she'd gotten him from the SPCA. Marion shopped carefully for things and usually bought the best she could afford, but dogs were different, she had said to Leona. Dogs were creatures, not objects, and she didn't believe in their being bought and sold.

Her apartment building accepted dogs and cats, so Marion hadn't bothered getting anyone's approval before she brought Spot home. He was a Labrador-Newfoundland cross. He stood thirty inches tall at the shoulder and weighed 120 pounds and was totally black. The first time Marion encountered a fellow tenant while taking Spot out through the lobby for a walk, a complaint was lodged. Marion was indignant, but in this matter she didn't even get support from Leona. It was Marion's continuing and ever more heated argument with the manager of the apartment building about her dog, Leona was convinced, that had sent her off house-hunting.

"You work for *Calgary Week*, don't you?" Vern was asking Emily, referring to a weekly newsmagazine with enthusiastic prejudices, political and moral.

"Yes," said Emily, and as she began to talk about the magazine, Leona was struck again by her lack of resemblance to Marion. She was shorter, slimmer, more hesitant, and her face was much gentler than Marion's. Her gray hair was short and curly and her eyes were a light blue. Leona thought she must be in her late fifties. There was a suppleness about her, and an air of physical vulnerability, which made her think Emily must have successfully battled disease over a long period of time; but she knew from Marion that this wasn't true. This day Emily was wearing baggy jeans and a navy sweatshirt under a fisherman's cardigan; she had obviously come to work. Leona felt a rush of affection, looking at her. She had bought some travel pills and taken them to Emily, to replace the ones she'd borrowed, and neither then nor since had Emily expressed curiosity about that evening in November. She hadn't mentioned it to Marion, either, Leona was certain of that, for if she had, Marion would have asked about it.

"Two trips with the truck, I figure," said Bruce Menzies, coming in from the living room. His blond hair was hidden beneath a tuque that came down over his ears.

"Where's your good wife, Menzies?" said Vern, leaning against a kitchen cabinet.

"She's meeting us at the house later, with food," said Bruce. "Come on, you guys, drink up, let's get at it."

"Wait a minute, wait a minute," said Vern, clutching his cup. "Her heater doesn't work, I'm still freezing."

"Work, that's what you need," said Bruce. "Lots of hard work, that'll warm you up."

"The *Star* isn't the same without you, Marion," said Vern sorrowfully. "I don't know how much longer I can go on there, now that you've left."

"Don't be ridiculous," said Marion. "I just left yesterday."

"You should have come to your party," said Bruce, grinning. "It was a hell of a party."

"What party?" said Marion. "There wasn't one. I told them I didn't want one."

"Yeah, but we had one anyway," said Leona. "We all went to the pub. Jesus, Marion." She looked at her friend in dismay. "It's going to be awful on Monday, without you there."

"For hours we toasted your memory," said Vern. "I think I'm going to quit. Maybe get a room in your house, Marion. What do you say?"

"I say you're out of your mind," said Marion.

"Let's get this show on the road." Bruce pulled his gloves from his pockets and put them on. "Vern, help me load the furniture on the truck, okay? Marion, the rest of you should fill up the cars with boxes and stuff."

"Jesus, listen to the general here," muttered Vern. He glanced at Bruce. "Okay, okay, I'm here, aren't I? Ready, willing, and almost able."

Marion went into the hall to get her jacket from the closet, and appeared again at the kitchen door zipping it up. She looked at each of them. "Thank you for coming to help me," she said, almost formally, in her high, clear voice; it made Leona think of music, and running water. Marion's face was flushed, and her eyes seemed greener than usual. "I very much appreciate it."

There was a sudden wrenching in Leona. It was as though Marion were disappearing from her life, about to board a plane or a train for a place Leona had never seen, shedding her friends and accommodations with an equal ease, abandoning Leona to despondency.

"You're very welcome, Marion," said Emily, and they all looked around for something to carry outside.

By the time all four vehicles were finally crammed full of furniture, boxes, and, in Marion's small station wagon, clothes hanging on a rod across the back seat, Vern was shivering violently.

"Jesus bloody Christ," he said, climbing into the Honda. "My hands are going to drop off."

"Sit on them," said Leona.

"If you'd told me your heater didn't work, I wouldn't have forgotten my gloves."

Leona gave him an exasperated look, and cuddled deeper into her down-filled jacket.

"What the hell are we waiting for?" said Vern, craning to look outside.

Bruce was securing the load of furniture in the back of his maroon pickup truck. The only thing he used the truck for, as far as Leona could tell, was doing favors for people. One year there had been a strike of garbage men and then he'd used it to trundle garbage to the dump, his own and his friends'. He drove to work in a '64 Chevy Impala which he called his American Graffiti car because it was red and white and low-slung. It was this vehicle, too, in which he disappeared for a few days from time to time, whenever he fell off the wagon. He was a good worker, so the benevolent *Star* always took him back, and so did Norma, his wife.

Bruce stepped back from the truck, waved, and got in the cab. The small convoy moved off; first Marion's blue station wagon, then Emily's yellow Volkswagen, then Bruce's maroon pickup, and finally the red Honda.

"Have you seen this house?" said Vern, rubbing the window with his arm so he could see out.

"No," said Leona. Marion had been adamant. She wasn't going to let anyone see it, she said, until she'd redecorated the interior.

It was a slow procession, down Tenth Avenue and across the Louise Bridge and along Memorial Drive, beside the Bow River, solidly frozen. By the time they turned off Memorial, Leona had decided she really must get her car heater fixed first thing next week.

She looked out curiously at the street which as of today was Marion's street. It was unusually wide, because it was in one of the oldest parts of the city, and many of the houses were old, too, though some had been torn down and replaced by duplexes or low apartment buildings. Snow lay deep upon lawns and sidewalks, but a few people had emerged from their dwellings, well bundled against the cold, to slowly and laboriously shovel steps and driveways; their breath made thick clouds in the January air, and they squinted against the sun, which was brighter now that the ice fog had begun to clear.

Leona pulled the Honda over to the curb behind Bruce's truck, and Vern looked eagerly through the windshield to see which was Marion's house.

"That must be it," said Leona, as Marion approached a low iron fence in front of a tall and narrow house, white except for the bottom story, which was painted brown. Leona got out and crunched through the snow to the sidewalk.

"Christ, it's got three floors," said Vern, catching up to her. On the walk in front of Marion's gate they joined Emily, and the three of them looked up at the house, narrowing their eyes against the sun.

"Stay where you are!" Marion called out. She was just about to climb the steps to the front door. "Don't move!" She proceeded up the steps extremely slowly, her head bent.

"What are we waiting for?" said Bruce, coming up behind them, carrying boxes.

"I don't know," said Leona, rubbing her gloved hands together.

"Come on, Marion," said Vern. He burst through the open gate, his bare hands clutched to his bare ears. "Get a move on, open the door."

Marion whirled around. "You idiot!" she screamed. "Look what you've done!" She bent over, as if in pain. "Idiot! Damn fool idiot!" She straightened and shook her head in fury, staring at them, a huddled group of four, now, halfway up her walk.

"She swore at me," said Vern, awe-struck. "She never swears. What did I do?"

Marion stood on her front porch taut with rage. Leona thought she looked mythological, a goddess guardian, her jeans tucked into brown leather boots, her emerald green jacket and tuque reflected in the flash of her eyes. Her feet were apart, her gloved hands in fists. Leona gaped at her, shocked by her anger and envying her, too. Spontaneous fury held no risks for Marion's heart, while merely witnessing it had caused her own to lurch.

"What did he do?" said Bruce uneasily, shifting the boxes in his arms.

Marion threw up her hands, and lifted her face to the sun. "Ah well," she said, and looked at them again. "It's nothing. He didn't do anything."

She pulled open the glass door which became a screen door in sum-

mer, unlocked the inner door and opened it. "Come on," she said to
her friends, who hadn't moved. She turned, holding the door open, and
smiled down at them. "Come into my house," she said.

CHAPTER 3

In early March, Leona began to suffer spasms of dissatisfaction with
her job. She didn't try to stifle them but embraced them heartily. A
specific, manageable dissatisfaction was just what she'd been looking
for.

Discontent with work wasn't new to her. It afflicted her at regular
intervals, and usually resulted in her getting a new beat. The job then
took off in a whole new direction and her enjoyment in her work was
restored.

Right now, she badly wanted to take off in a whole new direction.

But this time a new beat didn't feel like quite enough.

"Maybe I could write a column," she said hopefully on the phone to
Marion. "Do you think I could persuade Ziggy to let me write a column? What do you think?"

"What on earth kind of a column?"

"I don't know. I'd have to think about it, work up some samples for
him. What do you think?"

"You've got columnists coming out of your ears down there. Wait
until somebody dies, or quits. You're not going to have any room in
that paper for news pretty soon, that's what I think."

Leona would have liked to argue with her, but she knew Marion was
right. She could imagine the skepticism that would appear on Ziggy's
face as he took her sheaf of sample columns in his hand, held them at
arm's length, and stared at them in polite disbelief. He didn't hold
much with personal journalism, and suffered the columnists he had
only because they had been comfortably ensconced before he took over
as city editor.

"Talk to Ziggy," said Marion. "Tell him you're ready for a change.
He'll have some ideas."

The next morning in the women's washroom, Bridget and Gloria-Rose were again chatting away at the mirrors. Leona joined them. She had to know that her hair and makeup were in order before she approached Ziggy.

"I was just telling Bridget," said Gloria-Rose, "there's a man in my building who's allergic to money." She studied herself critically in the mirror, tucking loose strands of hair behind the braided loop at the back of her head and checking her makeup.

"Oh yeah?" said Leona. She dropped her shoulder bag on the counter and began hunting through it for her comb.

"Had a long talk with him by the elevator, I did, and he's allergic to money." Gloria-Rose was a large woman of fifty, with a quavery, warbling voice. Her hands were in almost constant motion, fluttering, clasping one another, seeming to plead. She was notoriously inefficient. She mislaid messages, and let unwanted people past her into the newsroom, and took half a day to type a letter. But she had been with the paper for more than ten years, and unless she suddenly went mad, or took to swiping handbags, Leona figured she'd be there forever.

"Why did he need money at the elevator?" said Bridget, who was leaning against the wall by the paper towel container, arms crossed. She was about thirty and overweight, but she carried herself regally.

"Have you ever heard of such a thing?" said Gloria-Rose, amazed.

"Yeah, I have," said Leona, heading for the door.

"He's in the oil business," said Gloria-Rose vaguely.

"Is it change or bills?" Leona heard Bridget say. "Or both?"

Leona sat at her desk, which she was glad to see was bare of photographs, lit a cigarette, and glanced casually over at the city desk. Now that she'd made up her mind to talk to Ziggy she wanted to do it as soon as possible. But she had to wait until the eight-thirty first-edition deadline had passed.

The city desk was still waiting for cutlines.

"What the hell's up with you, Herbie?" Bruce yelled from his desk, which was beside Ziggy's. "Two lines, for Christ's sake, that's all I want."

Herb Wingate was a junior reporter who had been with the paper only six months and still got flustered by deadlines. Leona knew that Bruce threw last-minute cutlines and rewrites at him deliberately, trying to get him used to it. She saw Herb leaning tensely over his VDT, staring at the screen as though it were speaking softly to him. A final burst of silent typing, then with a flourish he pushed the button which stored his cutlines in the computer and made them instantly available to the city desk. "Done!" he shouted across the newsroom.

"Jesus, congratulations," said Bruce, and a couple of reporters applauded and cheered. Herb flushed, then turned in his chair to make an awkward bow.

Jesus, thought Leona, smiling.

She watched Ziggy lean back in his chair, hands behind his head. He was talking to Bruce, who had dispatched Herb's cutlines and was taking a break before hauling out his clipboard and making his rounds.

Now's my chance, thought Leona, and she went over to him. She was tense but exhilarated, her usual state when plotting a career change. "Can I talk to you sometime this morning?" she said.

Ziggy smoothed his hair with both hands, stood up, and gestured at the stairway to the cafeteria. "Sure. I'll even buy the coffee."

She picked a table as far as possible from the one by the window which was occupied by some people from the wire desk.

"What's up?" said Ziggy. He put the coffee on the table and sat down opposite her.

"I'm restless," she said, and grinned at him.

He nodded thoughtfully. "Have you ever thought of taking up jogging?"

"No, seriously, Ziggy. I've been on education for more than two years now. Every time I write a story it sounds vaguely familiar, you know? It's time I moved on again, right?"

"This time I'm actually ahead of you, Leona," he said, stirring sugar into his coffee. "How would you like to work on the desk?"

She looked at him blankly. "What desk?"

"The city desk. We're going to put on a third person. Are you interested?"

"I was thinking of another beat."

"What is there left that you haven't already done? Sports, agriculture, entertainment—they don't come under me, but I could put in a good word for you, I guess," he said, smiling.

"No, thanks," said Leona, nettled. "I was thinking—I don't know. I guess I hadn't thought beyond something new."

"The desk would be new."

"Yeah. I've never done any desk work."

"Can't get much newer than that."

"I don't know. What would I be doing?"

"Handing out assignments, working with people on stories. What Bruce does. We've got thirty reporters now. That's too many for me and one assistant to handle."

"Are you offering it to me?" said Leona. "Or just sounding me out?"

"I'm offering it to you. I'll have to get Jack to approve it, but that won't be a problem."

Jack Hiller was the managing editor. Most of the reporters tried to avoid him because of his caustic manner and lack of patience.

"Tell you what," said Ziggy. "You think about it. Let me know in a couple of days." He stood up to leave, coffee cup in hand. "I ought to warn you. You'd have to get in here by seven, sometimes six-thirty. And we don't get paid for overtime."

That evening the streets were wet and gritty, and as Leona crossed the bridge on her way to Marion's house, she saw that the ice on the river was much thinner and that in some places cracks had appeared, revealing black water. There would be another spring, she thought with satisfaction, even though she knew it was still weeks away.

She heard the dog trumpeting on the other side of the door when she rang Marion's bell. He sometimes made her nervous, even though she knew he was gentle. When Marion opened the door she was holding on to his collar.

"Come in, come in," said Marion. "We must immediately drink a toast to your new career. Get rid of your things, while I take Spot back to the kitchen."

"I don't have a new career yet," Leona called after her. "I haven't decided whether I should do it or not."

"Of course you must do it," Marion called back, out of sight now in the kitchen.

Leona, smiling to herself, took off her jacket and her boots. A door with glass panes to her right led into the living room, and on the left was the stairway to the second and third floors. She put her boots on a rubber tray on the floor of the closet, and hung up her jacket.

She went up the hall to the kitchen, a large room running the width of the house. Marion had arranged comfortable chairs and bookshelves and her television set on one side, turning it into a sitting room. Emily had given her a small stereo, as a housewarming gift, so she could listen to records here as well as in the living room. To the left another hallway, very short, led to a small bathroom and the bedroom, which was also where Marion worked. These rooms and the hall were an addition to the original house.

The dirty dishes from Marion's dinner sat on the counter, under one of the three windows in the kitchen-sitting room. Next to the window a large Boston fern hung from a hook in the ceiling.

"My God, you've got a plant," said Leona, amazed. "Did Emily give it to you?"

"Emily knows better. My mother brought it. Sit down, let me get you a drink." She was wearing jeans and a brown sweatshirt, and although her shoulder-length hair was combed, she hadn't put on any makeup.

"Are you getting any work?" said Leona. "Renting any rooms?"

"I've been working quite furiously at *getting* work," said Marion, handing Leona a scotch on the rocks, "and I plan to advertise the rooms at the end of next week."

She sat in a big stuffed chair, purple, worn on the arms, and put her feet on the coffee table. Spot, who had been standing in the middle of the kitchen ponderously wagging his tail and watching her, walked over to her chair and lay down with a sigh. His legs looked too thin to carry him easily, but Marion said he could run like the wind when he had enough space to run in. Newspapers and magazines cluttered the coffee table, the sofa, and the end table next to Leona's chair.

Marion lifted the glass she'd brought for herself. "Congratulations on your new job," she said, smiling, and drank.

"You think I should take it, then," said Leona eagerly, leaning forward on the sofa.

"Of course." Marion jiggled her glass and observed the slosh of golden scotch over chunks of ice. "You're a very capable person."

Things come easily to me, thought Leona suddenly. She had never had trouble finding jobs, and never had one she didn't like. Every time she began feeling bored or impatient, something new and interesting came along. But it's not as though things are *given* to me, she thought; I work hard, I *make* things happen for myself.

"Good," she said. "You think I should do it. Good." She drank some scotch. "I'll do it, then. I'll tell him tomorrow." There'd be a lot to learn on the desk, she thought. It would be a job that would call on different qualities in her than reporting had. I hope I can do it well, she began to say to herself, but her modesty was a pose, and impatiently she flung it aside and delighted, reckless, in a surge of confidence.

She put down her glass and stood up, restless with energy. She rubbed her hands and paced the room, watched by Marion and Spot. She felt galvanized, filled to bursting with ambition and purposefulness. She stopped and looked at Marion, and felt a shock of fierce pleasure; things would go well for Marion, too, she was certain of it. For a moment she stood, helpless, wanting to offer Marion quantities of acute perceptions, of dazzling concepts, each articulated with a splendid precision.

"What on earth are you doing?" said Marion disapprovingly.

"I have no idea," said Leona, and gave Marion her husky laugh. "I'm just stuffed with energy." She waved her hands.

She sat on the edge of the sofa. My reach, she thought, most certainly does exceed my grasp.

"It's beginning to drain away, now," she said.

"And a good thing, too." Marion finished her drink and got up to refill her glass.

Leona sank back into the sofa. She was very comfortable in this room, even though it had been created by Marion expressly for herself. There was a sureness in the way furniture and belongings were collected together that Leona found soothing. The room made a statement about Marion—about her untidiness, her attachments, and in the absence of more personal things, which she must keep in her bedroom, even about her pressing need for privacy. Leona felt serenity there, and coveted it.

"My apartment's got something strange in it," she said abruptly, examining the braided rug on the floor.

"Good heavens," said Marion, coming back with her drink. "What? Bugs?"

"It's a kind of—moribund expectation."

"Well. I don't like the sound of that," said Marion, still standing.

"I noticed it a few months ago." Leona looked up at her. "I thought it was just impermanence. I thought maybe all apartments had it, because after all, you pay by the month, everybody knows you won't be there forever."

Marion nodded from her purple chair.

"It's a kind of a month-to-month lease on life, you know?" Leona grinned wryly. "With somebody else's curtains, and somebody else's carpeting, and people lining up patiently out there somewhere"—she waved a hand toward the window—"waiting for their turn to move in."

"I don't want to get into any morbid conversations, Leona," said Marion sharply.

"Well, shit," said Leona, her face getting hot. "Who the hell else am I going to have them with?" She picked up her scotch. The glass was cool in her hands; the scotch had a soothingly medicinal taste.

"You could buy a house, too, you know," said Marion. "You wouldn't have any trouble getting a mortgage. Especially now. You'll be getting a raise."

Leona looked at her in astonishment. "My God. I guess I will. I hadn't thought of that." She shook her head. "I don't think I want a house, though. I don't think that would help."

"Certainly not if you took your moribund expectations with you, it wouldn't." Marion watched Leona. "Look at you," she said after a while. "Sitting there all grim in the face. You need a shot of something. I'm going to give you some Beethoven." She got up to put on a record. "And another drink," she said, taking Leona's glass from her hand.

"You see, the thing of it is," said Leona, rushing to say it while Marion was out of sight, "I've been thinking quite a lot lately about what it was like, living with Peter." She flinched a little, waiting for Marion's response. She waited for what seemed a long time, long enough to regret having said it, to argue with herself about that, and then to become defiant. "Turn it down, for God's sake. I can't hear the notes properly."

Marion turned down the stereo and handed her a fresh drink. Leona glanced at her quickly, feeling sullen. Marion looked quite calm. The exultant Emperor Concerto filled the room, strengthening Leona.

Marion put her feet back on the coffee table and looked at her curiously. "Why have you been thinking about him, for heaven's sake?"

"It was good to have someone there," said Leona. "It was good to be the two of us, instead of just me."

Peter had given her a tape of this music, to play on her car stereo, which was now broken. She liked it so much she'd given the record to Marion. Its joyful power sometimes made her grin delightedly—she could actually feel the smile take hold of her face; and sometimes it caused something unbearably sweet and restorative to steal up into her throat; and sometimes she just wanted to join in, roaring a husky tuneless la-di-da accompaniment to the sections she knew best.

"He took care of me," she said apologetically, "Peter did."

"Took care of you," said Marion slowly and with contempt. She took a large sip of scotch.

Stubbornly Leona thought about him. She would wallow in her loss again, after all this time, because she damn well wanted to, and to hell with Marion. She'd probably cry, with all that scotch inside her, but what the hell. She stared down, solemn and grieving, at her sock feet, and started to giggle.

"Took care of you," said Marion again. "My great aunt Fanny, Leona, you do have an enormous ability to deceive yourself."

Leona threw back her head and roared with laughter, and thought this not an unfitting accompaniment to the jubilance of Beethoven.

"He probably wasn't even any good in bed," Marion muttered, downing the rest of her scotch.

Leona bent over and clutched her stomach, moaning, tears of laughter in her eyes. "Oh yes," she said breathlessly, "that's not fair, Marion, he was, really."

"That's something, then," said Marion reluctantly.

"Oh Christ," said Leona, slumping back into the sofa, one arm still across her stomach. "I hurt." She wiped her face with her hand. "He wanted to have children, he said. Someday."

"I'm not at all surprised," said Marion. "Men are terribly keen to reproduce themselves, I've noticed."

Leona's chest bubbled with laughter. She sat up straight. "Don't do that. Don't make me laugh again, Marion."

"I didn't make you laugh in the first place. You made yourself laugh. Remember that, Leona," she said, getting up, "next time you feel this inexplicable yearning to share your living space with some inadequate male. You're your own best company. One more drink," she said, scooping up their glasses, "won't do us any harm."

"Look who's talking about sharing her living space. You're going to be sharing yours with several total strangers in a couple of weeks."

"I certainly am not," said Marion indignantly from the kitchen counter. She came back into the sitting room and handed Leona her glass. "They aren't going to be allowed past that door," she said, pointing, as she sat down. "If they try to come past that door, Spot will bite their feet off, won't you, Spot?" She held the dog's head in her hands and nuzzled him between the ears.

"What if they're terrible people?" said Leona, grinning. "What if you end up renting your rooms to weirdos?"

"I have no intention of doing that. I'll turn them away, if I don't like the look of them. And I won't even let them come to look at the rooms, if I don't like the sound of them on the phone."

The record came to an end and clicked itself off.

"Oh, Marion," said Leona. She sat back and closed her eyes. "I have so much exhilaration these days. I don't understand where the despair comes from." She opened her eyes. "It bewilders me." She looked at Marion and smiled. "I've got to go, while I'm still sober enough to drive."

Marion shut Spot in the kitchen and went to the front door with her.

"Thank you, Marion," said Leona, booted and jacketed against the raw chill of the March night. "For the scotch, and the conversation."

"I don't have any despair in my life," said Marion thoughtfully. "But I don't have a great deal of exhilaration, either."

She looked almost wan under the bright hall light, her face, without makeup, exposed and assailable. She had wrapped her arms around herself, hugging her breasts.

Leona dropped her purse on the floor and moved toward Marion, hands outstretched. She put her arms around Marion and felt her friend embrace her. Leona's cheek pressed against the softness of Marion's brown sweatshirt; Marion's breath warmed the top of her head. "Oh dear," said Leona, half laughing. She pulled away and saw Marion smiling at her, saw Marion's head bending toward her, felt Marion's lips on her cheek, the softest possible touch of skin to skin.

"Good night, Leona. Drive safely."

CHAPTER 4

Leona started working on the desk at the end of April. She didn't see much of Marion for the next couple of months. She had to get up at six o'clock, because of her new hours, and that meant going to bed at ten, and it took her several resentful weeks to get used to this.

She liked the work, and didn't miss reporting at all. She lived happily without overtime, was not distressed by the disappearance of her by-line, and actually enjoyed spending the whole day in the newsroom instead of rushing off to cover things and interview people. She was mildy surprised, having expected to suffer at least a few pangs of nostalgia.

She saw Marion at a couple of weekend parties during this period, and they talked now and then on the phone. Marion was slowly but steadily getting work, and had sold several pieces which would appear in the coming months in regional magazines. And she had rented her rooms. A new deskman from Ontario was living in one of them. He was a man of about Leona's age, not tall, with a wiry body, curly hair and a friendly manner. His name was David Bermas.

Late one afternoon near the end of June, Leona was at Marion's house for dinner and David Bermas was to be there, too.

"This is not going to be at all a special meal," said Marion firmly, turning from the oven to fix her green eyes on Leona. With a potholder she lifted the lid of the casserole and looked at it critically, and sniffed.

"It smells wonderful," said Leona from across the room, where Spot lay near her feet.

"It's just something I had in the freezer, that's all," said Marion, closing the oven door. "I've made a salad and I'll heat up some rolls and that's it. Nothing special at all." She set the timer on the stove, picked up her glass and sat down opposite Leona. "What do you think, should we just eat in here?"

"It would be less trouble to go into the dining room," said Leona, "if it's trouble you're thinking of. There's junk all over the kitchen table, in case you hadn't noticed."

"It's not the trouble. I just don't want this to be in any way an occasion," said Marion. "I don't want him to think I'm going to be making a habit of this. I told him when he moved in, 'I'm not running a boardinghouse here,' I said."

"He might not even remember to come. They say on the wire desk that he's a bit vague sometimes."

"Well, that's wonderful," said Marion.

"Wait till he shows up, then decide where to eat. If the table isn't even set yet, he'll know it's not an occasion." Leona grinned at her.

"Just wonderful," said Marion.

"Is he nice? He seems nice. But I don't have much to do with him at work."

"He's fine," said Marion. "I don't know whether he's nice or not. I barely know the man."

"How come you've invited him to dinner, then?"

"I'm not at all sure," said Marion cheerfully. "He seems a pleasant enough sort, and I thought he might be lonely. He never has any friends in to visit. Spends all his time up there typing something."

"Typing what?"

"I have no idea." Marion stood up. "Let's have our drinks in the other room for a change."

In the living room Marion curled up in the bay window, her arms around her knees, and Leona arranged herself on the sofa, propped up against an enormous pillow.

"You like it on the desk, don't you?" said Marion absently.

"Yeah, I do. It's kind of tough getting up so early in the morning, but yeah, I like it."

"I knew you would," said Marion. She was looking out the window. "I should tell you," she said, "that my mother's sick."

Leona was immediately interested. Marion seldom engaged in any kind of conversation about her mother. "How sick? What's the matter with her?"

"I don't know yet. But Emily says she's going to die in a few months." Marion sounded thoughtful, bemused, but her voice held an echo of astonishment.

"Marion, that's terrible." Leona sat up quickly, and swung her feet to the floor.

"Well," said Marion, turning to look at her, "I can't stand the woman, as you know."

Leona's arms ached to encircle her, to soothe and comfort; yet this obviously wasn't called for. "I know that's what you say, but, Jesus, Marion, I've never quite been able to believe it."

"Oh, it's true, all right," said Marion, nodding. "Can't abide her. Detest her. Always have. Still, it's odd to think of her dying."

"I don't know what to say. I feel terrible," said Leona, helplessly.

"I know. It's quite peculiar, isn't it?" Marion sat quite relaxed, hugging her knees. Her head was slightly tilted.

"What did she do to you, for God's sake?"

Marion stared out the window. "Well she didn't want to have me, that's the first thing."

"But that must have happened to half the mothers in the world, back then. I'm sure I must have come as a hell of a shock to mine, too."

Marion put her feet on the floor and sat straight-backed on the windowseat. "I'm sure you're right," she said briskly. "Anyway, the whole business will take some getting used to. My poor father, he's miserable, of course, he loves the woman to distraction. Couldn't even tell me about it himself. Had to ask Emily to do it." She brushed from her hands invisible crumbs, or dust, and poked the dog with her foot. "I think we'd better eat in the dining room after all, don't you? I'll set the table."

As she passed, Leona reached for her hand. "Marion."

"It's all right," said Marion. "I just wanted you to know. So that as things go along, I can tell you about them, if I want to, which of course I may not." She gave Leona a quick smile and went off to the kitchen.

Leona sat still, staring blankly through the window.

A few minutes later David Bermas appeared on the sidewalk and turned through Marion's gate.

"Here's your tenant," Leona called out.

He strolled up to the steps and inspected the raised flower beds on either side, and reached in to pull a few weeds, which he dropped on the grass.

"Christ, what's he doing?" muttered Leona. "He's weeding," she called to Marion, "can you believe that?"

He looked up at the window and smiled in at her.

"He's not coming in. He's going around the back."

"He always does that," said Marion, bringing cutlery to the dining room table. "He's got things planted out there."

"Really?" said Leona, amazed. "What kinds of things?"

"Flowers and vegetables, those kinds of things," said Marion vaguely. She shot an indignant glance at Leona. "He's dug up some of my grass back there."

Leona went into the kitchen and peered out the window into the backyard. About a third of the lawn had disappeared. Neat lines of white string marched in suspended rows back and forth across the rich black earth.

"He brought sacks of stuff," said Marion disbelievingly as she joined Leona at the window. "Fertilizer, and things like that. And dug them in there."

"But what do you do with the dog? That used to be Spot's yard."

"Sometimes I take him for walks, and sometimes I make David take him, since he's created the need, so to speak. But usually I just wait until it's dark and then let him loose out the front door."

Leona, dazed, noticed the flower garden which was springing up along the fence at the back and both sides of the yard.

"It'll be quite nice to sit out there, I suppose," said Marion, taking the casserole from the oven. "For those of us who have time for relaxation, among whom I certainly do not include myself."

"He's coming in," said Leona, retreating from the window.

"Hello, hello, hello Spot," said David, as the dog pressed against him, its tail whipping back and forth with joy. He rubbed behind Spot's ears and whacked him affectionately on the flank. "Lie down, now. Down," said David. He wiped his feet on the mat. "Everything's looking pretty good out there. Hi, Leona."

"Hi."

"I'm not late, am I, Marion?"

"Not quite," said Marion, energetically tossing a salad.

"That's a very good-looking garden," said Leona.

"Yeah." He sat down. "Anything I can do?" he asked Marion.

"No, everything's ready. I'll put the casserole back in the oven for a few minutes and get you a drink."

He sighed happily. "Nice and warm out there. I was beginning to think you didn't get summer in this place."

"There are no guarantees," said Leona. "We take each year as it comes."

"Do you want another drink, Leona?" said Marion, handing David a beer. Leona noticed that she hadn't had to ask him what he wanted.

"No thanks, I still have some," she said. "Apart from the weather," she said to David, "how do you like Calgary?"

He shrugged, and smiled. "It's okay. Interesting. Nice people."

"And the *Star?*"

He smiled again. "Same thing." He gestured around the room with the bottle of beer. "Found a good place to live, don't you think?"

"Yeah. How do you get along with the other tenants?"

"Hardly ever see them. That lady who lives upstairs—what's her name, Marion?"

"Clara. Clara Zeeman," said Marion, sitting down with her drink.

"Clara. Yeah. I hear her a lot. She's always muttering. Have you noticed that, Marion?"

"I make it a rule," said Marion firmly, "never to notice the idiosyncrasies of my tenants."

"What do you mean, she mutters?" said Leona. "What does she mutter about?"

"It's mostly in Dutch," said David, "so it's hard to tell. I think she's complaining about the stairs. She lives on the top floor."

"She's a cleaning lady," said Marion to Leona.

"My God, really?"

"She's got ten ladies she 'does for,' as she says," said David. "Two a day, five days a week."

"As soon as she loses one of them," said Marion, "I'm going to ask her to do for me."

"And then there's the guy who lives down the hall from me. He drives a truck." David sat up and rested his elbows on his knees, clutching his beer. "This guy's got a motorcycle, Marion lets him keep it in the garage. He comes out the front door all decked out in leather stuff, and a big black Plexiglas helmet, puts on a hell of a swagger. But you meet him in the hall, he says things like 'good evening,' and every time he has a bath, you go in the bathroom and the whole place has been scrubbed down with Lysol."

Marion nodded. "So far so good. I just hope neither of them ever leaves. I might not have such good luck the next time around."

"Don't worry about it," said David, grinning. "I'll be here for a while yet. I'll help you screen out the loonies."

"I think we'd better eat," said Marion, and she got up to put the food on the table.

Halfway through dinner, David turned suddenly to Leona. "I keep forgetting. I was supposed to say hello to you for Peter Blakey."

Leona looked at him in confusion. "Who?"

"Oh, good," said Marion delightedly. "She's finally forgotten all about him."

"Blakey," said David. "Peter Blakey. We were both covering something in Halifax. When I told him I was coming out here, he said to say hello to Leona Hadden." He looked at Marion. "She doesn't even remember him. Poor guy." He gave himself another helping of the casserole.

"I remember him," said Leona. "I lived with him for two years, for Christ's sake. Of course I remember him."

"Oh," said David, glancing at her.

Leona delicately tore a roll in half. "How is he?"

"Fine, I guess. I don't know. I only met him at that conference. Oh, he's going to Vancouver. He did say that. I guess he's there now. Had a desk job starting sometime in the spring."

"Wonderful," said Marion grimly, looking at Leona.

"That son-of-a-bitch." Leona pitched her roll onto her bread-and-butter plate and flung herself back in her chair, arms folded, face flushed.

"I don't think I should have mentioned this guy," said David.

Late that evening Leona tossed her clothes into the dryer and slammed the door shut. She dropped into one of the metal folding chairs set up along the wall in the laundry room, beyond the door, and lit a cigarette. It was a gray-green room without windows, since it was in the basement of her apartment building, and not a place where she cared to spend a lot of time.

Life was pretty funny, she thought, but she was not amused.

She had refused to go to Toronto with Peter not just because she was sick of his sleeping around, but also because she didn't want to live there. She wanted to go back to Vancouver eventually, and heading off three thousand miles in the opposite direction hadn't seemed the smartest way of going about that. She had planned to get working on it right away, as soon as he left, but she'd kept putting it off, and putting it off, and now . . .

Shit, she thought, throwing her cigarette onto the concrete floor and mashing it beneath her foot.

She sat back, hands in her lap, leaning against the wall. The dryer tumbling her clothes around was the only machine in operation. The top-loading washers and dryers stood in two rows, facing each other, their doors open, like soldiers at ease, except for hers.

She deeply resented having to think of him in Vancouver. The place was changed for her now, she thought moodily, thanks to Marion's tenant, busily scattering his news. She would have been better off never knowing he was there. Yet she couldn't blame David. She would have heard about it from someone else, sooner or later.

Gloomily, she crossed her arms, and spun for herself a fantasy in which on one of her trips home they met on the street. On Georgia, it would be, in front of the soaring glass façade of Eaton's. She would be tripping lightly down the steps into the courtyard at the corner of Granville, and he would see her and hurriedly approach. "Leona!" he would call out, and she would turn and look at him quizzically, not immediately able to place him. (Bullshit, she said to herself, but swept on, enjoying it.) "My God," he would say, taking her hand, "Leona."

She heard the elevator, then heels clicking quickly along the hall leading to the laundry room, and sat up straight, feeling foolish.

Emily came in with a large plastic bag and begun unloading clothes into one of the washers.

"Hi," said Leona.

Emily turned with a small smothered shriek, clutching a dark blue bath towel to her chest.

"I'm sorry," said Leona, standing hastily. "I didn't mean to startle you."

Emily leaned against the washer and shook her head, smiling. "I was so wrapped up in my thoughts, I didn't even think to look around." She dropped the towel into the washer. "It's been a long day."

"Let me help you." She went to Emily and helped her load the rest of the clothes.

"It's my birthday on Sunday," said Emily. She wore a rose-colored dress, and looked as though she had been out for the evening.

Peter's birthday was in June, too, Leona remembered, fitting a yellow sheet on top of the other clothes in the washer. She couldn't recall the day, though, which was satisfying.

"No celebration," said Emily. "Not this year." She sprinkled soap powder on her laundry and closed the washer and turned on the machine.

"Marion told me about her mother," said Leona. "I'm sorry. It must be very hard for all of you."

Emily stood still, her hands flat on the top of the washer. After a moment she turned to Leona. The harsh lights in the laundry room shone implacably upon the aging of her flesh. "I saw the strangest thing tonight," she said. "There was a man lying in the dark. He seemed to be asleep."

"Where?" said Leona, puzzled.

"I wish I'd had my notebook with me," said Emily. "I could be more specific." She flushed, and turned away to fold the plastic bag. She did it swiftly, competently, and again made Leona think of her mother. "I must get back upstairs," said Emily. "I'm not going to put these things in the dryer until morning." She smiled at Leona, composed. "Good night," she said, and Leona heard her heels tap-tapping quickly up the hall, and heard the elevator door open, and close, and heard the car ascend.

The dryer stopped, and Leona started folding her clothes.

He would take her hand and say, "Leona. My God . . ."

He would want her to have dinner with him, but she would be busy. Probably.

The son-of-a-bitch.

CHAPTER 5

On the last Saturday in October, the day before Halloween, Leona was in a shopping center in northwest Calgary, looking for a birthday gift for her mother. She would have described herself as strolling through the mall, but actually she was bustling, propelling herself along with short sharp steps, a heavy shopping bag in her hand and a purse over her shoulder. She had put aside her cape in favor of a long down-filled jacket; it was unseasonably cold. A scarf hung around her neck, fleece-lined gloves were stuffed into her pockets, and her boots were high, almost flat-heeled, warm, with corrugated soles for walking through snow or along icy sidewalks. Although she would have insisted that she was relaxed and enjoying herself, she was beginning to feel too hot, and slightly frazzled, and she bitterly resented this early taste of winter, even though she knew it would go away. Worst of all, nowhere had she been able to find the hooded poncho she was determined to buy for her mother, and she was furious to have spent so much time and energy driving out to Market Mall only to be once more disappointed.

She hovered around the benches grouped near the entrance to Woodward's department store until an overweight woman with flushed cheeks and tangled hair hoisted herself up and dragged her two children off down the mall. Leona edged into the vacant space on the bench, and was immediately joined by a teenage couple. The teenagers fell into an embrace. Leona shifted position until her back was to them, and dug into her purse for her cigarettes.

It was as she straightened up, her purse on her lap, cigarettes in one hand and a red disposable lighter in the other, that her heart stuttered, grew still, then leaped in panic, hurling itself repeatedly against her rib cage.

Oh shit oh Christ.

She wanted to call out timidly for help. She imagined turning around and tapping the shoulders of the teenagers; excuse me, please, but could you give me some assistance? She imagined their astonishment, the interrupted kiss still trembling in the air between their open mouths, as they stared at her.

She grabbed at her shopping bag and stood up, her heart pitching wildly in her chest, its dinning surely audible; but nobody paid any attention except for a weary bearded man in cords and a jeans jacket leaning against the wall nearby; he watched her hopefully and pushed himself off the wall, ready to claim her seat on the bench.

Leona walked unsteadily toward the nearest exit to the parking lot, her shoulder bag held tightly to her chest. Her heart's panicked beating accelerated, but still it didn't hurt her. She knew that the compulsion to keep moving was an instinct unlikely to accompany a heart attack. And surely the painlessness of the experience must be another indication that nothing serious was going on. But she was nevertheless terrified; her heart was obviously aghast about something.

"Okay, okay." She spoke to it comfortingly, aloud but quietly, trying not to move her lips, although God knew if she could wander through this crowd without anybody noticing the volcanic thundering of her heart she could certainly get away with talking to herself. "I'll take you off to my doctor," she promised her heart, which responded by ignoring her; it was like a frantic animal thrown by something invisible into suicidal terror, unable even to register the importunate soothings of its master.

The coldness of the fast-dying afternoon seemed to muffle its lunatic thrashings. She'd come outdoors on the wrong side of the shopping center, and had to tramp halfway around the sprawling complex to get to her car. By the time she reached it her face and ears were throbbing and her fingers and toes were numb, but at least her heart's frenzied beating had subsided. Next time it happens I'll just run outside and bury myself in a snowdrift, thought Leona; I'll freeze the sucker immobile, that's what I'll do.

She creaked open the door of her Honda and threw her shopping bag into the back seat. She got in and shut the door and rested her arms on the wheel, and her head on her arms.

She had expected never to have this happen to her again.

On Monday she called her doctor, using a pay phone in the lobby of the *Star* building because she didn't want to be overheard. She decided that doctors take hearts quite seriously. She had barely gotten her symptoms out of her mouth when she had an appointment for the same afternoon. And she wasn't kept waiting at all, not even in the little cubicle where she usually sat cooling her heels for at least fifteen minutes before her doctor swept in, frowning at Leona's apparently indecipherable file, or perhaps just trying to remember who she was.

Her doctor was a woman in her early sixties who seemed to believe she had a practice overflowing with hypochondriacs. But this day she didn't number Leona among them. She was in no hurry, listened with great concentration to Leona's heart for a long time, and briskly asked many questions to which Leona, with mounting hopefulness, was able to reply "no." No pain, no tingling in the extremities, no shortness of breath.

"But it scared the hell out of me."

The doctor nodded.

"I thought I was having a heart attack."

The doctor nodded again. She said she couldn't hear anything abnormal in Leona's chest.

"Well, but it's not happening right now," said Leona.

The doctor assured her that she had not had a heart attack, nor was she likely to have one. Leona was uncertain how to accept this. Something peculiar had definitely occurred in her chest cavity. She thought she owed her troubled heart more than what the doctor was providing.

"You have to get off the pill, that's the first thing," said her doctor. "And stop smoking."

"I only drink decaffeinated coffee now," said Leona helpfully, pushing her hair back behind her ears.

"Stop smoking, and stop taking the pill. If you have any more problems, come and see me again."

The doctor was on her way out the door when Leona blurted, "Wait!" Her hand was in the air, an involuntary gesture of appeal.

The doctor turned. "Yes?"

Sitting on the examining table, inadequately clothed in a paper gown, Leona felt like a supplicant. "I have a lot of trouble," she said, straining for dignity, "getting to sleep."

The doctor whisked out a prescription pad and scribbled on it. She tore off the prescription and handed it to Leona. "Only twelve of them. You won't need them after a week or so." She smiled tentatively, and Leona realized with a shock that she was not a graceless woman; merely shy. "Try not to worry. Your heart is fine. Sound as a dollar."

On her way home Leona stopped at a drugstore to get the prescription filled.

Her heart remained docile, quiescent in her chest.

At night, arms behind her head, she lay quietly, confident of sleep, and reminded herself that she wasn't going to have a heart attack; the doctor had promised her. But this didn't comfort her. She dreaded another occurrence of that agitated pounding. Her heart might not be ill, but it was suffering attacks of great alarm. What if next time it were unable to contain itself? What if next time its reckless thudding tore it from its moorings, or cracked open her aorta?

Thank God for chemicals, she thought, as sleep drifted over her, obliterating anxiety and loss.

CHAPTER 6

Leona went to work the next day. When she awoke in the morning nothing extraordinary was going on in her body. Staying at home thinking about things wasn't going to help and in fact might provoke a recurrence, she decided. If it happened at work she could always just walk out of the newsroom, straight to her damn doctor's office, and let her figure it out. So she got out of bed, dressed, ate a piece of toast and an orange, and walked to work in the dark of early morning, as though everything in her life were normal.

But Bruce Menzies didn't go to work that day. His wife, Norma, called to say he was sick.

He didn't come in on Wednesday, either. Leona did, and her heart continued to behave itself, which was a good thing, because Bruce's absence created a lot of extra work.

"What's with Menzies?" said Vern Thursday morning when she made the rounds with the clipboard.

"Sick," said Leona. "What have you got coming today?"

"Sick?" said Vern meaningfully.

"Yeah, Vern, sick. As in unwell. Indisposed. Ailing. What have you got for us today?"

"What's the matter with him? Too much firewater?" He chortled, looking around for an audience, but nobody was near except Leona.

"Jesus Christ, Vern, do you plan to do any work today or are you going to spend all your time minding other people's business? Now what the hell have you got coming, I said?" She badly wanted a cigarette.

But Vern wasn't the only one to speculate about Bruce's condition, and by Friday afternoon even Ziggy was uneasy.

"I'll drive out there on the weekend," Leona told him, "and check things out."

It wasn't until she got home that evening that Leona realized she was afraid to drive alone to Bruce's house. She was afraid her heart might make her have an accident. She was afraid to be out of reach of help.

Despising her weakness and her fear, she called Marion and asked if she would go with her, and could they use Marion's car because the Honda was being serviced.

"You people have no faith," said Marion impatiently. "The man hasn't gone on a bender for months." But she agreed to go.

The world was getting steadily colder. At night the stars burned unnaturally bright, all extraneous materials between them and earth exterminated by the ever-increasing cold. There was no snow. The days and nights remained clear.

"How's your mother?" Leona said to Marion as they headed south out of town on the Macleod Trail.

"Oh, let's not talk about my mother," said Marion cheerily. "It's a beautiful day, look at the mountains, Leona, they're all white and positively Alp-like."

Marion hadn't brought up her mother's illness since she'd mentioned it in June. It must be much worse now, thought Leona, and she glanced at Marion, but Marion's pale skin was smooth and her green eyes seemed untroubled and her hands on the steering wheel were relaxed.

"How's business?" said Leona. "Are you keeping the wolf from your door?" She was having to look hard for things to say. Without work to distract her, she seemed unable to think about anything but her heart. I'm so wrapped up in my damn self, she thought disgustedly.

"Just barely." Marion sounded grim. "Things have dried up recently. But they may improve in the near future," she said, more confidently. "What I need is something regular, so that at least I'll be able to depend upon a minimum amount of money coming in every month."

"Where do you find such a thing?" Leona's eyes were drawn to the mountains, brilliant against the clear winter sky, a gateway made of cold white marble.

"I might find it at the *Star*. They want to talk to me about writing a column."

"You're kidding," said Leona, turning to look at her.

"I know," said Marion with an apologetic grin. "It's ironic, isn't it?"

"Don't worry about it. I'm happy doing what I'm doing. What kind of a column?"

"Something for the editorial page. Woman speaks out firmly on all manner of things. That sort of stuff."

"Good. That's terrific." Leona felt her heart skip, then strike a heavy beat. She held her breath, but it found its rhythm and settled down to a steady tick, tock, like a clock wound just in time.

They turned off onto a two-lane paved road which led east through Fish Creek Park. The land rolled away on either side. The mountains were behind them, now, and the sun, too, already starting its downward arc.

"I hope Bruce is all right," said Leona, and reached for her handbag before she remembered that there weren't any cigarettes in it. She told herself to be glad that Marion didn't smoke, but she wasn't.

For several minutes they drove in silence.

"This is where you turn," said Leona.

"I know, I know," said Marion, wheeling the station wagon suddenly to the left.

She drove more slowly now, because the road was gravel. An occasional house could be seen, surrounded by shivering trees, but mostly the land stretched flat, gold and brown, with fences at right angles marking off enormous fields.

"Is there something wrong, Leona?" said Marion carefully, watching the road.

Leona's heart lurched, and she cursed it. "What? How do you mean?"

"You look a little peaked, I thought. That's all. Not your normal ebullient self."

Ebullience, thought Leona. That's what I used to have. She considered this, wonderingly. "I'm just thoughtful today, I guess," she said to Marion, who nodded and didn't look at her.

They turned into a long driveway lined with some kind of tree which Bruce had planted four years earlier, and which still hadn't achieved a height of ten feet. He talked with great satisfaction about those trees, and the six others he had planted near the house. He had made sure to space them far enough apart so that when they reached their full height and bushiness they wouldn't crowd each other; so far, thought Leona, you could drive an earthmover between them without touching a branch on either side.

They pulled up by the front steps and Marion turned off the motor. They looked at one another for a moment before getting out.

Marion knocked at the door, which was opened almost immediately by Bruce's son, Garry. "Did you bring your dog?" he said to Marion, craning to see behind her.

"No," said Marion. "Is your father home?"

"Why not?" said Garry. "This is a good place for a dog to visit."

"My dog doesn't like cars," said Marion, and Leona gave her a reproving glance.

Norma appeared behind Garry, smiling. "My God, this is a surprise.

Get out of the way, Garry, let them in. What are you two doing away out here?"

"We wanted to have a look at the park," said Leona. "And once we got that far we decided to keep on going. Maybe we should have called first, though."

"I don't think there are any phones in the park," said Norma, with a slight smile. "Come on in." She pushed Garry gently out of the way and put out an arm to welcome them. She closed the door behind them and ushered them into the living room, whose high wide windows faced out upon a deck, a large area of brown grass, limitless flat fields beyond, and the abrupt and distant mountains.

"Oh God, it's beautiful, I always forget," said Leona. Tears stung her eyes and were as suddenly gone.

"Let me see if Bruce is awake," said Norma. She turned to leave the room.

"Oh, don't waken him," said Marion hastily.

"I won't," said Norma, and disappeared.

"Maybe if you take him out just for a block or so every day," said Garry. He flung himself into a chair.

After a minute Marion looked at him, and saw that he was staring at her patiently. "I beg your pardon? Were you speaking to me?"

"He probably just has to get used to it, that's all."

"He means Spot," said Leona.

"Yeah," said Garry. "All dogs like to ride in cars. Yours just isn't used to it, that's all." He leaped to his feet and approached her. Marion drew back slightly. "How do you get him places, if he won't ride in cars?"

"I didn't say he *wouldn't* ride in them," said Marion coolly. "I said he didn't *like* to ride in them."

"He'd think it was worth it, once he got here. Look at that," said Garry, pointing out the window. "Look at all those miles and miles he'd have to run around in."

"Why don't you get a dog of your own," said Marion, "if you're so fond of them?"

"We're going to, some day."

"He's still sleeping," said Norma, coming back into the room. She wasn't much taller than Leona. Her short black hair had some gray in it, and she looked weary, but at ease. "He's had real bad flu. But the doctor says he's going to be fine. He may not be back at work on Monday," she said to Leona, "but maybe Tuesday, and Wednesday for sure. How about some coffee?" she said, looking from one of them to the other. "It'll just take a minute."

"No, really, thanks, Norma, but we're on our way home," said Leona. "I'm glad he's getting better. Tell him everybody says hello."

"It's been quite a week," said Norma. "But Garry's been a big help."

"I take his temperature," said Garry. "That's my job."

"Thanks for coming," said Norma at the door. She looked at them speculatively. "You can report that he's alive and getting well."

From the car they waved at her, standing on the step with her arm around Garry's shoulder.

"I feel like a spying shit," said Leona as they drove away. She sighed and stared out the window. "All those miles and miles of nothing." On the other side of the mountains lay British Columbia, and on its Pacific shore was Vancouver, a languid, glittering city in a green and pleasant land. A big city. She had walked its streets and beaches when she went home in the summer, and had seen not a soul she knew.

"We weren't spying, exactly," said Marion, and laughed, but it turned into a shudder. "I am very tired of sick people. He's probably all rumpled and smelly." She opened her hands on the wheel, closed them again to grip it more firmly. "I'm glad we didn't have to see him."

Leona had rested her head for a moment against the window but she had to lift it quickly because the road was bumpy, and Marion had speeded up. "He's just got the flu," she said sharply. "Slow down, will you? I sure know where not to go for sympathy, if I ever get sick." She turned away, because of a sharp pain in her throat. "I hear you went out with Vern a while ago. Jesus, I was amazed."

The car was rattling furiously along the gravel, sending clouds of dust billowing up behind. "Sheer desperation, that's what it was, my dear," said Marion. "Won't do it again, I can tell you. The man wanted to solve my sexual problems." Her laughter pealed into the car, filling Leona's breathing space.

"What sexual problems?"

"I don't have any. But he wanted to solve them anyway." She turned onto Fish Creek Road. "Oh, that's a relief, pavement at last." She shifted into fourth gear.

"He's going to be calling you every week now, you know."

"He calls me every week anyway. I'll just tell him no. I don't have any difficulty telling people no."

"Marion, stop the car."

Leona sat as straight as she could, her hands on the seat on either side of her. The car came quickly to a stop on the edge of the road. Leona got out and started walking along the shoulder, her fists clenched, got to keep moving that will do it goddamn useless heart . . . she struggled with it, willing it to subside, walking faster and faster, and then she stopped, facing the mountains, and concentrated on the sun which was suspended just above the highest peaks. She closed her eyes but the sun stayed there, visible. She felt her troubled heartbeat subside. In a moment Marion's arm was around her shoulder but still she shivered in the cold wind, able to feel it, now.

"I'm all right. Really," she said.

"What is it? What's wrong with you?"

They stood side by side, looking at the mountains blazing in the sun. Leona turned, leaned against her. "Oh, Marion. I'm so scared. I'm so fucking scared."

"I am quite sure," said Marion, as they headed back into Calgary, "that your doctor's right, and there's nothing wrong with you. But you absolutely *must* go back to her, and tell her you want to see a specialist. You *must* do that, Leona, or you're going to worry yourself to death."

Leona, reclining in the passenger seat, which Marion had wound halfway down, was lulled, sleepy, and at peace. She nodded. Marion glanced at her sharply. "I will, Marion. I promise."

"You should have told me. Right away, the first time it happened. Really, Leona, what a useless sort of friend you are, sometimes."

Leona, smiling, closed her eyes.

CHAPTER 7

She knew Marion was right, and intended to go back to her doctor almost right away. But sharing her worry, she found, had diminished it. Hard work, sleeping pills, and confiding in Marion had united to bring a measure of tranquillity she was reluctant to disturb.

Depriving her heart of nicotine might have something to do with it, too, she admitted. She hadn't had a cigarette for more than a week now. But it was still exceedingly difficult not to smoke.

Marion called four days after they had driven out to see Bruce.

"No, Marion, I haven't called her yet, but I will. I'm going to do it. Really."

"Remember now, tell her you want to see a specialist," said Marion. "You want an expert opinion, that's what you want."

"I'll remember," said Leona patiently. "I'll tell her."

But she continued to put it off.

Jack Hiller, the managing editor, called her in to see him the following week, on a Friday morning. He was sitting back in his chair, feet crossed on the corner of his desk, fiddling with a pencil in his hands.

He watched her as she crossed the expanse of carpet and sat in a leather chair opposite him.

"Well, Ms. Hadden. You're going to be holding the fort at the city desk for a couple of days, I hear."

"Just for a couple of days, yeah. The two days before Christmas." Ziggy and Bruce were giving themselves a long Christmas weekend.

"I've called you in here to discuss the December 24 paper," said Hiller, his dark eyes glinting from behind his glasses in a manner which made Leona uneasy. He had black hair and looked as though he had once been a fullback, though she didn't think he had.

"Oh?" she said cautiously.

"I want a full page of good news," he said, looking at her down the barrel of his pencil.

She looked at the row of windows that filled one wall of his office. She thought that if they demolished the walls that separated his office from the newsroom, the people out there could have some daylight coming in on them. She looked back at him, politely. "You want a what?"

He smiled at her. "I want every beat reporter to bring you a good-news story, and I want you to assemble a full page of these wondrous and salutary scribblings, for the delight and edification of our Christmas Eve readers."

"You mean, 'good,' as in 'about nice things,' not 'good,' as in 'well done.' "

"Precisely. Except that I also expect them to be well done. Of course."

"Of course."

He lit a cigarette and held it between his teeth, puffing. She thought that if it weren't for the cigarette he might be grinning at her.

"They aren't going to like the idea much. The reporters."

"Ah, but this newspaper isn't put together for the benefit of the reporters, now is it?"

Leona sighed. "Do you want to know what I think about this?"

He considered, puffing. He took the cigarette out of his mouth and put it in the ashtray on his desk. "Not particularly. But if you'd like to tell me, by all means, go ahead."

Leona sighed again. "I don't know what I think about it. I'll wait until I've seen what they come up with." She stood up to leave.

"Just remember, Ms. Hadden, that what they come up with will depend to a large extent on you."

She turned from the door to look at him. "And a Merry Christmas to you, too," she said.

"I have every confidence in you," said Hiller gravely.

Back at the city desk, Ziggy and Bruce didn't share her outrage and dismay, but it was easy for them, thought Leona; they wouldn't even be there.

"We tried that one year in Winnipeg," said Ziggy, his hands linked behind his head, legs crossed at the ankles. He was wearing a gray suit, a white shirt, and a bright red tie. "Could have been interesting, too. Only problem was, on the night of the twenty-third there was an eight-car pileup on the freeway, a warehouse burned down, and two planes collided at the airport. They were both trying to land at the same time."

"Beautiful," said Bruce, with a grin.

"What the hell will I do, if something like that happens?" said Leona.

"Use your best judgment," said Ziggy. "Page One would take most of any catastrophe stuff. And the stories that spill over onto the local pages—well, either you scrap the good-news page, or bury the real stuff on the inside."

"Great," said Leona.

The reporters were indignant, as she had expected. They insisted vigorously that there was no good news on their beats, and that even if there had been, they had too many important stories to write to bother with fluff.

"Don't give me that stuff," said Leona to Vern and the other two city hall reporters. "If you can't find me something nice, find me something funny. You'd think I was asking you to rewrite the Bible. Find some alderman who brings poor people home for Christmas dinner, or something."

They broke into laughter at this, and one of them, sympathetic at last, said, "This is an edict from the Hill, isn't it?"

"Yeah it is," said Leona. "And you're taking the whole week between Christmas and New Year's off, so do something kind for the city desk so you can enjoy yourself and not feel guilty."

She stomped off to see the education reporter, who was a lot easier to deal with.

By lunchtime she had talked to them all, and got grudging promises from each of them. The two people covering the legislature had refused to get anything that might make the politicians look good, but said they'd dig around among the civil servants. The police reporters agreed to do a piece on the toys the cops collected, repaired and wrapped each year for disadvantaged children. And the medical reporter would try to find a miracle, or at least a well-timed unexpected recovery.

Leona slumped in her chair, exhausted. Her hand went to her chest, and she patted herself there. "My God," she muttered to Ziggy, "it would be easier to write the whole page myself."

"Sure it would," said Ziggy.

"Excuse me, Leona," she heard, and looked up to see Silka Witowsky standing at her desk. "I know I'm not a beat reporter," said Silka, "but I could probably get you a Christmas story somewhere, if you need another one. I think it's a wonderful idea, a page full of good news." She was wearing tailored slacks and a silk blouse, and Leona, looking out across the newsroom, saw half a dozen male heads turned in her direction; they liked to watch her walk. "It gets so depressing," said Silka, "reading about the economy, and shootings, and people hurting one another. I think it will give people a real lift, a page like that."

"It'll give me a real pain in the ass," said Bruce, from his desk on the other side of Ziggy's.

"Take her up on it, Leona," said Ziggy. "In case one of those yahoos doesn't come through."

"I'll take anything I can get, Silka," said Leona. "Thanks." She watched Silka walk back to her desk and saw heads swiveling to follow her passage.

Silka had arrived four months earlier, straight out of college, and had filled the last job opening that had come up since the budget cuts. She had arrived in the newsroom unannounced and filled out an application form and showed Ziggy some of the things she had written at school.

Later that morning Leona had met Vern and Ziggy in the cafeteria.

"Well, whaddya think, Zig," said Vern. "Are you gonna hire her?"

"I think I might," said Ziggy quietly, watching as Silka and Bruce approached their table.

"She was looking a little lost up there," said Bruce uncomfortably, "so I brought her down for coffee."

She was in her early twenties and had long dark brown hair with a satin shine to it, and brown eyes. She wasn't beautiful, but she was striking, with high cheekbones and a pronounced jawline and a long, elegant neck. Mostly, though, her attractiveness lay in the lithesome way she moved. Her body was very much aware of itself, and she dressed it extremely well. Her waist was small, her legs were long, and she was effortlessly limber. Leona thought she must be an athlete of some sort; maybe she throws the discus, she thought, looking at her, not knowing much about it.

The girl had sat down hesitatingly at their table and smiled quickly, not looking at anyone in particular. The men began speaking in tones more hearty than usual. Leona glanced at them, amazed.

"So," said Vern, "you think you'd like to join us, do you?" Leona saw him watching the girl's bent head, which she raised to smile at him. She had a lot of straight white teeth. Wonder how long she's had her braces off, thought Leona.

"I think I would, yes," said Silka. Leona had thought pearls might drop from her lips, but her voice, although pleasing, was quite normal.

"I think we're going to be able to make room for you," said Ziggy. Leona looked at him curiously. He was smiling at the girl, and his hands were methodically destroying the Styrofoam cup that had contained his coffee.

Silka sat up eagerly and leaned forward, resting her hands on the table. "Really?" she said. "Do you really mean it?"

Ziggy and Bruce and Vern all laughed at this, indulgent chucklings.

"I'm very grateful for the opportunity," said Silka. "I'm extremely interested in mass communication."

Leona took a quick sip of her coffee. Along her spine ran ripples of embarrassment.

"Ah," said Bruce politely. "Mass communication, hmmm."

"What do you mean by that, exactly?" said Vern. He smiled at her encouragingly, and folded his hands on his protruding belly.

The girl turned to him. "It's so important that we understand each other," she said. Leona wondered if she herself had ever been that young. "Newspapers have such an important role to play, don't you think?" she said, turning to Ziggy, her satin hair swinging.

"Yes, I do," said Ziggy courteously. "But I wonder—"

"But then," said Silka, frowning into her coffee, "so does television. It may be that the electronic medium is more suitable for me than newspapers." She looked up at Ziggy apologetically. "Of course it's too early to tell. And newspapers offer more scope for learning and exploring."

"Learning and exploring," said Vern to the light fixture above his head.

"And I see," she said, smiling at Leona, "that there's room for advancement for women here."

Leona, who had been feeling like a spectator, looked back at Silka, her mind blank. She had a very direct gaze, this girl, and Leona thought to her surprise that she spotted some intelligence in there someplace.

And she'd been right, she thought now, watching Silka settle herself at her VDT and bend her head over the pages of her notebook. Silka asked a lot of questions, learned quickly, and did good work.

If only she didn't *care* so much, thought Leona wearily, getting up to go to lunch.

She ate in the cafeteria quickly, so as to be finished before anyone started smoking.

Back at her desk she munched an apple and tried to work out which of the Christmas stories she could count on, and how good they were likely to be.

After a while Bruce came back, stretched, and sat at his desk.

Leona drummed her fingers on the arms of her chair, wishing for a cigarette.

"Did it ever occur to you, Bruce," she said, "that none of this stuff we do every day means anything?"

He turned to look at her. Eventually he nodded.

There was nobody else at or near the city desk, and only a few reporters in the newsroom, working at their VDT's or talking together.

"We just keep running the same old stories," said Leona.

He nodded again.

"For a while you think it's useful." She nudged a wastebasket with her foot. "But none of it accomplishes a damned thing," she said slowly. It occurred to her that in order to be saying these things she must be angry or despondent, but she didn't seem to be either.

Bruce got up and sat on Ziggy's desk. He took one of her hands in both of his. His hair shone like gold. "Some things get accomplished, some of the time. Some things are worth doing." He looked down. "You've got pretty hands," he said, and grinned at her.

Reluctantly, Leona pulled her hand away.

"You've gotta get your pleasure from the work, Lee. Just the day-to-day stuff. Making a story better. Meeting the deadlines. And sometimes giving people information they'd maybe just as soon not have. Pride in the craft, kid, and all that." He stood up. He seemed to loom over her. He really was awfully big, thought Leona. "Hang in there, Lee." He returned to his desk.

Leona picked up her shoulder bag from the floor. "I'm going out for a while," she said. She got her cape from the locker and left the building to walk for half an hour through the Devonian Gardens, whose humid air and recorded birdsongs and lush greenery were too far above street level to convince her of anything, but where at least there was no talk.

That afternoon Marion called to ask again whether she had been back to her doctor, and when Leona admitted that she hadn't, Marion became exasperated, then angry. Leona couldn't blame her. But it's my damn heart, after all, she said defiantly to herself when they had hung up.

After dinner she wandered around her apartment, dusting things, straightening pictures on the walls, changing her bed, since she planned to do her laundry the next day.

She was restless, in need of company. She didn't want to see Marion and get harangued some more. She decided to call Emily and invite her down for tea.

And then the buzzer sounded from the lobby. It was Bruce. She thought he sounded drunk, but she pressed the button that opened the downstairs door.

"Shit shit shit," she muttered, hurriedly combing her hair in front of the bathroom mirror.

"I just thought I'd drop in and say hello," said Bruce when she opened the door. He looked like a great golden bear, with his blond hair and heavy caramel-colored jacket.

Leona sighed. "Hello, Bruce."

"May I come in?"

She stepped back, and he walked carefully into the hall, his hand on the wall, lightly, as though he were interested in its texture. "Whoops," he said as he ran out of wall, and staggered a little.

Leona took his arm and led him into the living room. "How about some coffee?" she said, helping him into a chair. She stood in front of him, hands on her hips. "Black, okay?"

"Okay, Lee, sure."

She heard him humming to himself while she fixed instant decaffeinated coffee in two mugs. When she took it into the living room he smiled at her.

"Norma's going to be worried," said Leona sternly.

"Oh, that Norma, she's a prince of a girl," said Bruce. He slurped delicately at the coffee. "Christ, that's hot." He put the mug on the table next to his chair. "Leona, I notice you aren't smoking anymore. How come?"

"Smoking isn't good for you."

Bruce nodded, looking at her intently. His eyes were the color of a clear summer sky. "You were the most cheerful thing we had around that place, until lately." He paused. "Maybe you ought to start again. Smoking."

Leona laughed, with a mild hysteria. "Drink your coffee, Bruce. I've got to get you sober enough to drive home." She had meant to sound brisk and positive, but her voice trembled, and she put a hand over her mouth.

Bruce got up quickly and sat next to her on the sofa. "I'm not the smartest guy I know," he said, stroking her hair, "but I know there's something going wrong with you." He grinned at her. "I'm not completely sober, I admit it, but I'm not completely drunk, either." He gathered her in his arms and rocked her gently. "Couldn't do this sober. Too shy. Planned to get a bit corked today anyway."

Leona struggled in his embrace, just for form, and decided he probably hadn't even noticed. She lay against his chest, aroused and expectant, and thought she heard his heart in there beating steadily, calmly. It was exceedingly pleasant, being held close against a large, well-muscled male body.

But soon she was frowning. He continued to hold her, patting her back soothingly, but it was probably precisely how he held his son when Garry fell off his bicycle. Leona waited for him to turn her slightly in his arms, to lift her chin so that he could kiss her, but it was clear that he had nothing in mind beyond comforting her. She was looking down at his lap, and lascivious longing must be all over her face, she thought; she turned to press her face into his chest, stifling a hopeless giggle. He pulled away, then, his hands on her shoulders, and looked at her worriedly.

"Are you crying, Lee?"

"Oh no, Bruce, really, thank you, I feel much better. I really do." In a rush of tenderness she kissed his cheek. "Thank you."

"What are friends for, eh?" he said affectionately. "Do you want to talk about it? Whatever's going wrong with you?"

"No, Bruce," she said with regret. "But thank you."

At the door he stooped to kiss her forehead, but Leona raised her head too much and he kissed her lips instead. His mouth brushed hers, retreated, returned, kissed her more firmly. He stood up straight and looked down at her. They waited. Then he touched her hair, and left.

When he had gone she pounded her head, gently, against the wall next to the hall closet. "For one little minute, there, Norma, by Christ . . ."

Suddenly she lifted her head, stunned, remembering that she no longer took the birth control pill.

Oh well, she thought, sighing, and pushed herself away from the wall.

It was very quiet in her apartment.

She turned on the television and tried to watch it.

Her apartment was a hollow place. Bruce's presence had given it a temporary abundance; his departure seemed to have gutted all of its rooms. Leona was furious with herself, for allowing only other people to bring warmth and life into what was supposed to be her home.

CHAPTER 8

Vernon Titus Palmer shot through the door ahead of her. "Merry Christmas!" he said, wrapping his arms around Marion.

"Out of the way," said Leona, pushing him aside.

"Merry Christmas," said Marion, smiling at them. She was wearing a floor-length dark green velvet dress that had long sleeves but revealed quite a lot elsewhere. Leona was slightly shocked. She looked closely at Marion, but could see no sign of grief.

Emily had given her the news of Marion's mother's death a month earlier. She hadn't seemed terribly upset. Maybe she wasn't all that fond of her sister-in-law. Leona had immediately phoned Marion, empathetic sorrow heavy in her chest, but found that Marion was perfectly calm, even cheerful. Leona had put this down to shock. She had thought of sending flowers to the funeral, but since she had never met either of Marion's parents, this didn't seem appropriate. She had thought of sending flowers to Marion but couldn't imagine how they might be received.

A week after the funeral, Marion called to invite her for Christmas dinner. Leona accepted with relief, since her job didn't allow her to go home this year. They had talked next not of Marion's loss but about Leona's heart, and conversation had lapsed again into argument.

Leona, harassed, began to wish she had resisted the urge to confide in Marion, who was apparently not going to leave her in peace until her advice had been taken. But Leona remained profoundly reluctant to go off to a specialist. As the days passed, and she braced herself for the next confrontation with Marion, she admitted to herself that she was a coward; she was afraid that a cardiologist would find something her own doctor had missed.

"Come in and meet my father," said Marion on Christmas afternoon, after stacking their coats and scarves and boots unceremoniously at the bottom of the stairs. She led Vern and Leona through the glass-paned door into the living room.

On the sofa opposite the door sat Emily, wearing a wool dress in a soft shade of red. Next to her was a woman Leona had never seen before, with startling orange hair. Marion's tenant, David Bermas, stood next to a chair beside the sofa, and Marion's father sat to Leona's right, as she came through the door.

He was a man of medium height seated in a low chair that forced his knees to stick up higher than seemed comfortable. He had glasses, and what hair was left on his head was gray. He wore dark gray trousers, a white shirt, a dark blue tie and a gray cardigan, buttoned up.

Vern went straight over to him. "Please accept my condolences," he said solemnly, "upon your recent bereavement." He took Henry Tyler's hand and shook it tenderly.

How tasteless, thought Leona, devoutly wishing that she, too, had prepared for this moment.

"I'm sure you must miss your wife very much," she murmured to him, and was horrified to see Mr. Tyler's eyes fill with tears.

"Buck up, Dad," said Marion. "Here, have a piece of Emily's fudge."

He took a piece and sat holding it expectantly, as though it were something he would soon have to pass along to someone else.

The red-haired woman turned out to be Clara Zeeman, Marion's cleaning-lady tenant.

In the window seat, which was just barely big enough to accommodate him, Spot lay on his back with his eyes closed and his legs in the air. He seemed in a kind of ecstasy, chewing gently on a large rubber hamburger.

David brought in coffee, cream and sugar, and mugs, and began serving coffee.

"I don't think I got your name, earlier," Marion's father said to him.

"David Bermas. I live on the second floor."

"Oh."

"He works at the *Star*, Dad," said Marion. "He's a deskman."

"And here, he's a typewriter," said Clara Zeeman. Leona couldn't place her accent, then remembered being told it was Dutch. "Just like Marion. Type type type, all day long, all night long. I hear them, oh, I hear them all right."

Leona couldn't stop staring at her. She looked to be in her mid-fifties, and the muscles in her face had begun to slacken, but Leona thought she was beautiful. She had rather small brown eyes, under her flaming red curls, and she wore a pantsuit made of a bright blue shiny synthetic material. Toenails painted almost purple peeked out from under the straps of her sandals and she'd put on far too much mascara; but there was a sweetness in her face that fascinated Leona. Her voice was sweet, too, and hesitant; maybe she was self-conscious about her accent. She ducked her head a little, as she accepted a mug of coffee.

"Clara lives on the third floor, Henry," said Emily.

"Are they all here, then?" said Marion's father, looking around. "Are all your tenants coming here for Christmas?"

"Not the motorcycle man, I hope," said Clara grimly.

"He's working today," said David, passing around cream and sugar.

"He might stop in later, if we're still up when he gets home," said Marion, smoothing her eyebrows.

Henry, watching her, said, "She always used to say—"

"I know, Dad," said Marion, taking her hand away from her brow. "That I'd rub them off."

His sorrow was rather more public than Leona would have expected. She thought with interest that Marion, who didn't appear to resemble her father in any way at all, might actually take after the mother she had loathed.

"Do you live here, too?" said Henry to Vern. "Is this the motorcycle man?" he asked Clara. He seemed confused.

"Would that I did," said Vern, rubbing his balding head. "Would that I did. But I don't live here, no. I've got a little place of my own."

"A house?" asked Henry.

"An apartment. It's got no lawn and no eaves troughs," said Vern proudly. "But it's a nice enough little place, isn't it, Marion?"

"That motorcycle man," said Clara. "Mike, he says his name is."

"I forgot something in the hall," said Leona. She stood up abruptly. Spot tried to scramble to his feet, forgetting where he was, and fell off the window seat.

"Look at that crazy dog," said Clara.

Leona came back into the room with a record, which she thrust at Marion. "Here, put this on." It was Pavarotti's *O Holy Night*. "It's a present."

"Oh, good," said Marion, her voice clear and high, fervent with relief. "I couldn't find a single Christmas record this morning except for Elvis Presley, of all things. I don't know where it came from, but it seems to be the only one I've got." She put on the record. The first cut was "Ave Maria." "I want to speak to you later, my dear," she said in a low voice to Leona.

"Like an angel, he sings," said Clara.

"I've had quite enough coffee for one day," said Marion, "and I'm off to get myself an alcoholic beverage."

She went through the dining room into the kitchen, closely followed by David and Spot.

"I saw the paper yesterday, Leona," said Vern.

"Oh yeah? That's above and beyond the call of duty, reading the paper on a day off."

"I've got to tell you, I sort of liked that good-news page. You did a good job there."

"It wasn't me," said Leona, flustered. "I didn't write the stuff. I didn't even have much to do with the makeup."

"I did some makeup for a while," said Emily tentatively. "At the magazine."

"I've always meant to ask," said Leona, turning to her, as Vern got up and headed for the kitchen, "exactly what do you do there anyway?"

Emily ran her hand through her short, curly hair. Leona noticed that she seemed nervous. She was usually struck by Emily's serenity—or maybe it was just reserve. She moved deliberately, with grace. Her hands never waved or flapped, as Leona's seemed to do so often, but rested quietly in her lap or on a tabletop when they had nothing useful to do.

"I was hired as a receptionist," said Emily. "Gradually I began doing other things as well."

Leona thought of Gloria-Rose, and wished that Emily had wandered into the *Star* at an opportune moment, instead of into *Calgary Week*. "How did you come to work there in the first place?" she asked.

"I told her it was a mistake to leave the oil company," said Henry, staring at his knees. "That was a long time ago."

"Oil company," said Clara disparagingly. "They've got too much money. I suspect those people."

Just then Marion came into the room. "Drinks, anyone?" Leona thought she was stunning in her dark green velvet dress and wished she herself had worn something more dramatic than a pair of tweed pants and a silky brown shirt.

"Do you know," said Emily, suddenly authoritative, "that sounds like a very good idea."

"I may go away for a while after the new year, Marion," said Henry laboriously in the middle of dinner.

"Where, Dad?" said Marion, surprised.

"Maybe to Hawaii for a week or two. Your mother didn't like Hawaii. There won't be any memories there."

Leona, embarrassed, bent to her food. She was quite certain that Marion's father would find memories at the bottom of a coal mine.

"Sounds good, Mr. Tyler," said Vern heartily. "Get yourself a bit of sun, a bit of surf."

Leona caught Marion's eye and looked hurriedly away.

"By yourself, Henry?" said Emily.

"I thought so, yes. Unless," he said hopefully, putting down his fork, "you'd care to come with me, Emily?"

"Hawaii, that would be nice," said Clara to Emily.

"Of course there's your job," said Henry vaguely, looking at the food on his plate. He looked older than his sister; Leona guessed that he was retired.

"Well, actually there isn't," said Emily, setting down her wineglass. "I don't have a job anymore. I've been laid off."

"Perfect!" said Vern, beaming at her.

"Emily, that's terrible," said Leona, shocked.

"Vern, stop drinking and eat," said Marion angrily. "Emily, when did this happen? Why didn't you tell me? That dreadful Grebbs, it's typical, laying somebody off at Christmastime."

"Actually it happened in October," said Emily. "I wonder if I might have a little more wine, David. There's no need to be concerned, Marion. I'm certainly not destitute, and I've been doing some work at home, to keep myself busy."

Leona tried to imagine having no job to go to. She couldn't see beyond panic.

"Maybe you could come with me, then," said Henry, with an almost imperceptible lightening of spirits.

But maybe she's even relieved, thought Leona, who knew that her parents were counting the months until her father's retirement.

"It might not be possible, Henry," said Emily gently. "But we'll see."

"This is a very nice Christmas," said David, "and I know it's going to be a good new year, too." He smiled at Emily, and filled her glass again. He'd hardly said a word since they sat down to eat, thought Leona, looking at him mistrustfully.

She wanted a cigarette. It irritated her that nobody at the table smoked.

"Yeah, it is," said Vern. "A very nice Christmas."

"I'm glad," said Henry, "that my presence hasn't put a damper on things."

"A damper?" said Vern, incredulous. "Great Scott," he spluttered, and glanced pleadingly at Marion.

She burst into laughter which bubbled on so long and so gloriously that Leona began to giggle, stuffed her napkin into her mouth but still couldn't stop, and soon everyone was laughing but Henry and Clara.

Clara reached over to pat Henry's hand where it lay, abandoned, next to his plate. "You never mind these crazy people," she said comfortingly. "Just you think to yourself what your wife would say, watching them."

At the end of the meal, Leona got up to help Marion clear the table. When they had set the first load of dishes upon the kitchen counter Marion turned to Leona, her eyes bright, her face flushed.

"I absolutely *demand,* my dear, that you go back to your doctor. I've had quite enough of your endless procrastinating. If it hadn't been for my mother's dying riveting my attention I would have swept you up long ago and taken you there myself." She took Leona's hands. "I want your solemn word, Leona. And it's purely selfish, I assure you. I am sick to death of worrying about other people."

"I've got an appointment for the sixth of February," said Leona.

"With whom?"

"With a cardiologist."

Marion hugged her. "Thank God. You've got a small amount of sense after all."

"It's purely selfish," said Leona, her voice muffled by Marion's green velvet shoulder. "I'm sick to death of worrying about myself."

It was better to be brave, she had decided, and get the bad news straight from an expert, than to go on waiting in fearful ignorance for catastrophe.

CHAPTER 9

In February Leona went to the cardiologist, who examined her and sent her to the hospital for a series of painless and interesting tests.

In March she returned to his office, where her heart was pronounced entirely normal, completely healthy.

In April she took two days off and went home to Vancouver for a long weekend.

From the plane, the sight of the green city spread between mountains and the sea loosed in her a flood of joy which took her completely by surprise.

She seldom went home at this time of year, and had forgotten that April can be almost summertime in Vancouver. It was often a time when God overlooked Alberta; the earth there was uneasily suspended between winter and spring, the snow might be all gone but the ground remained brown and sullen. But April in Vancouver was pink with cherry blossoms, bright with azaleas, white with the flowers of the dogwood trees.

It was a city in which the four seasons seemed inextricably mingled, thought Leona, peering avidly out the window as she drove her rented car north on Boundary Road, Vancouver on her left and Burnaby on the right, heading for the freeway entrance. There was never a clear demarkation between one season and the next, and spring was the longest of them all. It dawdled along like *Gone With the Wind*'s Butterfly McQueen, progressing languidly, absentmindedly, through harsh winter rains; humming to itself from months away; permitting glimpses of itself from January on. She remembered only days into the new year finding a faint fragrance of spring in the air, perhaps from primroses lifting astonished blooms above the thick, wet January snow. In February bushes began to throb and flush, and willow trees glowed golden, and more flowers appeared; but still the air was very cool, and the rain was cold. In March there were more frequent bursts of sunshine, and by April spring sprawled languorous across the city, decking itself out in blossoms and lush green grass.

Leona knew this, but rediscovering it now brought her extraordinary delight, as though the city were sharing her own sense of renaissance, born the moment of the cardiologist's pronouncement. She heard herself burbling aloud inside the rented car at frothy pink trees, and banks of tulips. She stared, amazed, at people outside mowing their green lawns. And the intensity of color in spring-leafed trees made her healthy heart ache.

She stopped the car before she reached the freeway and took off her winter coat. At least she hadn't brought her snowboots. She put her seatbelt on, adjusted her sunglasses and, with the window open, drove on, breezing down the highway with the sun at her back and spring lapping at the edges of the road and, on the horizon ahead of her, Mount Baker rising high and white into the afternoon sky, benign and gleaming above a cluster of green hills.

She loved this land. From Calgary she saw the mountains in the west not as a barrier but a gateway. Only seventy-five miles away, they tumbled down what was left of the continent and dumped her at the edges of the ocean, and that was home.

Half an hour later she turned off the freeway at Abbotsford, the town where she had grown up and where her parents still lived. She hardly bothered to look anymore for the familiar haunts of her childhood; they were almost all gone, bulldozed into oblivion to make room for shopping centers or apartment complexes. But when she pulled into the driveway of her parents' house it looked the same as it always had, and just standing by her car and staring at the place, she was wrapped in instantaneous nostalgia.

The front door opened and her mother stepped out onto the porch.

Sometimes Leona thought her mother was the only woman in the world shorter than she was.

She held out her arms, laughing, and they met on the grass halfway between the porch and Leona's car.

At the kitchen table she watched as her mother made coffee. Her mother was slightly stooped, with gray hair cut neatly short and gray eyes, large and lustrous. She wore what used to be called a housedress and perhaps still was, for all Leona knew, and sensible shoes, and a bibbed apron which when not in use was kept on a hook on the inside of the broom-closet door. The windowsill above the sink held a row of African violets.

Leona watched, contented, as her mother poured the coffee and brought it to the table. No matter how many years passed, no matter how many things happened, her mother changed only outwardly, and even this occurred with a graceful inevitability as though she herself had planned it.

She fetched cream and sugar, took off her apron and hung it up, patted her hair, and sat down at the table. Immediately she took Leona's hands in hers. "You look tired, dear," she said. "Have you been working too hard?"

"Probably I have." Leona smiled at her mother, whose name was Jane. "I like the work, but it's still hard to get up so early. Even after a whole year, I'm not used to it."

To Jane, the workings of a newspaper remained mysterious. Leona could see that the concern on her face was mixed with confusion. She couldn't understand why it was necessary for anybody to be at work so early in the morning when the *Star* was what was commonly known as an evening paper. Leona had tried to explain it to her, but her mother's world, her mother's life, had become so far removed from her own that certain kinds of communication were often difficult and sometimes impossible.

Nobody important to me has ever died, Leona thought suddenly, and looking at her mother she couldn't believe that this would ever happen. She felt more worn than Jane, more buffeted, even though this was arrogant and unrealistic; she felt it unlikely that she would survive her mother—not because she felt physically at risk, but because she couldn't imagine the world without Jane.

Her mother believed in God, quite firmly, even though she never went to church anymore. She read to herself from the Bible every night and had years earlier determined to live her life according to the teachings of the New Testament. She was a woman in whom strength and humility had forged an astonishingly salubrious alliance. Living was not particularly easy for her. Leona had often seen her struggle with anger, prejudice, and envy. But she had a touchstone, something changeless against which to judge herself, and Leona, floundering around for precepts within herself, felt like someone looking for signposts in a place where there was no light; it was impossible not just to see them, but even to know whether they were there.

Her mother continued to hold Leona's hands, searching her face, and finally Leona said in the quiet, sun-filled kitchen, "I thought for a while that I might be sick, Mom. I thought there was something wrong with my heart. But there isn't. I went to my doctor, and she sent me to a specialist, a cardiologist, and I had a lot of tests, and there's nothing wrong with me at all."

He had offered no satisfactory explanation of what she had experienced. Apparently it was possible that she hadn't experienced it at all; that her heartbeat hadn't quickened, but that her mind had thought it had. Leona had listened to this with incredulity. She wished, later, that she had pressed the cardiologist for more details, demanded alternative interpretations, argued with him. But the relief which swept through her when he told her she was healthy was so immense, and produced in her such joy, that her lingering doubts seemed trivial.

"What made you think there was something wrong with your heart?" said her mother.

Leona gently removed her hands from Jane's warm firm grasp, and flexed her fingers. "It started pounding one day. It was probably a good thing, in the long run. I go for walks a lot now, and I'm off the birth control pill. And I'm not smoking, either." Though I may change my mind about that, she added silently.

Her mother looked down at the table, smoothing the cloth, which was embroidered, nosegays of violets in each of its four corners. "I'm worried about you," she said, and lifted her head to look Leona straight in the eyes. It was one of her more disconcerting habits. People never got sidelong glances from Jane, and the acuteness and concentration of her gaze was often unsettling.

"There's no need, Mom," said Leona. "I'm perfectly all right. Really."

At dinner she beamed upon her parents beneficently, as if they depended upon her.

"Have some more meat loaf, Sam," said her mother, pushing the platter closer to her father. He exchanged a glance with Leona.

"Leave him alone, Mom. You're going to make him fat."

"Meat loaf won't make anybody fat," said her mother.

"When are you going to move back out here, Leona," asked her father. "Seeing you once or twice a year—it isn't good enough." He pushed his half-glasses farther down his nose so he could look at her over them.

"Oh, I don't know, Dad. Sometimes I think maybe never." She pushed her mashed potatoes around on her plate. "I like my job. I like my friends." She looked up at him and smiled. "I just wish all of that were in Vancouver, instead of Calgary."

"We miss you," said her father, and cleared his throat.

Leona got up and kissed his cheek. It was already stubbly, because he shaved early in the morning before going off to open his drugstore, and his beard grew quickly. She saw that it was silver, and imagined him with long silver hair growing from his cheeks and chin. Maybe it would even grow out white, and he would look like Santa Claus, or a rural patriarch.

"Meantime, though," he said, "you're only an hour away on the plane."

Leona sat down and picked up her fork.

"What do you want to do while you're here, dear?" said Jane.

"I'm going into Vancouver tomorrow, Mom," said Leona casually. "To look up an old friend." She lifted her head and shook her hair away from her face. She smiled at Jane, and felt the privacy in her smile; her mother could see it, she was sure.

CHAPTER 10

This is all very casual, said Leona to herself the next morning, in her parents' bathroom, putting in her new diaphragm. She straightened, swept back her hair, and looked directly at her face in the mirror, intending to stare down her own chagrin. But it was an ingenuous face. There was no embarrassment there at all.

She drove into Vancouver with the car windows down. The air was warm and sweet-smelling and to the north some white mountains flared against a blue silk sky. Her rented car rolled along the highway and among the woods on either side the dogwoods flowered, and behind them were pastures and sometimes fields of raspberry canes. Leona's hands on the wheel were delicate and graceful and as she moved slightly in the driver's seat she felt her body as something curved and indolent, full of poise and beauty. The breeze which came in through the open window ruffled her hair into thick waves and her eyes behind their sunglasses saw that the earth was seductive and so, sometimes, was she.

She had called him at work from Calgary and had felt furtive about it, as though someone like Marion might be hiding in her kitchen, listening and disapproving. He had answered on the first ring.

"Peter Blakey," he said, and she opened her mouth, but couldn't remember what she had been going to say. "Hello?" he said; no impatience, just curiosity.

"Peter, it's me," she said. But there was no reason for him to remember her voice, he hadn't heard it for almost four years. So she said her name, and at the same time, he said it: "Leona," he said, and sounded surprised, which was okay.

"I'm coming out there in a couple of weeks," said Leona, "to see my parents. Do you want to have lunch?" She marveled at herself. She thought she had struck exactly the right tone, casual but friendly, detached but not quite cool.

He sounded pleased. "We'll have a long lunch," he said. "Lots of martinis."

"Actually I drink scotch now," said Leona, with a savage pleasure that disconcerted her.

"Okay," said Peter. "Then we'll have lots of scotch."

His voice hadn't done a damn thing to her, she thought with satisfaction when she'd hung up the phone.

Now she drove through the sunny spring morning toward Vancouver, passing signs to Clearbrook and Aldergrove and Langley and the U.S. border and the Victoria ferry, wearing a brown summer skirt and a yellow short-sleeved blouse with small pearl buttons and occasionally wishing she had a narrow-brimmed straw hat. Maybe she'd go to Pacific Centre and look for one, she thought; she had lots of time. But she knew she probably wouldn't do that. She was serene and confident in her rented Pontiac and would stay in it, driving around the city, until it was time to meet him.

Sex, that's what she needed. She was driving herself into Vancouver on a therapeutic mission. She hadn't even bothered to ask him if he was married or living with somebody. She didn't want to know; she just wanted some good hard sex with him, that's all, something to get the old machinery clanking again, something to send her back to Calgary with her hormones purring, her eyes sharp, her hunting instincts on the alert.

It was unlikely that he wouldn't want to go to bed with her, she thought coldly. She didn't think he'd ever met a woman whom he didn't want to take to bed.

The first time they'd gone out together it had been for lunch. She couldn't remember afterward what they had eaten, either of them. She remembered sunlight striking her wineglass; it seemed to pour into it, and mix itself up with her white wine. She remembered that the table was covered with a white linen cloth, but she couldn't remember what restaurant it was. She remembered a dark red rose in a bud vase. And that Peter's face had looked dark against the whiteness of his shirt—it must have been summer; he tanned quickly, she remembered that, too.

That evening he had called, and they talked about nothing at all, and later Leona had had a bath, and in the bath had felt her body blossom like a flower caught by time-lapse photography, and it ached plaintively, so to soothe it she stroked it, gently then urgently to a climax and then lay in the warm, scented water with one hand firm between her legs until the throbbing subsided.

Sex, that's what it mostly was with him, that's for sure, thought Leona contemptuously, swinging the car over the Port Mann bridge. They had spent a great deal of time making love, and it was very good, except for that one occasion near the beginning, shortly after they moved into an apartment together, when right at the summit of things Peter had cried out somebody else's name, the son-of-a-bitch.

She sped furiously along the freeway, passing Coquitlam and New

Westminster and Burnaby, but couldn't keep her anger alive for long. All that stuff had happened years ago and had nothing to do with her life now. All she wanted today was his body. It was very satisfying to lust so ruthlessly, to want nothing more from him than a good fuck.

She turned off the freeway onto First Avenue and was in the city, no longer approaching it but there, and her stomach lurched uneasily.

There had, of course, been other things as well. He had brought her massive drippy sandwiches in bed late at night, marching naked into the kitchen to make them. She had done his laundry along with her own. He had wiped her face with cool cloths and fed her orange juice when she thought she was dying of the flu. She had dragged him off for X rays when he hurt his knee playing racquetball.

When he went out for a few drinks after work and was late coming home she knew that he'd probably gone to another woman's bed. But what the hell, thought Leona, I got over all that.

She turned onto Main Street, crossed the Georgia Viaduct and drove slowly through the downtown city to the bar near Stanley Park where they were to meet for drinks before lunch.

He wasn't late, but she was early. She walked along the beach for a while, looking out at the freighters anchored in English Bay, and the Saturday sailboats gliding among them, and the dark green wedge that was Stanley Park thrusting into the water, but she didn't really see these things, and finally she went early to the bar, blinking as she plunged into its near-darkness.

She found the ladies' room and combed her hair. She got a table in the corner and ordered a vodka martini without even thinking.

She saw him as soon as he came in and watched him dispassionately for the few seconds it took his eyes to adjust to the reduction in light. He was wearing jeans and a white T-shirt with a collar, open at the throat, and her first thought was that he must still play racquetball. He's in pretty good shape, she thought distantly. He saw her and his head tilted a little, the only sign that he might be nervous. Leona's heart was thudding; fuck off, she told it, watching him approach.

He stood by the table, his hands flat in the back pockets of his jeans. "Hi," he said.

Well Jesus, thought Leona. "Hi."

She wished he would sit down.

He was looking at her steadily. Leona found this enormously disconcerting. Her face was red, although he probably couldn't tell because
the light was so dim, and her hands seemed to have grown larger.

"You're looking good," said Leona. He smiled, and she felt a thrill of
horror; had she made a sexual innuendo? She went over the words in
her head. No, she decided, it was a perfectly straightforward remark.
She crossed her legs, and heard the swish of pantyhose as one leg
stroked the other.

"So are you," said Peter. Finally, he sat down.

Looking at him she found it hard to imagine him in bed with someone else.

There were some new lines in his face, and she thought he had a few
gray hairs, too, among the brown ones. What was it, she thought de-
spairingly, that made him so goddamned sexy to her? She had thought
it might have worn off, and although that would have been sad and
disappointing, it would also have been an enormous relief. But it hadn't
worn off.

All angles he was, except for the dimple in his cheek, and the softness of his thick brown hair, and Jesus, he'd sat down right next to her
instead of across the table and she picked up her glass so as not to place
her hand on his thigh my God those are tight jeans, thought Leona,
sipping her martini.

"It's good to see you, Leona," he said when his drink had come, and
raised his glass in a toast.

They talked for a while about unimportant things. He asked with
careful politeness about friends in Calgary, and Leona, relaxing, felt
time sliding by. He sat next to her as a wholly physical entity. She
didn't even wonder what thoughts were in his head, it was so impossible to know what they might be. If he had been a stranger she would
have wondered more what he was thinking, but he wasn't a stranger,
and because he wasn't, he was more unreachable than anyone else
could have been. She was glad she hadn't called him when she thought
she'd had a heart attack. She finished her drink, and Peter ordered her
another. She sat, watching him talk and becoming pleasantly sad, wondering what was going to happen.

In the middle of their third drink he suddenly moved restlessly in his chair, shattering the illusion of physical relaxation. It was as though he'd pulled a switch somewhere, and she felt, and remembered, the restrained impatience in him. It was a very sexual thing, and her calm disappeared, and her body was again alert.

"I want to talk to you about something," he said, his elbows on the table, his hands around his glass. "I was trying to figure out whether to phone you, or write you, or what, when you called. I'm glad you called. It's much better to discuss this face to face."

He's going to get married, her mind told her promptly. She shut it down, suspending all thought, and waited, pretending to be tranquil.

"It's a bit difficult," he said. "I don't know how you're going to feel about it."

She continued to wait, imagining herself drifting in the air in a big basket suspended from a balloon.

"I got a call from your managing editor last week," said Peter. "They're going to be making some changes—you probably know about all this. Hiller wanted to know if I'd be interested in applying for the city editor's job, when Ziggy gets moved up to news editor."

Leona was stupefied. "Jesus. You'd be my boss."

"What do you think? Could you handle it?"

"Handle what?" she said coolly, and felt a surge of anger. "Why shouldn't I be able to handle it? Could *you* handle it?"

"I've had a while to think about it," said Peter reasonably. "And I've decided yeah, I could handle it. It might be uncomfortable for a while, but we'd get over that. That's what I think. What do *you* think?"

"Oh Jesus, Peter."

"We might work pretty well together." He leaned back in his chair and thrust out his legs.

She tried to relax—her muscles had knotted up—but succeeded only in laying stiff arms along the arms of her chair. She felt as though she were made of wood, and not even carved by loving hands, just chunked together carelessly, brutally nailed together. But she was filled with a mindless joy.

"I didn't think you'd ever want to leave here," she said. "I wouldn't."

"I don't want to leave forever. But I want to be a city editor. Do you think I'd be a good city editor, Leona?" She saw that he was excited by it but mocking himself and somehow mocking her as well.

"I don't see why not," she said after a minute. "I'd be a good one. Why not you?"

He looked at her carefully, his grin fading. She wanted to laugh. "Are you going to apply for the job?" he said.

Her limbs had knitted back into flesh and she was able to smile, and say, "Don't worry, Peter. If I'd wanted it, I'd have spoken up." She finished her drink. "Bruce doesn't want it, either, in case you're interested. He says he doesn't need the hassle."

He still looked uncertain. She wanted to get up and embrace him, feel the smooth hard planes of his back and shoulders, hug to her the innocence and the mystery of this once-known stranger.

"You're not married yet," she said.

"No. I live alone, too."

"Ah," said Leona, looking intently at the olive in her empty glass. She nodded wisely.

"How about you?"

She looked up, feigning surprise. "Me? No, me neither."

He nodded too, and smiled. Leona thought it was the first time that afternoon they had looked at one another straight on. It felt as though the air between them was breaking up and flying away. She could hear him breathing and could hear no other sound. It was too intense to be borne, so she looked away.

He put some money on the table and stood up. "Come on," he said, holding out his hand to her.

They walked to his apartment through warm sunshine. In the lobby of the building, in the elevator, in the hall leading to his door she felt him near her, following, and her body expected his lips against the back of her neck, or on her hair, but he didn't touch her until they were in his bedroom, where she could see no sign of a person she knew. She stood in the middle of the room, her head averted from him, wondering where her ruthlessness had gone, waiting blindly for him to touch her.

He put an arm around her shoulders and rested his cheek against the top of her head, and then turned her around so that she faced him. She couldn't look at him but allowed herself to be embraced, and with closed eyes knew he was bending his head, so she lifted her face and he kissed her. If she were blindfolded and twenty-five men came to her one by one and kissed her, she'd know which one of them was him.

It happened over what felt to Leona like a very long time. It was like being immersed slowly in warm water at first, and everything felt terribly familiar, yet new and strange. Their hands went automatically to the places they had once liked to touch and her body responded in the same ways he had made it respond before: his hands convinced her that she was voluptuous, that her skin was soft, that she was a gift.

It was a slow lovemaking, and with her eyes closed, his hands rippling her body, strange things happened in her mind: she saw a sweep of highway, a wide four-lane stretch of highway which had no cars upon it, so that the road itself seemed to be moving, sweeping gloriously down the mountainside in an endless downward curve; and then she saw small white cabins clustered under dozens of willow trees, and there was some water nearby, too; she saw these things in her mind, felt them in her body, highway and mountainside and willow trees and water, as Peter touched her with the delicacy and absorption of one touching the petals of a flower—a purple clematis, she thought, the size of her palm; she saw the flower shivering on its fragile vine and felt it brush against her with the touch of velvet; all these things moved through her mind as she lay with Peter upon his bed. Then he stopped touching her and sighed and fell back, arms loose above his head, and she did the same things to him, touching him with hands and mouth; the petals of the clematis became his skin, the sweep of highway the sweep from chest to genitals, and beneath his arms the hair grew warm like moss.

They were wise, she thought, as they loved one another, to show each other only the familiar things. There was a thoughtful courtesy about this lovemaking which pleased her and made her heart ache. She had felt sexual attraction for him so strong it was mind-shaking. She had avoided touching him, not wanting to be set off like a firecracker. But once he had embraced her, once it had begun, that part of it had become subdued by her preoccupation with ineffable familiarity. It had the potency of nostalgia, the depth of melancholy. It was like looking back over her shoulder and seeing her personal history, not way back, wavery in a long-ago heat haze, but so close she could feel its breath upon her cheek, and she was in danger of being overtaken by a self she thought she had shed, outgrown, left behind in a perpetual dream.

As they lay quiet afterward, not speaking, it occurred to her that conversation might be a problem. But her body was heavy with sweetness, damp with love, and her brain was in neutral; she left it there. Soon Peter reached over to squeeze her hand. She thought of telling him about her heart. But she didn't. There was nothing to tell, after all. She pulled the sheet up to her chin.

"I've never enjoyed making love to anybody as much as I enjoy making love to you," said Peter.

This confused Leona, because for her it had been such an unusual time in bed; very pleasant, eminently satisfying, but strangely cerebral. She wanted to ask him what images had flashed into his mind as he made love to her, and whether these were different images than when he had made love to her before.

"I'm glad," she said. He had a desk in his bedroom, too, as she did, she noticed, and a lot of books on white shelves. "When did you discover this?" she said, and didn't much like the dry tone she'd used. Voices get tones in them while they're still silent in your head, she thought indignantly.

"It's been creeping up on me for some time. But I got totally sure of it just now."

Leona thought it would be kind to tell him that the same was true for her. But she would have to do some hard point-by-point comparing before she could be absolutely certain that it was. This knowledge gave her a small shameless thrill, until she realized that Peter wasn't waiting for her to say it anyway. Maybe he just assumed it was true, which would be cause for some irritation on her part, Leona thought, or maybe he didn't care; perhaps this conversation was of merely academic interest to him.

She was definitely chilly. Despite all this familiarity, she didn't feel easy or sure enough to cuddle up to him for warmth. As if he had read her mind, Peter reached for the blanket and tucked it under her chin, then lay down again. She turned to smile her thanks.

He lay loose-limbed, uncovered, his ankles crossed, knees slightly apart, his sex cradled sleepily between his thighs. His waist was thicker than it had seemed as she touched him; their hands, then, had lied to them, tracing remembered bodies, not real ones. Dark hair curled across his chest. She saw the tufts of hair beneath his arms and wanted to put her face there and nuzzle and smell in the smell of him.

When some time later he sat up and reached for her hand it almost shot out in front of her, so eager it was to be held. There was a stiffness in her throat which if she didn't get rid of it would become pain and maybe even tears. I am not free of him, she thought; what a dreadful dreadful thing.

"If I go back there," he said, his lips on her hair, "it's going to start all over again. You know that."

He pulled down the sheet and the blanket and took one of her nipples into his mouth and squeezed her other breast gently with his hand. Oh shit Christ, thought Leona and wrenched up his head and kissed him and this time it was very fast, very hard, and they were ruthless with one another.

CHAPTER 11

All the way home to Calgary she thought about him, which she had planned to do, but couldn't summon the detachment she had hoped to bring to bear upon their situation.

She sipped vodka and looked through the window of the plane at the tops of the mountains and thought about his body, and about hers, which ached and throbbed from its unaccustomed activities. She struggled to consider things logically, clinically, but kept feeling his mouth on her, the strength of his arms around her, the hardness of him inside her. You've just been creaky with disuse, that's all, she told herself, and now you're oiled up and ready to go again, you ought to be grateful. But she couldn't fantasize about any body but his, although she gave it a halfhearted try, wrenching blond Bruce into her mind; he faded away almost instantly.

She tried to see him in Ziggy's chair, at Ziggy's desk, but that was impossible. She had no sooner wrestled him into position than she had them copulating on the top of her desk.

He was right, of course. They would start all over again. They'd sleep together, and probably live together, and the whole damn thing would happen all over again.

But it would be worth it, said an exultant voice inside her head, as she got off the plane and found her car. Oh Christ it would be worth it, I *need* him, she thought, resting her head against the front seat of the Honda, closing her eyes. We could strike a trade, she thought, sitting up and starting the car. If he'd make do with just me, I'd have him a kid.

If he still wants one, she thought, driving out of the parking lot.

The day was fresh and sunny, the air much cooler than Vancouver's. The world was not yet green here. And how lucky she was, thought Leona, to have two springs this year.

Around her as she drove into Calgary were great chunks of prairie not yet filled in, and every so often the skeletal beginnings of yet another complex of buildings devoted to light industry. Downtown skyscrapers thrust upward arrogantly, each struggling to reach higher than the next, and the Calgary Tower had been dwarfed long ago.

But she could see in the brush that huddled in clusters here and there the red flush of free-running sap, and the air definitely felt different, lighter, hinting of the greening leafing whoosh that would be spring.

A yellow sun rode low in the afternoon sky, and loving shadows lay upon the land.

That evening, Peter phoned.

"You got back okay," he said, and asked about her flight.

"I don't have to let them know for a while yet," he said finally. "I've got a couple of months. They aren't going to make the shifts until sometime this summer."

"You haven't decided yet, then," she said neutrally.

"I decide, and then I undecide. I want the job. I want *you*. Christ." He hesitated. "We didn't talk much."

"No," said Leona. She laughed. "We didn't."

"Christ."

"I miss you."

"Yeah." There was another pause. "I'll let you know first. Before I call Hiller."

"Good. Thanks."

"Sleep well, Leona."

"You too."

She hung up. "Shit," she said, and grabbed for the box of tissues on her chest of drawers. The phone rang again, and when she picked it up she almost said his name but didn't, which was a good thing, because it was Marion.

"How was Vancouver?"

"Beautiful. Gorgeous. It's practically summer out there."

"You didn't happen to run into your old friend, that person, this time, did you?"

Leona felt her face flush. She sat on the edge of her bed. "That person," she said carefully, injecting frost into her voice, ignoring the tears on her face, "probably doesn't spend a great deal of time at the airport, or in Abbotsford, which is where it was that I went."

"Good. That's a relief," said Marion. "I'm calling for a specific purpose, actually. It's going to sound a bit odd, but I'd like to ask you a favor."

"Sure," said Leona, wiping her cheeks. "Shoot."

"It's Emily. Can you keep an eye on her for me? Oh dear, I feel like a fool—" Her voice trailed away.

"Why?" said Leona. "What do you mean?"

"No, I've thought it through," said Marion firmly, "and I've decided. Would you please call her now and then, or drop in to see her; not often, just now and then. I think it would help her to feel more secure."

"Secure?" said Leona, now totally bewildered. "What's wrong? Did something happen to her?"

"She phoned me Friday in the dead of night because she thought someone was trying to break into her apartment."

"Shit," said Leona, glancing at her bedroom door.

"Nobody was, of course. But it makes me uneasy. She's never been nervous before. She might feel more relaxed if you reminded her occasionally that she's got a friend in the same building."

"Of course I will," said Leona. "I'll be happy to do it."

"Good," said Marion with relief. "Good."

She would have to tell Marion eventually that Peter might be coming back, she thought later, making herself some instant coffee. But she dreaded it. Marion had never liked him, not even at the beginning. As time passed and she got wind of what was going on she had stopped even speaking to him, and as Leona's unhappiness grew, so did Marion's anger.

Then he had left for Toronto, and Leona had closeted herself in the apartment, feigning illness that was not really feigned, just indescribable. She spent those days ridding the place of everything that had anything to do with him, and cleaning. She vacuumed, dusted, scrubbed, polished. Then she mended, sewed on buttons, and polished all her shoes. She also smoked even more than usual and drank a lot, too.

She shuddered, remembering, as she took her coffee into the bedroom and climbed under the covers.

On the fourth day after Peter's departure her doorbell had rung. She couldn't ignore it because that apartment building didn't have buzzers in the lobby; someone was standing in the hall right outside her door. And she knew it was Marion. She let her in.

"What on earth is going on?" said Marion. "They said you had a cold and weren't even answering your phone." She looked accusingly at Leona. "You don't look like you've got a cold."

"I haven't got one," said Leona, plopping herself down on the sofa and spreading her arms across its back. "I've been cleaning. Do you want a drink?"

Marion stood with her hands on her hips, looking down at her. "It's that man, isn't it?"

"So what," muttered Leona, picking up her martini.

"You puny sniveling thing," said Marion furiously. "Are you going to let him do this to you? You miserable idiot."

"You don't know a damn thing about what's happening to me," Leona shouted. "You have no right to call me sniveling. I am *not* sniveling."

They sat quietly together in Leona's living room. Leona noticed that it had begun to rain. She could hear pattering on the window, behind the closed drapes. In the kitchen the refrigerator started to whir.

"I'll bet you've been mooning around here all day," said Marion, "scuffling your feet. When you're not busy cleaning, of course."

"What makes you think you know anything about me?" Leona stood up and went to the window and pulled the curtains back, so she could look moodily out upon the rain.

"You aren't doing anything at all that's good for you," said Marion.

"Oh for Christ's sake," said Leona, and stomped back to the sofa, and threw herself upon it. "Good for me, what the hell does that mean?" She looked suspiciously at Marion. "What is all this, anyway? What is all this do-gooding? It isn't like you, Marion."

"Yes," said Marion calmly. "It is a surprise, isn't it. But I'm your friend, and things have gone far enough, and so here I am."

Leona sat up and looked at her feet in worn blue sneakers. She placed them neatly side by side. "I would have gone with him, Marion, if it was Vancouver he was going to."

"I know."

"I just couldn't see myself going on being hurt without anything else around for me to love."

"I know."

"But, Jesus, I wish I had gone with him to Toronto." Tears were pouring from her eyes. Marion sat next to her, and handed her a pocket-size package of Kleenex.

"I know," said Marion's clear voice, and Marion's arms embraced her. "The first thing you've got to do is move out of this apartment."

"I think he loved me, though," said Leona into a handful of Kleenex.

"I know a nice building," said Marion soothingly, "right downtown. My aunt lives there."

Leona turned off her bedside lamp and lay down. She pushed the past firmly from her mind. They were perhaps not much different now, she and Peter, but they were a little older and surely at least a little wiser. She thought about the weekend, and fell asleep with her hand cuddled between her thighs.

CHAPTER 12

They wrote to one another, which surprised Leona. Letters that were light, affectionate, and licentious. Sometimes he spoke of his restlessness, which cheered her; sometimes he wrote with enthusiasm of his job, or Vancouver, which temporarily depressed her. He never mentioned other women, of course. She knew there must be some in his life but was relieved not to have to put names or faces to them.

Leona had progressed from daily walks to frequent jogging, and often as she ran she thought she might be using this activity as a female equivalent to cold showers. Peter's letters, which came once or twice a week, were very graphic, and although she loved them, they unsettled her.

At work she continued to enjoy herself, and her spirits were so high that Bruce grabbed her in the cafeteria one day and kissed her enthusiastically on the mouth, then shook her lightly by the shoulders and said with a grin, "That's more like it, kid." She felt a welcome flicker of heat in her belly, and thought hopefully that maybe a person could be sexually interested in more than one man at a time after all.

There was gossip around the newsroom about the changes that were to take place on the desk, but so far she hadn't heard Peter's name mentioned. But whenever these things were discussed, Ziggy's eyes wandered thoughtfully to her face.

Every day when she got home from work she checked her mail, changed her clothes, and headed back outside in baggy jeans, a short-sleeved T-shirt, and her carefully purchased running shoes. She had felt ridiculous at first, aware of every curious glance. She hadn't run for years. It wasn't a thing one did past the age of sixteen or so, she thought, unless you were trying to catch a bus, and it felt strange and awkward. At first she had walked a block, run a block, and then with relief walked again. But soon running became familiar. She was careful not to allow herself to become winded, and she was careful, too, to do warm-up exercises before she set out, and to walk the last two blocks home so as to arrive back cooled down. She had read all about it in books borrowed from the library.

She liked to run, and liked the feeling that her muscles were getting stronger, and she especially delighted in the fact that her totally normal heart wasn't at all bothered by her running.

Often as she ran she thought of Peter, and sometimes she thought of work, and sometimes images came to her, from nowhere—sun dogs in the blue-white sky of the coldest days of winter, the bottled fetus from *2001*, large-eyed and somber, a dog she had seen one January day delicately holding up a paw that dripped red blood upon the snow—images neither harmless nor frightening, offering no message, just suddenly there, behind her eyes, showing themselves to her, detached yet amiable.

On a day in June she got home to find another letter from Peter, and in it he told her that he was staying in Vancouver.

She felt the entire complex mechanism that was her body slow down. She sat on her sofa, the letter in her lap. I don't think I'll run today, she told her body politely.

Quite a while passed before she read beyond that first paragraph. In the rest of the letter he told her that he didn't want to hurt her again. He would stay where he was, and Calgary wasn't that far away. He would spend lewd weekends with her there, he said, and she would spend wanton ones in Vancouver with him.

She lay down on the sofa and pulled up her knees.

Her jogging was whistling in the dark. There was something wrong with her, all right. It wasn't so unusual for specialists to miss things. They'd do an autopsy on her, and snap their fingers in exasperation, peering into her cut-up body; so that's what it was, they'd say.

Nobody's heart acted the way hers had done if there was nothing wrong with it. She might go a year, two years, even more, without its happening again. But she knew it would eventually. And she knew there had to be a reason for it.

I guess we didn't talk enough, she thought, staring into the blank face of her television set. We should have talked more when we were face to face.

When it was almost dark, she got up and put on her baggy jeans and her T-shirt and her socks and running shoes. She put her keys in her pocket and went down to the lobby and out into the street.

She began to run. Her calf muscles protested at first, because she hadn't warmed up, but she pressed them on and gradually they relaxed. As she ran she felt tears on her face but she ignored them. They dried rapidly, evaporated by the breeze she created, running through the summer evening.

She ran steadily down the sidewalks of Calgary, skirting the downtown area, sometimes glimpsing the light-spattered river. She passed many strangers, and as she passed them she thought that individual lives were parallel lines, never intersecting; the best you could do was send kisses across the intervening space, and such a waste it was, such a pity, such a tragedy, ever to launch anything less; such monumental loneliness there is, and fluttery kisses is the best that we can do, and sex flares brightly, briefly, and is not enough.

She ran slowly and steadily, pain and bitter disappointment all-encompassing. But her mind kept niggling a message at her. She was at first oblivious, but finally paid some attention, and realized with growing triumph that the message was about her legs, which felt lighter than usual, her muscles more powerful. It required a mild effort of will to prevent herself from running faster than she knew she should. Exhilarated and powerful, she felt the concrete melt beneath her feet, saw things close as she passed them, devoured feet and yards more hungrily than she had ever felt her car to be devouring miles.

She continued to breathe easily, and her heart continued to beat regularly. She felt no heaviness in her legs, and her feet didn't want to slow down. So when she reached the end of her mile she kept on running, slowly, steadily, passing in and out of the light spilled upon the sidewalks by streetlamps, past restaurants and office buildings and apartment buildings.

Finally she turned toward home, and ran to the quieter, darker block near the end of which was her apartment. She kept on running, her sneakers almost silent upon the concrete, her T-shirt soaked now, her mouth beginning to feel dry; she would run to her building and then walk around the block to cool down. In and out of pools of light she ran, silently in a silent world, she heard only her own breathing, and the quick but steady beating of her blood, and no, she thought, there is

nothing wrong with this heart, but there is something wrong somewhere else that makes me think my heart is ailing, and as she ran she
was determined to find it; she would search every inch of her interior
self with the relentless lamp of pure investigation and she would bloody
well find the thing that had screwed up her life.

Ahead she saw a figure approaching, walking, a woman in a coat too
heavy for a June evening. She saw the figure pause just outside the
circle of light in front of Leona's apartment building.

She would start, thought Leona, with the day on which her heart
had first attacked her. She would dredge from her memory all the
things that happened on that day nineteen months ago and look among
them for clues, and she would go back from there, months, years, if
necessary, to figure it out.

She ran on, and now her legs were tired, and her breathing less
regular; she slowed down but continued to run, light enveloping her
like a swell of music each time she passed beneath a lamp, then letting
her go as she plunged once more into almost darkness.

The woman stood still ahead of her, much closer now; Leona
couldn't see her face, but she appeared to be watching her, and suddenly Leona in what seemed a single bound reached her, and the
woman stepped forward, and Leona, startled, came to a halt.

"Emily," she said, breathless.

Emily didn't reply.

"I think I've overdone it today," said Leona in gasps. "You're supposed to be able to talk while you run."

Emily stretched out a hand. Leona took it instinctively, and in doing
so pulled Emily into the light.

"Are you all right?" she said, looking hard into her face, and knew
immediately that she wasn't. Emily was a substance other than flesh.
Her face had cracked, and her eyes were mirrors. Oh my God, thought
Leona, she's been mugged, or she's going to have some kind of attack.
She pulled Emily closer to her panting, sweaty body, and was putting
her arms around her when Emily stiffened and stepped back.

"Yes," said Emily. "I'm fine, thank you." Her face was once more
skin and bone; her eyes saw Leona; she held Leona's hand and reas-
sured her. She smiled, and walked with care toward the glass doors of
their apartment building.

Leona was aware of the pounding of her heart, overworked but untroubled; oh yes, she thought, I'll have to look elsewhere.

She hurried after Emily and put an arm around her heavy-coated shoulders. "You're coming to my place," she said resolutely, "for tea."

But Emily, still more resolute, said no.

EMILY

CHAPTER 1

On the cold, gray November Tuesday that Leona had covered a fire for the *Star,* Emily Murdoch, much to her amazement and dismay, was also dispatched on an assignment.

This was amazing to her because she wasn't a reporter and had no ambition to become one. It was dismaying, because although Emily took pleasure in observing what happened around her and fantasizing about or attempting to interpret what she saw, these were private enjoyments not, to date, subject to critical assessment. The prospect of observing for public print caused her feet to grow cold, and her hands to become clammy on the telephone receiver. I'm too old for this sort of thing, she was to say crossly to herself, rallying, as she slammed down the phone.

The weekly newsmagazine for which she worked was located far from the center of town, in an industrial area off the Macleod Trail. The parking lot in front of the dilapidated building which housed the magazine offices and what passed for its newsroom was a small one, with spaces for cars belonging only to the publisher, the advertising and circulation managers, and the photographer, with two spaces left over for visitors. There was usually only one available for visitors, however, since the photographer's car invariably occupied two. The photographer would have liked to paint PRESS! all over his automobile but, denied this, he always just left it, rather than parking it, hoping people would sense that his abandonment had been hurried, and infer that he was preoccupied with tense and urgent matters inside the building.

The publisher's car was a ten-year-old Volvo station wagon, gray, or possibly dark blue. It was hard to tell because it was always very dirty. The publisher and his wife had four children of varying ages, and a large, hairy dog as well. Emily imagined the publisher, whenever he wasn't at work, driving about the city with wife, children and dog in the car with him. She saw him, in one of her fantasy flashes, clutching the steering wheel, hunched over it tensely, staring out the windshield, eyes darting from side to side, oblivious to the dry, restrained wife beside him, the children bouncing in the back seat, and, even farther back, the hairy dog drooling dreamily against the window. Every time she walked past the car, Emily glanced inside it curiously. It always contained a battered Kleenex box and half a dozen comic books without their covers, and there was dried dog drool all over the windows.

Emily parked her yellow Volkswagen Rabbit around the corner as usual that Tuesday morning. She got out and locked it and hurried along the sidewalk, wishing the snow would come. The earth was unrelentingly ugly in November, the trees bare, the grass brown, litter displaying itself nakedly beneath brittle, leafless hedges and bushes. It looks achy and unhappy, the earth does, thought Emily, and needs snow to gentle it down for the winter.

When she entered the magazine office she noticed that there was a new girl on the switchboard, wearing a look of blank amazement as the old girl instructed her. Emily went up the somewhat rickety steps to the editorial office, clutching the banister and thinking that it would take the new employee several days to master things, and that in the interim they could all expect some confusion. Nobody ever stayed in that job very long; the pay must be terrible.

She walked into what the publisher called the newsroom. Emily, who had visited Marion's newsroom, was uncomfortable when the term was applied to the place where she worked. She had been there two years, and was still ambivalent in her attitude toward it. She marveled that the magazine actually came out every week, and marveled even more that people read it and some of them took it seriously.

Emily looked upon work as her outlet into the world, essential as a channel down which to focus her curiosity. When she had worked, earlier, for a theater company, she learned about the theater; when she worked for a firm of architects, she learned about architecture; and during her ten years with an oil company, she learned a lot about that. Now she was learning about journalism of a kind.

She had been shocked to learn the day before that her niece, Marion, whose journalism career with the *Star* Emily so admired, was giving it up to freelance. Emily thought that if she were ever lucky enough to find a job which fulfilled her, and in which she could continue to grow, she would never give it up.

It was the day after publication, and nobody else was in the newsroom yet. Emily liked this day of the week. It was a pleasant break in an otherwise hectic schedule, and gave her a chance to do all the routine filing and sorting which she seldom had time for. She switched on the light and hung up her coat on the rack next to her desk; the empty wire hangers clattered tiredly as she shoved them together to make room for her imitation fur coat. The room was cold, as it almost always was, but she wore a heavy sweater over her skirt and blouse.

Emily was fifty-nine. Her face was beginning to crumple and the flesh under her upper arms was loose and she was flabbier than she wanted to be around the waist. But her eyes were clear and blue, her legs were slim and smooth, and her hair, virtually all gray now, was curly because she had it regularly permed. She had abandoned a legitimate claim on elegance, turned her back on it, when she left the oil company, but it clung to her anyway, and showed itself in her legs, and the way she moved, and the dry precision of her speech when she was annoyed.

She regarded the magazine for which she worked as a slightly shoddy product plagued by the inexperience of its reporters and the single-mindedness of its publisher, whose name was Homer Grebbs. It bumbled and stumbled along, propelled by his stubborn determination. She hadn't yet decided whether he saw it primarily as a way to make money, or as a forum for his own political and moral views. He certainly used it as a forum, but he also talked exuberantly now and then about his hopes for starting similar enterprises in Vancouver, Regina, and Winnipeg. His ambitions didn't extend east of Manitoba, because like many Ontario-born Albertans, his hatred for his home province was staggering. With the fervor only a convert can possess, he fanned the flames of the old East-West rivalry in the pages of his magazine, and with gleeful recklessness tossed his bridges into the blaze.

Emily turned from the coat rack and made her way to the far end of the newsroom, where the washrooms were. The faucet in the ladies' room dripped steadily, and the porcelain sink had produced rust in hopeless defense against the constant attack. She filled up the soap container from a large jug in the open cupboard, pulled out a new roll of toilet paper and installed it on the wooden holder. It was a small and dingy room, lit by a bare bulb hanging from the ceiling. Large patches of linoleum had worn away or broken off, revealing what looked like tarpaper beneath. There was a window, but it had frosted glass in it and the outside had apparently not been cleaned since the long-ago day of its installation. The magazine had a cleaning woman who came in once a week or so, Emily had been told. She had never seen her, and the only indication that she might exist was the fact that while the place never got any cleaner, it never actually got any dirtier, either.

Emily liked things neat and tidy, but she drew the line at cleaning the bathroom of the place where she worked. She had taken it upon herself to keep certain areas of the newsroom clean and orderly. These were her own desk, the coffee table, and the filing cabinets, and also the pigeonholes on the wall into which she stuck the sorted mail. She was not in the strict sense of the word a secretary—her job didn't really have a name—so she felt no responsibility for the publisher's little rathole of an office, in which piles of newspapers and magazines fought for space upon the floor and on the extra chair, and the dust and dirt on the desk and the long table against the wall flew panic-stricken into the air whenever he moved things around.

Grebbs had a small manual typewriter which he attacked with vast amounts of energy when he wrote his weekly column, or the political stories which were his self-assigned responsibility, or rewrote anything that didn't please him. At the beginning of each publishing week he handed out assignments and was determined that all stories would be written by the reporters to whom they were given; he was very conscious of his responsibility to see that his reporters learned by doing and redoing. But as the days passed and things went less than well and stories weren't being written as they should have been and time was running out, his patience trickled away. Finally he would grab the latest efforts and rush into his office with them, calling to the reporters to follow. They would huddle around his desk as he typed; he called out to them abruptly now and then. "See, this is the goddamn lead, see?" They strained to see but couldn't, really; it was as though he thought that watching him type would teach them story structure. Emily sympathized with him, but she sympathized even more with his fledgling reporters.

Sometimes on the day after publication they came in and waited around for him to appear, knowing that today he would be at his most relaxed and expansive, and they would attempt to discuss their stories with him, but this was often unsatisfactory. He talked to them willingly, but tended to wander, and when cast by his reporters in the role of teacher preferred to instruct them on other matters, discoursing at length from behind his desk, his feet on a pile of newspapers, his chair squeaking, about the importance of the nuclear family and the iniquities of Ontario. Emily could hear him from around the corner and was exasperated by his lack of discernment but pitied his innocence.

She took newsroom phone calls, typed letters for Grebbs and his two editor-writers, looked after the filing, took care of the photo files, and made sure there were enough supplies on hand. And recently she had begun to help out with the makeup of the magazine.

This last was a task quite unlike anything she had done before and she enjoyed it immensely. She didn't have to think judgmentally about the content of the stories and photos, just juggle them and trim them until they fit tidily and, if possible, artistically into the prescribed space. It appealed to her sense of order, and because she learned quickly, and was able to act decisively and with a show of confidence, she did it well enough.

Cutting stories had bothered her at first, since she had no training or experience as a journalist. When Grebbs first suggested that she lend a hand in this area, she was doubtful and asked Marion's advice.

"I've never done any makeup," said Marion cheerfully. This surprised Emily. "Except at school, I think," Marion added. "You'd probably enjoy it. I've always thought you were vaguely mathematical."

"It's not the mathematics I'm worried about," said Emily. "Anybody can measure something and decide whether it will fit into a given space. It's the ethics of it that concern me."

"My goodness, Emily, I don't think there are a whole lot of ethics lurking around that place, do you?"

"Maybe not," said Emily with asperity, "but I've got plenty of my own. And I don't like the thought of someone's story being made shorter by somebody who didn't have anything to do with writing it."

Marion hooted. "Oh my goodness, Emily, they would love you in my newsroom." Then she became serious. "Your judgment is as good as anybody else's. Just read the piece and get a sense of what it's all about, and then if you have to make it shorter, decide which parts are least important. That's all there is to it. And if there's time," she added, "you can always take it back to the reporter and tell *her* to cut it. Or him."

This last suggestion relieved Emily of a lot of worry, so she had agreed to do some makeup. She had now been doing it for six months and reporters were telling her to go ahead and cut their stories herself. She took this as a great compliment but was surprised to find that their confidence encouraged her to look at their work quite coldly and clinically and that she seldom found it at all difficult now to cut, chop, or even hack, if necessary.

This Tuesday morning there was of course no makeup to do, but a lot of mail had piled up and in the frantic search for file photos to go with some agriculture stories the photo drawers had been left in a mess. She made a pot of coffee and had just sat down at her desk to tackle the mail when the phone rang.

"Calgary Week."

There was a pause, and then she heard, "Uh, is this the upstairs?" There were whisperings, and then another voice.

"Sorry, Mrs. Murdoch, a little trouble here," said the soon-to-depart downstairs receptionist, and Emily heard a click, and then an impatient male voice: "Hello? Hello?"

"Yes, you're through now, Mr. Grebbs," said Emily.

"Emily, good, who's there with you?"

"Nobody. It's a bit early for anyone else to be in today. How's Edmonton?" He was in the provincial capital, interviewing cabinet ministers, those who would agree to see him, for a story on government budget cuts.

"Damn, not Harold? Or Max?" These were the editor-writers, the

only people on the staff, with the exception of Grebbs himself, with
any previous experience in what Grebbs liked to call "the news dodge."

"Nobody at all. Is it important? Have you tried them at home?"

"Don't answer. Damn."

"They could be on their way in, I suppose."

"Ought to be home. Ought to be reachable. You never know, now
this damn thing has come up. Can't reach the damn photographer
either, damn it all, no organization, it's unsupportable."

The photographer worked for other people besides Grebbs and was
often difficult to locate at short notice. This was one of the few things
that could throw Grebbs into a rage. His face became red and his voice
deepened and he waved his hands frenziedly and tossed his head so
that his graying hair, of which he had a great amount, blew out around
him. Emily observed him at such times with disapproval. He never
directed his rage at her; it never occurred to her that he ever would.

He seemed more preoccupied than enraged at the moment.

"Emily?" he said. "What's on your schedule?"

"What, today?"

"Right now, what time is it, just after nine, you'd have to be out
there by—they say ten-fifteen, but you can't trust the bastards; you'd
have to leave right now, what do you say?"

"Leave for where? To do what?" She looked down at her coffee, still
steaming, and a partly opened letter from the department of culture,
which appeared to be a press release.

"Let me fill you in," said Grebbs. "I think you can do this for us,
Emily. New for you, but what the hell, it's the spice of life, isn't it. We
need you, Emily. Come through in the breach. Good."

She was glad the conversation was taking place over the telephone. If
he had been in the office talking to her like this her confusion would
have demanded that she make and retain some eye contact with him.
Grebbs, a short and nervous man, had a skin ailment at which he
habitually plucked. She often wanted to tell him that this was only
making things worse, but instead would avert her eyes from his face
and the soft, absentminded snatchings that went on there. This made
their relationship vaguely unsatisfying to them both, since it was difficult to establish and maintain communication when their eyes scarcely
ever met.

"What breach? I don't know what you're talking about, Mr. Grebbs," Emily said sharply. "I've got a lot of filing to do, and there's a great stack of unopened mail sitting in front of me at this very moment."

"This is important, Emily. This is *news*. Came over the press gallery wire up here. Now listen, up in the boondocks somewhere, can't recall exactly where, can't locate the goddamn piece of paper, never mind, some guy went berserk last night, polished off half a dozen people with an ax." He announced this with relish; he was already writing the headline.

"My God," said Emily. "That's terrible." A watery sun broke through the cloud cover, sending a wavery beam of light through the dirty windows that filled most of the top half of the wall on the other side of the newsroom.

"Drunk, of course," said Grebbs, who disapproved of alcohol along with smoking, premarital sex, and the United Nations. "Just waded into his cousin's living room and started hacking. The Mounties have him locked up. The thing is, there was a kid, got hit but didn't die, fell on the floor and rolled under a bed or something and the guy forgot about him."

Emily's imagination couldn't keep up. She saw it happening in slow motion, a man big and bulky, his face black with anger, wielding an ax with two hands; she saw heads averted and arms thrown up to ward him off; she saw the ax move slowly down, then slowly up, spraying blood in wet red drops that made a pattern in the air. She could not see the fallen victims; she couldn't see a child.

"It's a boy," said Grebbs. "Don't know how old. Must have been pretty badly hurt, they're flying him into Calgary, and that's where you come in."

"What are you talking about?"

"Get yourself down to the airport, the old one, ask where the plane's going to land, get yourself out there and wait for it."

"Why?" said Emily desperately. "What for?" There must have been a lot of noise, she thought; the axman would have bellowed with rage, and the people would have screamed, and the ax would have made grunting, thwacking sounds.

"Color," said Grebbs. "Get me some color."

"Color? What? Me?"

"Little touches, eyewitness stuff, this is heartrending material we're talking about, Emily. What does the kid look like when he's loaded off the plane, maybe there's a solicitous nurse hovering over him, that sort of stuff; the plane sweeps in, lands gently, eager hands open the hatch or whatever—you know, Emily; color."

If there was ever a time to become hysterical, Emily thought, this was it.

"Mr. Grebbs, you cannot seriously expect me to do this. I am a secretary, Mr. Grebbs. Why don't I try to round up one of the reporters?"

"No time," said Grebbs. "You can do it. You don't have to talk to anybody. They won't talk to you anyway. Just watch and write down what you see, that's all. There's nothing to it. I'll put Max on the story tomorrow. Get moving, now, Emily—I'm counting on you."

I'm too old for this sort of thing, said Emily to herself, slamming down the phone. But she got up from her desk and put on her coat and found a notebook and a pen.

On the tarmack at the old airport she found a group of people representing television and radio stations and newspapers, and she looked for a familiar face, thinking that the *Star* might have sent a friend of Marion's whom she would have met. She saw no one she knew. It was a relief, actually. She felt like an impostor.

She huddled on the outskirts of the group, feeling the coldness of the day on her face and legs. The sun had sunk back behind the clouds. Emily thought it had probably died back there, so gray and desolate was the sky. The wind whipped down the long stretches of runway straight at the waiting reporters; Emily turned sideways, and bent her head into the softness of her coat. A couple of people looked curiously at her now and then, but she kept her face impassive. It occurred to her that they might think she was a relative, and attempt to interview her, a development which would have done her in completely; but nobody approached her or spoke to her. I'm identified by my notebook, anyway, she thought, and in the same instant realized that she didn't have it.

She saw it lying on the front seat of her car, which was parked near the airport's main building, a quarter of a mile away.

She turned quickly to hurry back to get it.

"Here it comes," someone murmured, and the cameramen got behind their cameras and the reporters shifted uneasily, having been told earlier that this was as close as they were going to get.

Emily searched her handbag and found a pen there but no paper. She thought of asking one of the reporters for some paper, but they were concentrated on the approaching aircraft. My God, thought Emily, what now? She fixed her eyes on the small plane. I will memorize, she thought; I will memorize everything I see.

The plane glided closer and closer to the runway, touched down, sped bumpily along the tarmac (I wonder if he feels that, thought Emily, I wonder if it pains him; but no, that's nothing I can see, she thought, and refused to memorize it), made a half turn and came to a stop near the corner of the building.

An ambulance backed up close to it, having appeared from around the corner, where it must have been waiting. The driver and an attendant, both in white, hurried out of the ambulance and opened the back door and stood waiting, looking up at the door in the side of the airplane; its motors had been switched off and it stood still and silent on the runway. (Perhaps there's nobody in it, she thought, or perhaps they're all dead inside, all hacked to pieces—Emily chided herself angrily for fancifying when it was facts she was here for, facts and color.) The ambulance people are dressed in white, she thought clumsily, writing it in her head, and the airplane is white, too, with green letters on the side.

The airplane door opened suddenly, jerkily, and someone she couldn't see clearly lowered a ladder. After another few minutes she saw a Mountie inside the plane; he appeared to be struggling gently with something (some*one?* thought Emily wildly); then he glanced behind him at the ladder and began making his way down slowly, leaning into the ladder for balance because both his hands were busy with the end of the stretcher, keeping the stretcher as horizontal as possible. The stretcher looks very white, thought Emily, storing it away. She could hear the shuffle of feet as television cameramen kept the scene in their viewfinders, and she saw reporters scribbling in their notebooks, but nobody was saying anything.

The other end of the stretcher was held by a second policeman who was now slowly making his own way down the ladder, facing out from the plane, leaning slightly backward. Emily watched, fascinated; what if they dropped it? She could see now a flash of yellow on the stretcher and above that, a smudge of brown.

The second Mountie reached the tarmack and in the few seconds it took the two policemen to adjust the stretcher and pass it into the outstretched hands of the ambulance attendants, Emily saw a small figure in something that looked like a yellow sleeping bag, a white face beneath brown hair, a white bandage over half his head; the zipper of the sleeping bag was done up all the way to his chin; Emily couldn't tell whether his eyes were open or closed.

Nobody else came out of the aircraft, but a tall, wide-shouldered man in a brown tweed suit with a brown tie and a lighter brown shirt stood by the side of the ambulance, watching closely as the attendants loaded the stretcher. They closed the doors and hurried to the front of the ambulance, whose motor was still running, and drove away around the corner of the building.

The television cameras were turned off and there was a buzz of conversation among the assembled reporters, but Emily didn't stay to listen to any of it. She hurried as fast as she could through the cold November morning back to her yellow car and before she turned on the engine she filled several pages of the notebook with the things she had seen.

As she climbed the stairs to the newsroom she empathized for the first time with the four young reporters who worked there. She couldn't deny her excitement, or her slightly shameful sense of self-importance.

The newsroom was still empty, but it seemed to welcome her, full of eager silent questions, and she went immediately to her typewriter to type out her notes. She retyped them three times, in an effort to be detached yet specific, and had just placed them in the center of Grebbs's desk when he called again.

"Knew you'd do it, Emily!" he crowed, when she had reported to him. "Knew I could rely on you!"

She went off to lunch feeling self-satisfied and content, and enjoyed telling of her exploit that afternoon to Max and Harold and the two reporters who wandered in.

She didn't know that the biggest shock of her day was yet to come.

It was a one-time thing, of course, she told herself that night, waiting for the television news. It was an impulse born of Mr. Grebbs's desperation, and nothing more.

She was on her living room sofa, wrapped in an old pink bathrobe, drinking a mug of cocoa.

Even so, she wondered if it might not happen again someday. She would get herself a small purse-size notebook, just in case, and make sure she had it with her always.

Her attention wandered during the national news; it was the local news that she was interested in. She had missed the earlier broadcast because of an encounter in the elevator with a distraught Leona. Emily remembered, sipping her cocoa, the look of disproportionate gratitude on Leona's face as she accepted the bottle of travel pills. Emily had felt at that moment that she owed the girl more than such cursory assistance; she owed her some genuine concern, warmly expressed. But Leona stood up to leave and thanked her profusely, and Emily had let her go. She felt a little depressed now, as she thought about it.

The local news began. She perched on the edge of the sofa and leaned forward, watching intently, waiting for coverage of the child's arrival at the airport.

It was the second item.

She was incredulous. She wanted to stand up and protest. But she remained seated, her eyes unable to leave the screen.

They had lied to her, her eyes. The sleeping bag was not yellow but blue. A nurse followed the stretcher from the plane, wearing boots, and a heavy navy cape over her uniform. The zipper of the sleeping bag was not done up all the way to the boy's chin; it was done up only to about his waist, and under it he wore a dark green down-filled jacket.

And there was no man in a brown tweed suit.

She could see on the television screen exactly where he had stood, watching the Mounties turn the stretcher over to the ambulance attendants; that's where he had stood, right there; but he was not there.

Emily watched until the news was over, and people had told her about sports events, and the weather. She kept expecting another item on the arrival of the injured boy. Perhaps she had imagined the first one. Or perhaps they had gotten it wrong, and would show a corrected version. But they never did.

Finally she switched off the set and thought, trying to make sense of it.

The only thing which made any sense at all was that she had recalled the event inaccurately; that in the few minutes it had taken her to hurry from the tarmack to her car, her mind had rearranged things, getting rid of some of her observations and supplanting them with other things.

But why, for God's sake? Why?

She went to bed shivering with cold and bewilderment, and then got up quickly, found pen and paper, and wrote down what she had seen on the television news, so that she could change her notes in the morning before Grebbs had a look at them. She cried then, for a minute, furious and humiliated, looking down at what she had written, because of course her mind might just now have done it to her again.

CHAPTER 2

On the day Marion was to move, Emily dressed carefully, putting on a pair of yellow longjohns under her jeans and a T-shirt under her navy sweatshirt. She had a good breakfast, too, figuring that it might be many hours before she had another chance to eat. And she gave herself plenty of time to drive to Marion's apartment, because fresh snow had fallen during the night.

She was excited for Marion, who was totally preoccupied these days with taking possession of her first house, and would have hugged her when she opened the door except that Marion didn't go in much for that sort of thing. Hugging and hand-holding and cheek-kissing were part of the social graces for Emily, things she did without even thinking about it when greeting people she knew. She was a sensuous woman and enjoyed the touch of skin, was fascinated by the varying fragrances these small ceremonies carried with them, subtle perfumes of cologne or aftershave or the dry unnameable aroma of skin itself.

She was slightly shorter than Marion and would have had to reach upward to embrace her. But even more discouraging was the possibility that Marion, though she probably wouldn't actively push her away, might stiffen and merely suffer her aunt's embrace. Not since Marion was a child had Emily put her arms around her.

So when Marion threw open the door and beamed at her, Emily only smiled back, and said, "It's a great day."

"Come in and have some coffee, Emily, you must be frozen." She closed the door and took Emily's coat. "I was hoping for a Chinook today, but no luck." In the kitchen she poured coffee into two Styrofoam cups. "You might as well sit down, Emily. Unfortunately all my friends aren't as reliable as you when it comes to getting places on time." They heard a honk outside the ground-floor window, and Marion looked out and waved. "I'm properly chagrined," she said. "Here's Bruce."

She brought him into the kitchen to meet Emily. He was a tall man, and broad, and seemed uncomfortable in Marion's kitchen, as though it were too small for him. He wore a tuque made of a coarse gray oily-looking wool, and he stripped off fleece-lined leather gloves to shake Emily's hand; he took it firmly but gently and released it almost immediately.

"Well, what do you think?" he said to Marion. "Furniture first?"

"Yes, I think so. There's not much of it."

"Do these things stay?" He pointed to the fridge and stove.

"Yes. Let me show you what goes."

Emily remained at the kitchen table while Marion showed Bruce around the apartment. She thought it might be the last time until she got home again that she would feel warm enough. She held the coffee cup in both hands, letting the steam rise into her face.

A moment later the doorbell rang again, and a balding man wearing a trench coat rushed into the kitchen, rubbing his hands. His ears were beet red. Emily thought he looked quite miserable, and at first didn't take him for one of Marion's volunteers because he was so obviously not dressed for the occasion.

Behind him came Leona, who greeted Emily warmly. She's such a tense little thing, thought Emily; so thin, so electric with energy. She looked at people with disconcerting directness, as if they were telling her things without knowing it.

The man with her was Vern Palmer. There was a slightly frenetic quality to him. It seemed he couldn't decide whether to be ingratiating or jocularly rude.

They asked Emily about her work. She remembered standing on the tarmack at the old airport, six weeks earlier, in the company of real reporters. She made it as clear as possible to Marion's friends that she wasn't a reporter. But she would like to have asked who had covered the child's arrival for the *Star*, and what he or she had said about it later.

Emily was a cautious driver and preferred to travel along snowy or icy streets as slowly as the rest of the traffic would allow. As she signaled and pulled out from the curb behind Marion, she realized that keeping up with her niece would require her to drive more quickly than was comfortable for her, and she forced herself to relax and refuse to be either pulled from in front or pushed from behind. She knew where she was going, and didn't need to be led. If the others got impatient they could always pass her. But in her rear-view mirror she saw the maroon pickup truck driven by Bruce establish and maintain a distance that pleased her.

The ice fog was beginning to lift, and Emily squinted in the sun, peering out into the winter-locked city. Her heart trembled a little each time the car slipped in the icy ruts in the snow. She knew she was going too slowly to do either her car or herself any great damage even if she did lose control, but she hated the sensation of helplessness when the Volkswagen traveled even for a couple of feet in a direction she hadn't intended. She began to brake gently, a long way from the corner where Marion's street intersected with a busier one, and when the car began to slide she let it go into loose snow, where it could regain its grip upon the road. When she'd made the turn onto Tenth Avenue she was relieved to see that it had been sanded. She sat up straighter and relaxed slightly. Marion's car was out of sight; the pickup kept its patient, respectful distance behind her.

She had had several days off around Christmas, and had spent most of them helping Marion in her new house. It was a big house and there was a lot of work to do, but Marion had tackled it with an almost ferocious cheerfulness. Emily wondered what on earth Marion expected the place to do for her. Still, she knew the unexpected possessiveness and joy in store for new house buyers. She had felt that way herself, about the house in Bowness she had shared with her husband and their son.

She had loved that house, and had hung onto it for ten years after her husband Victor died. It sat at the front of an extremely deep lot at the end of which passed the railway tracks. It was very near the river, and several large trees grew around it. But when she had to look after it by herself, the lot seemed to get bigger every year. Her son, Nelson, as he grew had no interest in gardening but didn't mind mowing the lawns; so more and more of the flower and vegetable gardens got dug up and seeded in grass.

She had struggled with that house for years. She remembered the day she decided to get rid of it. It was in August, more than nine years ago now, a couple of months after her fiftieth birthday. She had driven home from work and arrived even more hot and irritable than usual. The city had begun to grow very quickly; tall buildings were shooting up all over the downtown core, and it was taking her longer and longer to make her way through rush-hour traffic as she drove back and forth between the oil company's offices and her house. She pulled into her driveway, turned the motor off, and just sat there for a moment, feeling in her body the strain of the drive, the ache of weariness; then she climbed heavily out of the car.

She glanced at the garage which she used only in winter and saw how rickety it was, and noticed that the house needed painting. She went inside, where the carpets were getting threadbare and the windows were draped with the same curtains she had vowed to replace at least five years earlier. The kitchen sink was stained and there were a couple of rips in the linoleum. She realized suddenly and passionately just how much she disliked leaking faucets and crumbling eaves troughs and blistering paint and overgrown lawns. Nelson was by now at university in Edmonton, 180 miles away, and seldom came home. She was alone in a house which she was allowing to become a crypt.

She had decided on her fiftieth birthday to change her life. Getting rid of the house seemed a good way to begin. She put it up for sale the next day and after a buyer had been found drove away with scarcely a backward glance.

She found a one-bedroom apartment in a downtown highrise with an underground garage and laundry machines. Her apartment was freshly painted with long white drapes at the windows and french doors and a balcony. She was on the fourteenth floor and had almost the same view of the mountains as that enjoyed by her boss at the oil company. If the block of short old buildings across the street were eventually demolished and replaced by tall ones that would ruin her view, she would simply move again. Being mobile was really quite delightful. She got small shots of satisfaction, too, out of being the only one of her family to live in an apartment, as well as the only one of the four sisters to be gainfully employed.

"But you've only got one bedroom," said her youngest sister, Grace, when Emily had first moved. "Where are you going to put Nelson when he comes to visit?"

"On the couch," said Emily. "Besides, I think he's going to Toronto after next year. For graduate work."

"My God," said Grace, dismayed. "You don't mean it." Grace was one of Grebbs's most avid readers (a fact which Emily kept to herself), and shared his animosity for central Canada.

She didn't miss the house in Bowness at all. But she remembered loving it, and didn't find it strange that Marion should be falling in love with hers—as long as she kept things in proportion.

When she turned onto Memorial Drive, she saw Marion's small station wagon and followed it a couple of blocks behind. By the time she reached Marion's street, the wagon had pulled up in front of the house. She parked carefully behind it, and in the rear-view mirror saw the pickup, too, come to a stop.

Emily got out of her car and watched Marion walk slowly up to her house. Emily thought it only right that she should be the first one inside, letting the house welcome her privately before she opened it to her friends. It was, however, extremely cold outside, she thought, shivering, as first Leona and then Vern Palmer joined her.

"Christ, it's huge," said Vern.

But it wasn't, really, thought Emily. Once Marion had rented the three rooms she wouldn't find it big at all. Emily smiled to herself, imagining Marion as a landlady, and wondering how her tenants would react to Spot.

"Stay where you are!" Marion called from the bottom of the steps. "Don't move!"

"What are we waiting for?" said Bruce, approaching with a load of boxes.

"Come on, Marion," said Vern, who was trying to keep his ears warm with his hands. "Get a move on," he said, bursting through the gate, "open the door."

Emily felt a thrill of horror as Marion whirled around, her fists out in front of her, crouched as though under attack. She shrieked at him, calling him an idiot, bringing him to a halt halfway up the walk. The others had automatically been following him, and now they all stopped in confusion. Emily remembered a day a long time ago, when Marion wasn't yet in school, when she had shrieked at her father that way, Emily couldn't remember why. They were in the kitchen of her parents' house, the three of them. Marion's face was paper white, she was hunched over just as she was now, screaming at poor Henry, and suddenly Harriet had swept calmly into the room. "Stop it," she had commanded, not raising her voice, and Marion had immediately stopped.

"She swore at me," said Vern. "What did I do?"

Where are they? thought Emily suddenly, automatically looking over her shoulder, searching the street for her brother Henry's car. They ought to be here, she thought. But of course they weren't.

"What did he do?" said Bruce, who seemed ready to accept that whatever was wrong, Vern was likely to blame.

Emily watched her niece curiously. Marion unlocked the door and smiled at them and invited them in. They trooped obediently up the steps, and Emily followed, and inside it was warm, and Marion was serene.

CHAPTER 3

She heard the piano as she climbed the steps to her sister Grace's porch, and instead of ringing the bell she opened the door and closed it quietly behind her and stood in the hallway, listening. She didn't recognize the music. Emily had never been musical. "Not a musical bone in her body," her mother used to say, giving her a cheerful hug, when at Christmas the six of them and their parents stood around the piano singing carols which her father had played; Emily's lusty voice had sounded the only discordant notes.

But she knew that Grace was playing something classical. Classical music, however quick, however rippling, held within it always something melancholy; sometimes only wistful, sometimes downright sad, and sometimes so heavy with it, so fruited with despair that it was enough to make you cry, or run. It seemed to Emily that everything which held a touch of greatness held also a wild and hopeless despair.

After a while she took off her coat and gloves and crept softly across the long narrow carpet laid down the center of the hardwood floor and went into the living room, where the hardwood continued. A rectangular rug lay in front of the fireplace, two sofas facing it, a low mahogany coffee table between them. The piano was angled across the left-hand corner of the room, and Grace sat on the bench, playing, her back to Emily, the low gray light of a cloudy February Sunday falling upon her from two windows.

Grace stopped playing, and lifted her head to look out the window.

"That was lovely," said Emily.

Grace gave a little scream as she whirled around.

"I'm sorry, Grace. I didn't mean to startle you."

"I didn't hear you. Did you knock? Did you ring the bell?"

"I didn't want you to stop playing."

Grace let out her breath in a gasp. "You scared the dickens out of me."

"You should lock your door," said Emily, slightly irritated.

"You're probably right."

"You play awfully well. I wish I could play the piano."

"Oh, Emily, I'm so rusty it's just terrible." She went over to the fireplace. "I might as well light this, don't you think? It's so gloomy outside, and cold, a fire will be nice and cheery." She knelt to pull back the fire screen. "I hardly play at all anymore. The piano tuner came the other day and I thought as I watched him what a waste it is having the darned thing tuned every year and never playing it. So I decided to start again." She was twisting newspaper into kindling-sized pieces. Emily got down on the floor to help. "But my fingers are so stiff, it's dreadful, Emily. So discouraging. It's age, I guess." She arranged the newspaper twists on the floor of the grate and added pieces of kindling from a recess in the brick wall to one side of the fireplace.

"It's being out of practice," said Emily. "Age has nothing to do with it. I remember you used to have the same trouble every September when you started lessons again after the summer."

Grace sat back on her heels. "Is that right? Do you really remember that?"

Grace was fifty-two, well-dressed, well-shod, well-groomed, with an abstracted air which suggested that someone else looked after these details. She had a delicate face, with full lips and hazel eyes like her mother's. She also had a gaiety that Emily loved but which often seemed tentative; Emily wondered what Grace was like in the company of people other than her sisters.

Grace lit the newspaper and pulled the screen closed. "Let's sit in here for a minute, until the fire gets going. Then I can put in some big pieces of wood and we can leave it." She sounded happier. One good thing about Grace, thought Emily; with just a little bit of effort you can feel you've made a contribution.

"This is a beautiful room," said Emily, looking around. "It's a beautiful house." It was a spacious, two-bedroom house on a street lined with big old trees and surrounded by bigger houses, all of them on large lots, set far back from the sidewalk behind tall hedges or stone fences.

"It's too big for me, of course," said Grace apologetically, as she always did, "but I enjoy it." She got up to put logs on the fire and pour them sherry from a small bar in the corner of the living room. "Did you bring Olive a present?" she asked, putting the glasses on the coffee table.

Emily got up from the floor stiffly and sat on the sofa next to Grace. "I did not. She said no presents, so I took her at her word. Is Henry coming?"

"No, Harriet had to go to Edmonton for something, I forget what. I didn't really expect them to come, did you? We saw them at Christmas, after all." She giggled into her sherry. "I think she wishes Henry had popped into the world without a relative to his name, clean and uncontaminated, just for her."

They finished their sherry and Emily helped Grace with dinner, which was why she had come early; but she wasn't at all surprised to find that the only thing Grace had left for her to do was make a salad.

When later the sisters sat down at the table in Grace's dining room, Emily thought of family dinners from her childhood when there had been eight of them. We will dwindle more, she thought, we will disappear one by one until there's nobody left to hold a family dinner, nobody to come to one, there will be only silence.

It was a large table, even without any of the extra leafs in it. Grace was the only one who habitually served dinner on a table not completely clothed in linen with silence cloth beneath. Olive and Polly looked upon this with uneasy disapproval. There was something slightly uncivilized, they thought, about place mats. But Emily enjoyed the gleam of the polished oak coaxed out by candlelight. Grace had another habit that annoyed Polly and Olive, which was to serve the dinner onto plates in the kitchen, instead of putting platters and bowls on the table where people could help themselves. They always left something uneaten, as though reproving Grace for having thought she could accurately predict their appetites.

Still, they were comfortable in her house. On the few occasions when everyone was invited to Harriet's house, nobody was comfortable. Each of the sisters arrived in clothes none of the others had seen before, and they brought manners polished to a brilliant sheen and limbs which at least for the first part of the evening moved with a hardwon, concentrated elegance. Harriet and her collection of paintings were always too much for them, though. And there was Marion, too, who invariably came out with remarks which left the sisters' mouths agape. By the time they left, their noses were shiny and somehow at least one of them had managed to get a run in her pantyhose.

"Before we begin," said Grace, raising her wineglass, "let's toast Olive on her birthday. Happy birthday, Olive."

They murmured in response, and drank.

"Thank you very much, Grace," said Olive, who was sixty-three that Valentine's Day, and the oldest sister. Their brother, Henry, however, was sixty-six.

"This is very nice wine, Grace," said Polly.

"I'm glad you like it," said Grace.

"That magazine of yours, Emily," said Olive, cutting delicately into her fillet of beef, "gets worse and worse. My, my, this is certainly rare, isn't it."

"Oh, is it too rare for you, Olive?" Grace put her napkin down and prepared to rise. "I'm sure there's some in the kitchen that's more well done, let me get it for you."

"No, no, no," said Olive, lifting her fork to her mouth. "This will be fine. Don't trouble yourself on my account."

"It's no trouble, really," said Grace, standing.

"Sit down, for heaven's sake," said Emily. "She can eat around the edges."

Olive looked at her, astonished, threatening indignation.

"It is not my magazine, Olive," said Emily, "and I quite agree, it gets worse and worse."

"I really don't understand how you can work for that man," said Polly, who was fifty-five and didn't look like a blood relation of the others. She was tall, and heavy, and had black hair streaked with gray which she wore in a bun at the back of her neck, and she tended to be ponderous of thought.

"I like Emily's magazine," said Grace. Her loyalty was not to Emily but to Grebbs. Although she had never actually said so, Emily knew she hoped someday to be invited to dinner or a party at Emily's apartment and there encounter Mr. Grebbs in the flesh, a situation which most certainly would never occur. Emily was scrupulous, always had been, about not mixing her business and personal lives, and even if she changed her mind one day she would never go so far as to include Homer Grebbs among her friends.

"It isn't my magazine," said Emily again patiently. "I am simply a secretary there, that's all."

There was no point in trying to tell them about makeup. It wasn't that they wouldn't understand, but they weren't really interested in what she did. She would like to have told them about having been sent to the airport to takes notes that bleak November day, but she still shuddered just thinking about that.

Marion had actually laughed when Emily finally got up the nerve to tell her what dreadful tricks her mind had played upon her. "That's why we carry notebooks, Emily," she had said. "You can't trust your eyes or your mind without your pen. And even when you have them all working nicely together, good heavens, even then you're bound to leave out something important."

Emily never went anywhere now without a little notebook, and two pens, just in case one of them wouldn't work when she needed it, but so far she hadn't had to take any more notes, and she hoped fervently that she would never again be called upon to do so.

It would make quite a good story actually, she thought, if I could ever bring myself to tell it.

"I saw Henry on the street the other day," Polly was saying, pouring wine and mushroom sauce from a porcelain gravy boat onto her beef. "He looked quite distracted. Almost sailed right past me without seeing me. This is delicious," she said to Grace.

"I saw him in the Bay last week," said Grace, "and come to think of it, he was a bit pale."

They were silent for a moment, aware that death had cut a rather wide swath through their family, snatching up a sister and each of their husbands, not to mention their mother and father, though they really couldn't count that as unfair, since both parents had lived to see seventy. They were always alert to the possibility of fresh disaster.

Emily slowly drank some wine, put the glass down, and picked up her knife and fork. "I had lunch with him on Friday," she said firmly, "and he looked perfectly all right to me."

"Really?" said Olive. "You had lunch with him?"

Emily thrust a piece of broccoli into her mouth and began to chew. She wondered how she would feel about her sisters if she had just met them recently, as adults who were not also kin. Her relationships with them were at once more intimate and less personal than were her friendships with other people—not that she had many of those anymore. She couldn't look at her sisters for long without getting unwelcome echoes of the childhood they had shared, the parents they had seen—and still saw—so differently. After a while their presence stifled her. She felt restrictions wrapping themselves around her arms and legs and chest.

"Yes," said Emily, "and believe me, he's perfectly fine, perfectly healthy."

"I may take another trip in the fall, I think," said Grace brightly, "and I'm looking for some company."

"I'm sure I don't know why you think any of us would have enough money to gallivant around the world with you, Grace," said Olive. "You may not have to be careful with your money, but there are certainly those of us who do."

"I can't be blamed," said Grace, flushed but firm, "for the fact that my husband left me well provided for, and I have had the misfortune of remaining childless. And who said anything about gallivanting around the world? I haven't decided where I want to go, yet, but it's certainly not going to be around the world."

"As soon as I retire, Grace," said Emily, "I'll go somewhere with you."

"That's right," said Polly, staring at her in amazement. "You're going to be sixty in June."

They all looked at her. Emily looked back, not understanding, and then her skin began to prickle, and she thought her face might be getting red.

"Retirement isn't always the grand thing it's made out to be," said Olive, buttering a roll. "I'm convinced, for example, that retirement is what killed William."

"Oh, Olive," said Grace, embarrassed, "really, you do exaggerate. That's ridiculous."

"I thought William died of a heart attack," said Polly.

"He did," said Olive. "But he had the heart attack because he'd retired."

"How do you think Emily must feel," said Grace, "hearing you talk that way."

They all turned again to look at Emily, who said loudly, "People do not retire at sixty. People don't retire until they're sixty-five. Some people never retire at all."

"Retirement only kills men," said Olive, "which is why I worry about Henry." She was taller than Emily and Grace, but not as tall as Polly, and she was thin, and had an angular grace. Her hair was arranged in finger waves. "I've never been able to understand, Emily, why you've kept on working all these years anyway. It's not as though you've got a profession, or a calling. It's not as though you need the money, either."

"It isn't polite," said Polly reprovingly, "to discuss other people's financial situations. Even if they are your sisters."

"I work because I like to work," said Emily.

She saw Olive running frantically down a nameless street, skirts flapping about her knees, hands waving incoherently above her head; her hair flopped upon her flat-topped head like a wig, and her legs threatened to collide as she fled, bug-eyed with terror . . .

Emily snorted out loud, laughter of a kind, and her sisters exchanged wary glances. She saw this, and toyed with the idea of telling them about the scenes which were occasionally played out in her head, and which she called her fantasy flashes. But of course she didn't.

"There are things I can do," she said calmly to Olive. "And so I do them."

She thought it exceedingly inappropriate that Olive should be the one whose birthday fell on St. Valentine's Day. There isn't a loving bone in that woman's body, she thought, leveling upon her sister a stare which even from behind it felt metal cold, and she had the satisfaction of seeing Olive's eyes drop, and her hands disappear into her lap.

CHAPTER 4

Emily didn't notice until she was almost halfway home that she had forgotten her book. She took a book with her to work every day, to read while she ate her lunch in one of the restaurants in the shopping center a couple of blocks away, across the Macleod Trail. She probably wouldn't have bothered to go back for it except that it was Friday, and Monday was the May 24 holiday, and the book in question was the new Ruth Rendell mystery.

So, cursing under her breath, Emily got her car turned around and drove back to the office.

There was nobody else around. Emily let herself in with her key and went up the stairs to the newsroom.

She was struck by the emptiness of the place. It was as though everyone had not simply left to go home but vanished; as if they had all been ghosts, and now they had gone away to put out a ghostly magazine somewhere else, and nobody had thought to leave her a note.

She turned on the light, and saw her book sitting in the middle of her desk. She reached for it, heard the door below open and close, and then heard someone coming slowly up the stairs. At least it isn't Grebbs, she thought. He always rushed up the stairs, often taking them two at a time. Emily was reluctant to get into an after-hours conversation with anybody, but thought she could escape easily enough anyone but Grebbs.

The newsroom door opened and one of the reporters came in. She swept long black hair over her shoulder and turned a pinched face to Emily.

"Jenny. What's the matter?"

The girl started around Emily's desk. "I got laid off today." She stopped and looked at Emily. "Did you know about it?"

"Jenny. No, of course I didn't know. I'm so sorry."

"I'll be all right." Jenny sat at her desk, her back to the long row of windows. "I guess I'll go home to Red Deer and start looking for another job there." She opened a drawer and began moving things around inside it. "Grebbs gave me a check. A month's pay, that's not so bad. I'm just going to collect some things . . ." She put her forehead down on her desk and began to cry.

Emily went to her and stroked her hair. "I'm so sorry," she said.

Jenny lifted her head and rested it against Emily's stomach and put her arms around her. "It's my first job," she said, crying. "What a bitch."

"You'll find another one," said Emily, stroking, and she continued to say soothing things.

After a while she found a cardboard carton and helped Jenny pack into it the few personal things her desk drawers had had time to accumulate, and picked up her purse and her book and walked with the girl to her car, which was parked beside Emily's in the small otherwise empty lot in front of the magazine offices. She kissed Jenny's cheek, and waved as she drove off, and then Emily got into her own car, sober and shaken.

She had heard through Marion that the *Star* wasn't hiring, was in fact struggling to avoid laying people off. She didn't know the situation at the other paper but was sure it was, if anything, worse. Jenny at least had a home to go to, and parents who would look after her. But she had been proud of her first job and excited about supporting herself, and Emily was sad for her; 1982, she thought, was not a good year.

As she drove home she thought about small things which she had noticed, but had not put together. The receptionist hired in November was still there, six months later, despite the awful salary she was paid. The advertising and circulation managers had been looking grim and worried lately, and no longer had assistants to help them sell advertising space and subscriptions. The place seemed to be getting even dirtier, and Emily suddenly suspected that the services of the cleaning woman had now been dispensed with.

At least, she thought as she parked in the garage under her apartment building, she had no financial need to work, and in that she could count herself extremely lucky.

But she was weary, and distraught, and she leaned against the wall in the elevator and closed her eyes, and didn't open them until she felt the elevator stop and heard the doors opening.

It was hot in her living room. Emily put down her purse and book and took off her jacket. She would check the plants which sat out on her balcony. It was really too early in the year to have risked putting them outside, but Emily watched the weather forecasts carefully and if frost was expected she moved all the containers inside for the night.

She drew back the drapes, which she left closed each morning to keep out the afternoon sun, and unlocked the french doors and pulled them open. Heat struck her in the face and she closed her eyes for a minute against the sun's glare. She went out and felt the soil in the containers, but it was still slightly damp from the watering she had given them in the morning. The plants were all still small, and although some of them had buds, none were yet in bloom. She liked to watch them grow; petunias, marigolds, nasturtiums. She thought she might try a couple of tomato plants out there this year, as well.

As she went back through the french doors to the living room she noticed some spots on the beige carpet, just around the corner from the balcony; four small spots. She reached down to see whether they were pieces of fluff, or dirt, but they weren't; when she touched them, they smudged.

She straightened up, wondering at the wetness on her fingers, and looked at them curiously. There was something bright red on three fingers of her right hand. Uncomprehending, she rubbed her thumb across them, and the red wetness spread to her thumb.

Cautiously she sniffed at her fingers.

She stood quite still in the sunlight, looking, bewildered, at her hand, and then, holding her hand out in front of her, fingers carefully spread, she looked automatically at her bare arms, craning her neck to see down the backs of her arms, and then she looked at her legs back and front, and put her left hand up to her face and felt it gently, section by section, cheeks and chin and nose and forehead, and each time she touched her face she brought her hand out in front of her and looked at it, but there was nothing there.

She went into her bathroom to look at her throat, but it was not wounded. She saw the look of incredulity on her face, and saw her right hand, fingers still spread stiffly, palm up; the blood on them was already beginning to dry.

She rubbed her hands vigorously under the tap and went quickly to her bedroom, where she took off all her clothes and inspected her body, inch by inch, with the help of the full-length mirror on the back of the door. She went over her clothes, every stitch of them. She found nothing.

She threw the clothes on the bed and stood in her bedroom, thinking.

She then had an idea which at first she dismissed as foolish but which refused to be pushed away, and she considered it, frowning, standing naked in her bedroom and rubbing her hands, and as she continued to think about it, it began to make a certain amount of sense. She tied her robe around her, pushed her feet into slippers, and went into the living room.

From her purse she got the notebook and one of the pens. She went over to where the spots still shone wetly upon the carpet, opened the notebook, and stared down, concentrating. She went to her desk for a ruler, knelt on the carpet, keeping the skirts of her robe carefully away from the spots, and measured the distances between them, and those between the spots and the wall. She wrote these figures in her notebook. She recorded in her precise handwriting the sizes and shapes of the drops, and as best she could their color, and the texture of the liquid as she remembered it, wet and silky between her fingers. She made a note of the time of day, and the angle of the sun through the french doors—it was not such as to lay direct light upon the blood. She thought about describing her reaction when she saw it and afterward but decided this was irrelevant.

Finally she got to her feet, closed the notebook, and replaced it with the pen in her handbag. The exercise had made her feel calmer, more in control.

She wet a paper towel under the kitchen tap and scrubbed hard at the spots on the rug, and the paper towel became pink. She got almost all of it off.

CHAPTER 5

Sunday, June 27, was Emily's birthday.

On the previous Thursday evening, Henry had called to tell her that his wife was dying.

"Please tell Marion for me, Emily," he said. "I can't do it. I just can't say it twice."

If he was able to say it only once, thought Emily, he ought to have said it to his daughter. But people did strange things when they were suffering from shock.

Henry wanted to see Emily, and they arranged to meet at a restaurant the following evening, when he said Harriet would be sleeping. He had to talk to somebody, he said.

It was late when Henry called, and afterward Emily couldn't decide what to do. She felt an urgent need to speak to Marion immediately, yet was tempted to let her have the rest of this evening, and this night, untroubled by news of her mother's illness. There was always the remote possibility, though, that Marion would call her parents for some reason, and it would be terrible, thought Emily, for her to get the news over the telephone.

Emily went to see her niece.

"I'm so glad I didn't get you out of bed," she said when Marion answered the door, dressed in jeans and a short-sleeved blouse. "I'm sorry not to have called first, Marion, but it's very important that I talk to you."

Marion led her down the hall and into the combination sitting room and kitchen. "Get out of the way, Spot," she said as the dog tried to squeeze through the doorway ahead of her. *"Do* go over there and lie down. *Down*, Spot," she said firmly, and he collapsed in a heap in front of the door that led to the backyard. Marion turned to Emily. "Can I get you something, Aunt Emily? Coffee? Tea? A drink?"

"No, nothing, nothing."

"I'm astonished to see you here at this hour. Do you mind if I go on with this?" She picked up a wooden spoon and scraped steaming noodles from a pot into a large bowl. Emily could smell chicken, too, and some spices which she didn't immediately recognize. "I'm making a casserole. Leona's coming to dinner tomorrow, and one of my tenants, too." She glanced at Emily as she stirred the noodles into the other ingredients in the bowl. "I do hope you aren't the bearer of bad tidings, Emily. Bad tidings have absolutely nothing to recommend them, I find."

"That's exactly what I am," said Emily. She was appalled to realize that beneath her deep and genuine reluctance to serve as Henry's messenger lay an obsessive curiosity: How would Marion react, when she learned that her cold and uncommunicative mother was terminally ill? It was to deny this curiosity any satisfaction that she looked away, at the dog, Spot, when she said, "It's very bad news indeed. I can't think of a way to say it except just to say it. Harriet is ill. Henry says the doctors have said she doesn't have more than six months." Spot looked back at her, panting contentedly.

Emily heard Marion stop stirring. Time passed. Spot yawned, turned onto his side and looked toward Marion, his tongue hanging from the side of his mouth.

"What's the matter with her?" Marion sounded remote, but interested.

"It's cancer. But Henry isn't telling her that. You know how Harriet feels about cancer."

"Hmmm," said Marion. She sat down near Emily, in a large, worn stuffed chair she'd bought years before. It needs recovering, thought Emily, catching a glimpse of it, and of Marion, from the corner of her eye.

"When did you find out?" said Marion.

"This evening. Just before I came over here. Henry called."

There was another silence.

"She must be furious," said Marion, and Emily looked at her, then, and saw a faint smile. "I mean, good heavens, she thinks to be ill is to be careless; dying must be the height of imprudence, don't you think, Emily? My goodness, the poor woman." She got up and went back into the kitchen area, where she dumped the casserole mixture into a dutch oven. "My father must be quite overcome," she said.

"Yes, he is, of course he is. That's why he asked me to tell you," said Emily. "He shouldn't have, he should have—"

"I'd certainly far rather hear it from you, Emily," Marion interrupted, "than from him. My father always seems to be talking to himself, when he talks to me. It's quite disconcerting." She sat down again and put her hands on the arms of the stuffed chair. "Well. This is going to take some getting used to. I've never received this particular kind of news before. It's odd. There are no tried-and-true reactions to fall back on."

"I'm terribly sorry, Marion," said Emily. She began to get up to go to her, but Marion waved her back.

"I know of course the reactions I might be expected to have," Marion went on. "But they aren't appropriate. I have no intention of pretending to feel things I don't feel. Which is another reason, Emily, for my relief that it's you sitting there, and not my father."

"What can I do for you, Marion?" Emily felt grief like a stone in her chest. Her curiosity had vanished, dispatched into oblivion by Marion's isolation.

"They're a very secretive pair, aren't they," said Marion thoughtfully. "She must have had tests, she must have had symptoms for ages."

"Marion—"

Marion turned to look at her. "Oh, Emily, I'm absolutely fine," she said impatiently. "Surely you can see that. I'm certainly not going to burst into tears or start trembling with sorrow." She called Spot to her, and he sat close with his head on her lap. "There is nothing to be done, Emily. Nothing."

CHAPTER 6

It was a bright gold evening when Emily set out to meet Henry, and the slow-setting sun did strange things to downtown Calgary. The tall black-glass buildings seemed to lean across the street toward one another, preening themselves in the sunlight, transfigured into sheets of gold, reflecting each other, narcissistic in their mirrored gleamings. Construction equipment was silent, cranes stood on other streets lofty and awkward and somehow threatening, but unmoving, now, on this Friday evening, and all Emily could hear through the open window of her car were the sounds of ordinary traffic and sometimes shouts and laughter from pedestrians. She realized, driving as slowly as possible along this street of giant sun-gold mirrors, that she loved the city in which she had lived for more than three decades, and this gave her pleasure and comfort.

It was two days before her birthday, and this year there would be no traditional family dinner in her honor. It was a relief, actually. She could do without having people watch her as she turned sixty. But she also realized, with shame, that she resented Harriet for robbing her of this unwanted attention. She knew that a dozen yellow roses would arrive from Marion, as usual, but she wasn't sure that Marion, who was so much younger, would even remember how old Emily would be, let alone appreciate the awesome significance of becoming sixty.

Emily didn't like the sound of it, sixty; it had a harsh, clattering tenor, something remorselessly definite, which didn't appeal to her at all.

But decade birthdays are always difficult, she reminded herself, turning left, heading for Tenth Avenue and the Crowchild Trail.

Emily had married late, by the standards of the early 1950s, at twenty-nine, and had become pregnant almost immediately. She remembered her thirtieth birthday with embarrassment. Not yet married a year, aching and pregnant and filled with alarm, she persuaded her reticent husband to make love to her on the carpet in front of the fireplace in that old house in Bowness. He had been astonished and not very excited about the idea; in fact she recalled that in order to bring the thing to a satisfactory conclusion they had had to move into the bedroom.

Her fortieth birthday happened around the time of Victor's death, and was over and done with before she'd had a chance to register it. Forty was supposed to be a tough one, but she'd managed to miss it. Her fiftieth birthday, though, was a real crisis.

She was on Tenth Avenue now, traveling west, and the sun still burned high in the sky above the mountains, a jagged line of white seventy-five miles away but looking closer. Emily thought of them as a buffer and she liked to see them there, sometimes clear against the blue sky, as now, sometimes tearing the clouds apart, letting wisps of light and color flood between their teeth.

She had been so staggered by that fiftieth birthday that it sometimes seemed she had spent the rest of the decade trying to gear herself up for the sixtieth. But if that was the case, she hadn't done a very good job of it.

She had swished off the elevator on that Tuesday, June 27, ten years ago, and smiled her way down the hall to her small office, which was directly outside the large one occupied by her boss, who had a stunning view of the city and the Rockies. And as she dropped her handbag on her desk and reached to uncover her typewriter she had felt, with shattering suddenness, like a fraud. All day long she felt this way, and had to take herself sternly in hand, several times, forcing herself to concentrate on her work and talk to other people as though this were just an ordinary day.

After work she drove home through the traffic and unlocked her house and went straight to the bathroom, the most modern room in the place, to stare thoughtfully into the mirror. She saw looking back at her a woman who was the absolute picture of elegant serenity—her long hair pinned up in a tidy chignon, her makeup still glowing at the end of a warm early summer day, her dusty pink silk blouse tucked neatly into a suede skirt a darker shade of the same color—wearing alligator pumps and carrying a matching bag. She could see this creature as an executive of some sort—at the very least; more likely she was a politician, and not a municipal politician, either, a cabinet minister maybe, or even Canada's first female prime minister. She began to laugh, then, and laughed so hard she had to sit down on the toilet seat because her legs got weak and her stomach cramped.

When she had quieted down she removed her makeup, scrubbed her face, and brushed out her hair. That's better, she thought, nodding at the mirror; that's beginning to look better.

She made herself a large mug of tea and took it into the living room. Dusk had fallen now, but she sat without any lights on for a while, just thinking, feeling calm and resolved. There did lurk within her a certain amount of panic, but she decided she didn't have time to deal with it.

She had to get out of that job. Surreptitiously, it had been busily turning her into somebody else. She decided that the best gift she could give herself as a fiftieth-birthday present was a self with whom she could live comfortably for the rest of her days. She sat in the darkened living room sipping tea and trying to figure out what kind of a self that should be.

Emily, traveling north on the Crowchild Trail, watching for the restaurant sign, wasn't sure that she had ever figured that out. But at least she had, that summer, divested herself of house and job and determinedly begun a new life, of sorts; she tried not to chide herself now for not having been more specific; it was aimlessness which she despised and feared.

She spotted the restaurant and pulled into its parking lot. It was the kind of place where you had to stand in line for a table. Harriet would have been disgusted, she thought, and then it occurred to her that perhaps Henry preferred this kind of restaurant, but Emily decided it was more likely that on this occasion he hadn't given it much thought but had simply named the first one that came into his head.

He was already in the lineup, near the front, so they didn't have long to wait. Emily squeezed his hand and kissed his cheek when she joined him, but they didn't talk.

At the table they each ordered the smallest steak on the menu and said they wouldn't take advantage of the salad bar.

"I wish there were something we could do to help, Henry, all of us," said Emily when the waiter had left. "I really wish there were."

"I would have changed my life, if I'd known it was going to happen," he said, aligning the cutlery in front of him arrow-straight.

"How could you have changed it? It's not as though you could have spent more time together, or done more for her. You haven't wasted any of the time you've had, Henry. Think of the places you've gone, the things you've done together."

"I don't know how, but I would have changed it. I could have done something so that this wouldn't have happened to her, I know I could have."

Emily reached across the table to touch his hand.

"She's so brave about it," he said, looking up at her, and Emily saw the tears in his eyes. "I just can't bear it."

"Then you'll have to be brave too, Henry, won't you. You can't expect her to have enough courage for both of you."

"But she has, Emily. She's always had enough for both of us. And now she's going to need it all for herself, and I don't know where I'm going to get any, if I can't get it from her." He was rearranging the cutlery again, his fingers trembling.

"I think it must be much harder," said Emily carefully, "than when it happens suddenly."

It had happened suddenly to Victor. On a winter Saturday, when Nelson was off playing hockey. She and Victor had had lunch together from trays in the living room, but he hadn't eaten, he said his stomach was upset and he didn't feel well but it was nothing, nothing, and he'd have a cup of tea.

"But I have to be brave. I have to," said Henry. "I can't let her down now. It's the last thing I can ever do for her."

Victor had put on his coat and his gloves and the half rubbers that fitted over his shoes. "Victor for heaven's sake you really must break down and buy some boots." Emily remembered saying it. She remembered feeling exasperated. She had hated the look of those things.

"These are fine, Emily," Victor had said. "I don't walk through snowdrifts, you know. I just need them to keep my feet dry." He kissed her cheek and went out the door to take the garbage to the end of their long driveway. She hadn't even finished taking the dishes to the kitchen when she heard the door open.

"It's funny," said Henry, "but I've always been so sure, so certain, that I would die first."

Emily broke open a roll and buttered it, but that far-off winter afternoon kept crashing in on her, retreating for a moment only to let Henry speak of now, and Emily didn't want either then or now, she wanted to be back on Fourth Avenue with the golden highrise mirrors.

"Victor? Victor? Is that you?" She had walked through the living room and into the small entrance hall. He was three steps up, heading toward the second floor, where their bedroom was. His face was the color of the snow outside, and his eyes were glazed like the winter cloud-smeared sun, and he held on to the railing with both hands and said nothing, all of his consciousness focused on whatever was happening inside him; he was surprised, she could tell.

"All my thoughts were to make sure she was well provided for," said Henry, drawing the tines of his fork across the tablecloth.

Abruptly, it was gone, the tide of memory. She felt sick, and tired. It would be hard, now, she knew, to get rid of the pain, the regret, the bitterness, and she didn't want these things as companions on her sixtieth birthday; the thought of them clinging to her, weeping their useless tears, made her angry.

"It's unthinkable, Emily," said Henry. He raised his eyes from the table. The tears were gone, and he sounded almost conversational. "I do not know what I will do without her. It seems utterly impossible for me to continue to live, without her."

"I know, Henry," she said. Her voice was dry and rusty. "But you'll live, all right."

She was still remembering, but at least had the illusion of having decided to remember. She no longer felt swept along against her will in a great clatter of images and sounds.

"What was it that Victor died of?" said Henry suddenly. She thought for a moment that he had been reading her mind, but after all it was a natural enough question, under the circumstances.

"Coronary thrombosis." She had looked it up in the dictionary: "Coronary thrombosis—the formation of a thrombus, or blood clot, in one of the coronary arteries, resulting in interruption of the blood supply from the heart." She had wanted to know how it had happened, and why, but nobody could tell her.

Henry nodded. "Of course you had Nelson, didn't you. What was he, about ten?"

She had had no time to say goodbye. That was what had bothered her most, or at least that's what she thought, at the time. When they let her see him he was lying flat on his back and the face on the front of his head was not his. She had never seen such stillness. It was as though he had never lived.

"And you have Marion," she said to Henry, and confusion passed across his face.

Of course he didn't have Marion, thought Emily, driving home through the now dark streets.

And I don't have Nelson, she thought.

It was a lot easier to be an aunt than a mother. Especially when you were talking about Marion, who, although she made up for her physical reserve with devastating frankness in conversation, still gave of herself only that which seemed safe. She would dispute this, thought Emily, and protest that she was in fact very open about her feelings. "People always know where they are with me." Emily could hear her saying it. "There's no point in shilly-shallying around about things. I don't approve of courtesy if it's an excuse for dissembling," Marion would say cheerfully, her clear, rather high voice ringing with confidence.

Emily seldom wished for her son's presence, although she believed that each of them thought with affection of the other. Certainly there was no animosity there, she thought. She was back downtown now, looking for a store where she could buy a magazine or a paperback book before going home. She and Nelson had gotten on very well together. It was just that after Victor died, instead of growing closer they had gradually moved apart, and once he decided to go to college in Edmonton instead of Calgary, she knew she wouldn't see much more of him. He came out West on business a couple of times a year, and that was enough for both of them. He hadn't been out at all so far this year, though. Everybody was cutting back on everything, including business trips.

She saw the store after she had passed it, and had to drive a couple more blocks before she found a parking place.

Clouds had crept in from somewhere during the time she had spent in the restaurant with Henry, and the streets were covered with a film of rain, but no more was falling. She hurried around the corner, went to the end of the block, turned left and crossed the street. In the store she saw nothing that interested her among the paperback books or on the magazine rack. She made herself concentrate and had another good look, but there was absolutely nothing. And she had forgotten to go to the library that afternoon. She was unreasonably dismayed at the thought of having nothing at home to read. I have to do my laundry, anyway, she told herself. And then I can always watch late-night television. Tomorrow, she thought, leaving the store, I'll go to the library and to a bookstore, too, I'll make sure I have plenty to read on my birthday.

A few minutes later Emily stood immobile in a dark downtown lane, her concentration fixed on something lying on the ground. The blank surface of the lane looked wet and slick, and it shone dully in the light from the streetlamp at the end of the lane. Huddled against a brick wall, away from the light, an old man lay on his stomach with his knees pulled up, like a baby asleep in its crib. His right cheek was cuddled into the pavement, and his left hand clutched an empty wine bottle. His gray hair stood up in spikes and his eyes were tightly closed. A white shirt collar poked up from the old gray coat in which he was wrapped. He wore hiking boots and a pair of dark pants.

Emily turned slowly, holding her purse in both hands. She sighed, a soft, barely perceptible sound, and walked back toward the street.

The old man breathed blissfully in his sleep, but Emily as she looked down upon him had thought, oh how stiff and sore he'll be when he awakes.

She got to the street and turned left, passed an apartment block on the corner, and went into the small parking lot beside it, where she had left her car.

It surprised her that she had ventured into a lane, for heaven's sake, late at night. She wondered uneasily what had drawn her in there. The man wasn't even visible from the corner. She thought he must have moved slightly just as she passed the entrance to the lane, and perhaps then some light had flickered from the wine bottle. The combination of movement and glinting light would have snagged her eye, she thought, walking across the parking lot, trying not to hurry.

Her yellow Volkswagen was where she had left it, sandwiched between a blue dirt-striped pickup truck and a middle-sized bronze car of tidy sleekness. She unlocked the door and got in—but first, over her own jeering protests, she checked to make sure nobody was hiding in the back seat, and as soon as she was settled in the car she locked the door again.

She sat quietly, looking out through the windshield.

Any other night, she was sure, if her eye had been caught by something moving and glinting in a late night downtown lane, she would not have entered it but walked on. She couldn't understand what had possessed her to go in there. She remembered a feeling of detachment, and a sensation that she was invisible, or at least invincible.

This is ridiculous, she scolded herself, and massaged her temples, and started the car.

On her way home she thought suddenly of her notebook, and banged her hand in frustration against the steering wheel. There hadn't been much light in the alley, but she was sure there would have been enough to write by, oh, if only she had thought of it at the time, if only she'd gotten it all noted down, dry dispassionate facts, bloodless and unthreatening, thin letters on small pages of lined paper, so fleshless, so mathematically precise as to cause their inspiration to shrivel and die.

CHAPTER 7

Grebbs was direct but gentle. It was this Emily noticed as he spoke to her. She hadn't thought he could be gentle.

"I'm sorry, Emily," he said, standing over her desk on a day in mid-October, "but I can't afford you anymore."

She looked him in the eye for once. "I can't say that I'm truly surprised, Mr. Grebbs."

He had tried to wait until the newsroom was empty, but he could see that she was about to leave, too, for lunch. So he had said it right then, quickly, while Harold, one of the writer-editors, rustled his brown paper bag and bit into his tuna sandwich, trying both to hear and not to listen, from four desks away.

"It's a bad time for everybody, I guess," said Emily.

"We're all going to miss you very much." It had the stilted ring of something prepared in advance, and yet she thought he meant it, too.

"I'm not familiar with the procedure," said Emily, who sat wrapped in dignity. "Am I to leave now, or in two weeks, or what?"

"On Friday, I think," said Grebbs. "That'll be the fifteenth." He plucked at his cheek, then stopped this to run his fingers through his hair. "Hell of a thing," he said, and again, "hell of a thing," as he moved off to his office.

Emily looked over at Harold, who was hunched over his sandwich, turning the pages of *Time* too quickly to absorb anything written there. He glanced up to see her looking at him. There were no thoughts of him in her head, he just happened to be in the way of her eyes.

"Gee, I'm awfully sorry, Emily," he said, and swallowed what was in his mouth. Harold was about thirty, thin, with fine, fair hair and pale blue eyes. From this distance he didn't appear to have any eyebrows. He had been with the magazine for five years and worked almost as many hours every week as Grebbs did. He would be the last to go, Emily thought, and wanted to tell him that, in case he didn't already know it.

"So am I, Harold." She busied herself at her desk so he would go back to eating his lunch.

She had a proprietary attitude toward her desk. If she loaned anyone her stapler or her Scotch tape dispenser or even a pen or a ruler, she made sure she got it back that very day. It was important to her that the instruments of her job be on hand and in their proper places.

She heard the crackle of wax paper as Harold bunched up the crumbs left from his sandwich. From Grebbs's office came only silence. She still didn't want to stand up. It seemed that's where she had had the shock, in her legs.

She wished she had something to type. Eighteen months earlier, Grebbs had gotten a good deal on secondhand IBM Selectrics, the same kind of machine she had used when she worked for the oil company. She had been relieved and delighted to have one again, after years at first the theater company and then the magazine, punching laboriously away at elderly manuals. Now she stroked the hard plastic dustcover of her "new" typewriter and tried to come up with a reason to turn on its purring motor and put in a piece of paper and manipulate its keys with the speed and skill in which she took considerable pride. But there was nothing waiting to be typed.

They would get along without her quite easily, she knew. Yet she had not expected to be laid off.

She put her hands flat on the desk. She wore clear polish on her short, rounded nails, and a wedding band on her left hand. The skin of her hands was wrinkled, and there were some small brown splotches on them.

She pushed herself briskly away from the desk and stood up; her legs were fine, as strong as ever. She picked up her purse and her book, smiled at Harold, who smiled back guiltily, and left the newsroom.

She was supposed to have lunch with Grace, but by the time she had driven downtown and parked in a lot near the Palliser Hotel seeing Grace was the last thing she wanted to do. She stood on the hotel steps for a moment, preparing herself. Then she rushed inside, found Grace in the dining room and gave her a quick, almost incoherent excuse, something to do with errands, and the magazine, and the press of deadlines. Grace, half standing, napkin in her hand, stared at her tensely, trying to comprehend, nodding uncertainly, and when Emily dashed off she turned at the entrance to the dining room and looked back to see Grace still in that almost crouched position, waving the napkin as if in permanent farewell.

Emily walked the downtown streets for a while until the noise and dust of construction began to irritate her. Nobody would care if she was late getting back from lunch. She got onto a bus to the university. She hadn't been on a bus in years, and had to ask the driver what the fare was. He actually smiled as he told her, and made a remark about the weather, which was unseasonably warm, and which he said wasn't going to last.

There were only three other people on the bus. She took a seat by a window and the bus moved off with a comforting lurch, away from the cacophony of bulldozers and earthmovers, toward the river. This time next Monday, thought Emily, I shall have nowhere to go in the daytime. She thought she should be grateful that losing her job wasn't a financial catastrophe, as it would be for most people. She would be able to manage just fine on Victor's pension, which had been coming in regular as clockwork for twenty years now, and on her savings, carefully divided among savings bonds and term deposits and a few extremely stable stocks. My God, she thought, I have nothing to complain about, nothing at all.

But not going to work would be remarkably odd, she thought, smoothing her brown wool skirt over her knees. The first thing which had popped into her head after she had understood what Grebbs was saying was that now she would have to go job-hunting again. This had been accompanied by a slight weariness, some dismay, a little bit of irritation. It was one thing to find a new job because you wanted a change, and quite another to have to find one because your old job no longer existed.

And then it had dawned on her that she wasn't going to be able to find another job.

She kept forgetting the societal implications of being sixty. She didn't feel any different, in herself. It hardly even distressed her to look in the mirror. If her life was etched upon her face, so what, she was proud of it, to be unmarred would be to have been untouched. But at sixty, nobody was going to give her a job.

The bus was crossing the river now, a clear-water mountain river, not wide, with trees along its banks which in autumn looked like great golden umbrellas. They were tattered now, and even as she watched, more scraps of gold were torn from them and blown away by the wind. But the riverbanks were covered with cotoneaster, too, a low-growing bush that in the fall turned red and now spread restrained fire along the low slopes.

Emily decided that what faced her was a challenge, an amazing and a staggering challenge: how to live a full and useful life without a job. She thought it quite possible that for some people, anyway, jobs were often the barrier between them and their deaths. As long as you had something useful to do, death would take no notice of you. But hang around doing nothing all day and you'd be sure to catch his eye. Well, Emily had never in her life hung around doing nothing, and she wasn't going to start now.

She began considering her options. It was an activity which gradually became dispiriting.

She was too warm, sitting in the sun in her wool skirt and cotton shirt and tweed blazer. She moved her body away from the seat and reached behind her to unstick her blouse from her back. She remained in this position, looking out the window, until her skin felt dry, and then she sat back.

She was only a couple of blocks from Marion's house, she observed, as the bus trudged along Kensington Road. With a start, she realized the bus had already come this way once since she got on. She had been around the entire route, hadn't even noticed, and was now trundling around it again. But what were they going to do if she was late getting back to work, she thought; fire her?

The bus found the river again and traveled along beside it for a while.

She wouldn't tell anyone, not just yet. She had to at least make a start on planning her new life before telling anyone. Besides, Harriet was still dying, and joblessness lacked significance next to that.

Her hobbies had always been reading and walking and the occasional pleasure of other people's company. These activities were not expandable to fill entire days, and neither would be any other hobby she might develop, whether it was knitting or sewing or playing bridge or golf. Gardening might be sufficiently expandable, in another climate, but not in Alberta, where the frozen earth refused to admit a shovel from October until May. She thought this was probably why so many prairie people retired to British Columbia's lower mainland. But they retired in couples, not singly.

The bus slowed to enter the university grounds again, and Emily saw crowds of students hurrying between buildings; if you can't find a job, stay in school. She wondered if she should inquire about going to college, something she had never done. For a few minutes, peering from the bus window, she felt this would be possible and desirable and even potentially rewarding. But then the bus stopped and a group of students got on, and to Emily they looked competent and aggressive. She would have to take a course in taking courses. She had been away from school much too long. And what on earth would she study, and to what end?

The driver, whistling to himself and occasionally exchanging comments with the students sitting near the front of the bus, fiddled with something and caused the lettering above him to reshape itself. Emily saw that the bus was preparing to return again to the downtown area. This time she'd better stay alert so as not to miss her stop. She didn't want to be away the whole afternoon. She didn't want to be thought irresponsible.

The chatter of the young people around her was irritating. She knew she was probably as well educated as any of them, having lived for sixty years and read a lot, but this didn't seem to count for anything. She had no degree to hang upon her wall, and soon they would. Not that it could be expected to help them much. Nowadays it seemed you had to have at least two degrees to get anywhere. At least that's what Nelson said. He had two of them now, and a good job as well, even though it was in Toronto.

Emily knew that a lot of mothers in her predicament would at least seriously consider moving in order to be near their offspring. But not she. She fanned herself with her hand. What would be the point in living near Nelson? He wasn't married, there would be no grandchildren to visit. And she and Nelson didn't have a great deal to say to one another.

It was very noisy in the bus, with all the students talking and laughing. At least they were old enough not to keep getting up all the time and throwing paper airplanes and bellowing insults at their friends.

The sun flooding in on the other side of the bus was lower now, but still Emily felt too warm. Suddenly she regretted this peculiar impulse, leaping onto a bus, imagine, when she had a perfectly satisfactory car, quiet, with windows that opened, for riding about in. She thought about her car, anxiously. She had left it in an uncovered parking lot where anything might happen to it, a crane could drop a steel girder on it, an impatient careless driver might ram it, and had she closed the windows and locked the doors so no hostile person, young or old, could reach inside and cut up its upholstery? Emily looked intently out the window, trying to calm herself.

She stood quickly and pulled the cord, and when the bus stopped she got off. As it moved away she looked around her and saw that she had gotten off too soon, or too late, and didn't know where she was.

She walked purposefully down the street. At the next corner she had to stop to wait for the light to change, but even when it changed, Emily stayed where she was, jostled by hurrying passersby.

Finally she went into a drugstore to ask for directions.

CHAPTER 8

Emily was in the undersea world that lies between sleep and wakefulness when she suddenly shot upright in her bed, listening, or straining to see.

She reached out to turn on the bedside light.

Then she pushed herself out of bed and turned on the overhead light.

She went through her apartment, room by room, checking behind curtains and furniture, opening closet doors and peering inside. At the front door she checked the locks, which were all secure. She stood for a minute at the door, holding her breath, listening, and soon became convinced that someone was standing on the other side, out in the hall, listening with equal intensity. She ripped open the locks with swift, sure fingers and pulled open the door. So strong had been her imaginings that when he was not there she almost drowned in her own relief. Her head pounded with it, all her joints ached and trembled with it. She closed the door and locked it and went back to bed.

She turned on her side and tried to get comfortable.

She lay quietly, counting her heartbeats, and felt her body relaxing, seeking the slopes and hollows it had made for itself over time upon the mattress of her bed. Even her eyelids relaxed, and the sweet urgency of sleep cajoled her.

. . . and there he is driving noiselessly along the street in a dark car without lights or glass, with no reflecting surfaces at all, like a black, soft-padding dog slinking through someone's backyard. His car is only a shadow, nothing for the police to see. He parks it somewhere, in a parking lot probably, and eases out of it; no light comes on when he opens the door and no thunk sounds when he closes it. He lifts gloved hands and flexes them. His face is in shadow beneath the brim of some kind of hat. His body is big and his shoulders are wide and his legs are long and he is neither young nor old, just psychopathic—he had to be psychopathic, because no other kind of person would come after Emily.

He moves through parked cars like a snake, undulating between them, pushing the air apart. With his body creating a heavy thick silence as he goes, he walks up the sidewalk like a black soft-padding dog, moving close to walls. He turns into a lane, and the walls of the lane glisten blackly although there is no light there at all. He sees the man in the lane still curled up where Emily left him all those months ago and the psychopath stops there and looks down at him and sniffs the air and smells Emily, even though it was so long ago in another season that she was there.

He looks down at the bundle of clothes and spiky hair sleeping curled up in the lane, an empty bottle cuddled next to it. The psychopath pulls from inside his leather jacket a knife, and without even looking to see if anyone is watching he kills the man, just like that; Emily sees him do it. He lowers himself onto his haunches and with his left hand gives the old man's shoulder a little push that makes him roll over on his back. Emily can't see whether the old man's eyes open or not; oh, she hopes that they do not. The psychopath stabs him in the chest three times; Emily sees him hesitate first and for a minute thinks he might not do it, but he is only deciding not to cut the man's throat because of all the blood and even stabbing him in the chest he gets some blood on him. Emily hears the sounds of it, the thwack of the knife and the whoosh of air from the old man's mouth. The psychopath wipes the blade of his knife on the old man's clothes and stands up, and Emily wants to hide, she is sure that he has seen her, and then she remembers that he is coming after her anyway . . .

Damn, damn, damn, thought Emily. But she refused this time to sit up and turn on the lamp.

In the darkness of her bedroom, the time past 3 A.M., Emily got into a sudden argument with her imagination. It wanted her to go out and look in that lane right now, and see if there was a dead person there, or if the old man with the spiky hair was still alive and sleeping.

What a ridiculous idea, she thought.

But her body became stiff in the bed, it wanted to get up and put on its coat and march outside and look; the old man should be taken care of, he probably doesn't have anybody . . . she argued and argued with her imagination, and in the middle of the argument, fell asleep.

CHAPTER 9

Harriet died in late November. Nobody who went to her funeral was dressed entirely in black. Most people's winter coats weren't black, and Henry didn't own a black suit and wouldn't respond to Olive's urgings that he go out and buy one. Emily didn't have a black dress. She considered buying one, but decided it would be hypocritical. Her relationship with Harriet had been mutually courteous, and even considerate, but in the forty years they had known one another there had been no real affection between them. Emily didn't miss her at all, although she felt genuine sorrow for Henry, whose grief approached coma: he could hardly be persuaded to eat or shave.

The other sisters had black dresses, and wore them, and black hats, too.

Marion had a black dog, but she left him at home.

Emily watched both Henry and Marion carefully throughout the funeral service but wasn't called upon to come to their aid. Henry, in a daze, followed where he was led. Marion observed the proceedings remotely, and as soon as they were over she went home.

"Highly improper behavior," said Olive later in Henry's kitchen, putting out food for the people who had gathered at the house. "It shows no respect, not for Henry, and not for her poor dead mother. Where does she keep her good plates, do you suppose?" she said, opening Harriet's cupboards.

"She's a private person," said Emily, pouring coffee into a dozen cups. "I see no reason why she should be required to parade her sorrow in front of a lot of people she doesn't even know."

"She knows *us*," said Olive indignantly.

"She doesn't owe you a look into her soul," said Emily, "just because you're related to her."

"She owes something to Henry," said Polly. She was sitting at the kitchen table. "It's not right to desert your kin in times of trouble. What are all those people going to think? His only child. She ought to be out there in the living room with him, sitting by his side."

"You should be grateful," said Emily, "that it's Grace who's doing that, and not Marion."

"She certainly has some nice things," said Olive, staring into a cupboard filled with row after row of wineglasses in subtly varying shapes.

"Had," said Emily. "She hasn't got them anymore."

"I wonder what's going to happen to them now?" said Polly curiously, but neither sister answered her.

CHAPTER 10

Grebbs had given Emily the secondhand IBM Selectric typewriter when she left the magazine, which she thought extremely generous. He had carted it down the stairs and put it into the trunk of her car and stood there, his masses of gray hair whipping in the October wind, telling her again that he would miss her.

They had bought beer and pizza for a going-away party, but it wasn't a jovial occasion, since her departure wasn't her own idea. Grebbs had been subdued, and hadn't eaten any of the pizza, and of course hadn't drunk any of the beer, and Emily was relieved when enough time had passed for her to announce that she had to go.

It was then that he had stood and placed a hand on the dustcover and announced that the typewriter was going with her. She had been almost overcome, not so much because of the machine itself, since she didn't know what she'd ever use it for apart from monthly letters to Nelson, but because of the thought. She had to turn away and brush at her eyes with her hand.

A little more than two months had passed since that day, and Emily was finding the typewriter more useful than she had expected. She was wielding it as a weapon against the strangenesses which had entered her life.

She hadn't yet told anyone that she no longer had a job.

She seemed to be in a state of almost constant alarm. When she drove her car carefully over snow and ice, other drivers did wild and reckless things completely unexpectedly. When she walked along sidewalks, horrendously loud sounds would shriek into the winter air, causing her to duck and reach to cover her ears. If she crossed a street, she would hear what she thought were the sounds of a car screeching to a stop to avoid striking her.

Hurrying along under the arcade one day, trying to get into the Bay before her ears froze solid on her head, she noticed a woman moving along beside her. Emily turned slightly to glance at her. The woman was a total stranger, striding along wooden-faced—that could be from the cold, thought Emily, or not. She slowed down a bit, and so did the woman. All the way along the sidewalk they paced one another, the woman walking so close to Emily that her coat brushed against Emily's coat, and Emily felt the fear again, and stopped, leaning casually against the display window. The woman hesitated, glanced at her, and continued on her way. But Emily kept an eye on her, and only when she was safely past the entrance to the store did Emily dare to venture in.

It was ridiculous really, yet indisputable. The world was filled with menace.

Emily blamed it on the thin, cold air of winter. Everything seemed closer, sharper; light was blinding in its arctic ferocity; the body huddled into itself and felt, and was, more vulnerable. Once spring came, things would soften into normality, and fear would vanish. She believed this, but found it a struggle to remain calm in the meantime.

Her typewriter helped distract her. It sat on the desk in her living room, and she used it to type things for people. At the moment she was working on a manuscript for an English professor at the university who had some ostensibly new things to say about Shakespeare. She also typed term papers for students who were as uncertain of their grammar and spelling as of their themes. And she had done some work for a psychiatrist, transcribing tapes which turned out to be disappointingly uninteresting.

She sat at her desk, typing, and got satisfaction from her work, and since she had to collect the material from her clients and deliver the finished products back to them, she was forced to get out regularly into society, which she knew was a good thing.

If only she had not lately developed this ridiculous fear of the world.

She sat back in her chair. Her back ached; it was time for a lunch break.

In the kitchen she opened cupboard doors and closed them again, looking for something that appealed to her, and finally settled on a can of Scotch broth. She turned on the radio, but the CBC was offering the livestock report, so she turned it off. Humming to herself, she dumped the soup into a pot and added a can of water and put it on the stove to heat. She would have a piece of toast with it, and perhaps an apple, cut up and cored, and while she ate she'd sit in an easy chair with her feet up and read a library book.

While the soup warmed she wandered across the living room to the french doors and looked out onto the balcony. She couldn't see much, because of the thick frost near the bottom, which became jagged streaks in the middle of the glass. Containers sat out there, frozen to the concrete, the earth within them frozen, too. In the spring she'd have flowers again. Spring seemed a long way off.

She gathered her lunch onto a tray and took it into the living room.

There were aspects of living with fear which she didn't mind, she thought, spooning up her Scotch broth. It was a silent, heavy battle which offered her some dignity and pride. What she didn't like at all was the sensation of living furtively. The longer she kept her family in the dark about her situation, the harder it became to speak of it. Henry, she thought, probably wouldn't even hear her anyway. She saw him frequently, but had so far been unable to ease him out of his grieving, and went home from her visits exhausted and depressed.

She hadn't realized, until she left *Calgary Week*, how friendless she had become. The discovery had at first bemused her. Where had they all gone, the friends who she thought had peopled her life? She looked back through the years to find them and caught only glimpses, gray shadows ducking behind leafless trees so quickly she couldn't see their faces, just the flutter of a skirt, quick soundless feet scampering into hiding. They had come and gone with relentless, rhythmic regularity, a procession of them, often prized, sometimes beloved, but now it seemed that she had gone hand in hand with none of them, but rather had been suffused with affection as they lived for a while within her life, and stood dismayed, an arm raised in helpless protest, as she followed with her eyes their disappearance.

Emily put down the plate of toast and fruit untouched, and got up to take her lunch dishes back to the kitchen.

That's what comes of staying forever in a city of transients, she thought. The only immovable people in her life were her family. But really, she thought, rinsing dishes under the hot water tap, I could do a lot worse than that.

That afternoon, when she had delivered the first six chapters of the professor's manuscript and picked up the last six, Emily detoured to Market Mall to do some Christmas shopping. She pushed halfheartedly through the crowded shops, unable to decide what to buy for anybody. Henry would be the hardest this year.

She tried to remember what she had done for herself and Nelson the first Christmas after Victor died, but she had no recollection of that Christmas, none at all.

Suddenly, inexplicably after all these years, she felt longing for him as strong as in the months immediately following his death. Oh, how different it would be, she thought, letting herself slump against a wall near the entrance to a department store, if he hadn't died, if there were two of us now.

She pulled herself upright and got a Kleenex from her purse to wipe her eyes. She was tired and ached and dreaded the thought of going out into the cold to find her car.

In the crowd thronging the mall she caught sight of a figure which looked familiar. The woman was small and slight with a turquoise hat pulled low on her forehead, and over her ears. She wore bright yellow pants, and a heavy jacket which looked as though it had once belonged to a large soldier. As she drew nearer Emily recognized the woman as Marion's tenant, Clara Zeeman, whom she'd met several times during the summer and fall at Marion's house.

"Clara," Emily called, waving.

Clara pushed through the bustling shoppers and reached Emily's side. "Terrible, terrible," she said. "They would kill you, these people."

"I know. I've given up for today."

"I have now to get the bus," said Clara. "The stupid thing, it leaves here only every half an hour on Saturdays, can you believe it?"

"Why don't we have coffee," said Emily, smiling at Clara's accent. "Then I'll drive you home."

"Sure, yes," said Clara, "but I don't want to be any trouble."

"It's no trouble at all," said Emily, and they found a restaurant and sat down in a booth.

"Ah, it's an irritation, having only Saturday to shop," said Clara, pulling off her black wool gloves and pushing her hat higher on her head. Wisps of bright red hair stuck out from beneath it at the back. She put her purse on the table and next to her on the padded bench set a half-full shopping bag which had obviously been used more than once.

"What have you been buying?" said Emily.

"Ah, just little things, some soap, I like better soap for my skin than Marion gives us, and a bottle to take the roots out of my hair, and the last Christmas present, a present for my granddaughter. She's five, so pretty you wouldn't believe it."

"My son in Toronto is going to get married, I think," said Emily.

"It's true?" said Clara, her eyes wide. "You'll have grandchildren too before long, yes?"

Emily laughed. "He's just going to his girlfriend's house for Christmas, that's all. I shouldn't already have them getting married. And even if they do get married, they might not want to have children."

"They don't have to," said Clara, shaking her head. "Not like us." Their coffee was set before them, and she burrowed in her handbag for saccharin.

"Are you going to spend Christmas with your children?" asked Emily.

"After all I'm not," said Clara, stirring. "Is too expensive, you know? Too much money for me to go to them, and also for them to come to me. Also I would have no place to put them." She laughed, her face squeezing up, her narrow shoulders hunched beneath the large khaki jacket. "Marion, she said I should come downstairs, but I don't know . . ." She pushed the thought away with her hand.

"Oh, do come," said Emily. "I'm going to be there, too. We'll have a good time." She thought she sounded hollow. Christmas didn't beckon her with silvery seductive fingers this year. Its music was tired, its secrets shoddy, its promises counterfeit; even its red poinsettias were faded this year.

"Oh, yes?" said Clara. She ducked her head, picked up her coffee cup. "Maybe I come. Who knows." She took a cautious sip, put down the cup, and added another tablet. "Her mother died, yes? Marion's. So sad." She stirred the coffee, watching carefully until the saccharin had dissolved. "You're a widow lady, is that true?"

"Yes. For a long time now. You are, too, aren't you?"

Clara said, "Was lucky." She nodded, looking thoughtfully into her coffee.

Emily wanted to smile. "What, that he died?" She was pretty sure she'd heard correctly, but couldn't be absolutely certain because of the family of four, including two small children, who had just sat down at the table not far from their booth.

Clara sat back, holding her coffee cup in its saucer as though afraid the waitress would come back to snatch it away. "Ah, I don't know. He was a good man. He made me laugh," she said, and a smile of sudden sweetness swept across her face, and then was gone. "But he gambled." She drank some of her coffee.

"What, do you mean he bet on the horses?" said Emily awkwardly, because it was a phrase she'd never used before.

Clara nodded. She hesitated, then leaned toward Emily, her arms on the table. "It was so horrible, you wouldn't believe it. All his money he gambled. Sometimes horses, sometimes card games—it didn't matter to him. He would fly away to Reno and Las Vegas." She looked at Emily with wide eyes. "It was horrible."

"Good heavens," said Emily, dazed. She was full of impertinent questions. "Did he ever win?" she ventured.

"Sure he won," said Clara promptly. "And he lost. And then he won again. And then he lost again."

"You must never have known how much money you actually had." Emily tried to imagine this.

"He was such a gentle man. Everybody loved him, you wouldn't believe it. All his friends, all the people who worked for him—they all loved him." She threw up her hands. "He made them smile and laugh, they felt good with him, you know that?"

"More coffee?" said the waitress, materializing at their booth with glass pot in hand. Emily nodded, and she refilled their cups. At the table next to them the children were not so surreptitiously kicking at each other, and their parents, smoking cigarettes and staring into opposite corners of the room, were trying to ignore them.

"We had a lot of money," said Clara. "Ah, I don't say we were rich, but we had a lot of money. He did well in his business, we had a big house and a car and could buy things for the children."

"You mean, he could afford to gamble?" said Emily.

Clara looked at her intently. "Nobody can afford to gamble. Oh, maybe a millionaire, maybe a man like that, maybe he can afford it. But nobody else. Because—it's so stupid, anybody can tell you, anybody, if you gamble, you lose and you win and you lose and you win. And if you lose, you can't wait for more money to come, you have to do it right away and so you take money meant for other things."

"You mean he would take your savings?" said Emily incredulously.

"Ah, savings, yes, of course he would take savings," said Clara, "but money for food, that he would also take. It was a sickness with him, you see, the gambling. Like men who have to drink. Just like that, a sickness."

"Could you help him?" asked Emily.

Clara sighed, and linked the fingers of her hands upon the table. "I had first to help the children. I cut holes in the cushions of my chairs and there I hid money. When he won and handed me some money, laughing and hugging me, I would wait until he was gone and hide it in my chairs. Then when he lost and came to ask for money I would say, 'I have already spent it.'"

"My God," said Emily. What sickness in her own husband, she wondered, had death forever concealed?

"Soon, though, he didn't believe me," said Clara. "It was horrible, horrible. You wouldn't believe it. He would come banging through the door. 'I need some money,' he says, and I tell him, 'It's all gone, I spent it all.' 'I don't believe you,' he says, cold and flat, you know? He went to my kitchen and opened everything, threw things on the floor looking for money. I pushed the children outside. 'There's no money here,' I said, but still he threw things on the floor, looking; there were broken dishes; oh, it was horrible."

"Did he ever find it?" said Emily.

"No, he never found it," said Clara contemptuously. "And so we lived."

At the table next to them, each child got swiped by a parent, and began to cry, but then their Cokes and french fries came and they stopped crying and started to eat and drink. The parents exchanged grins across the table and looked less tired. The man had a beard and wore a duffle coat. Emily inspected his profile, looking for signs of addiction to gambling, drink, lust, or murder, but could see none. From this angle, anyway, he looked only affectionate.

"What happened to him?" she said to Clara.

"He won again and got into a plane to go to Las Vegas and it crashed."

"Were you glad?" said Emily.

Clara smiled. "I was not glad that he died, because he was a beautiful man and he made me laugh. But I am a very strong person. Who can know? Someday I might have killed him. A plane crash is better, yes?"

Back at home in her living room, Emily dug her notebook and pen out of her purse. There were times when it simply wasn't possible to take notes as things were happening; Clara would have thought her mad.

Released from the responsibility to record the visible, audible, capturable truth, Emily contemplated with pleasure the choices which offered themselves. She could write what Clara had said, as Emily recalled it, however inaccurately; and perhaps her own reactions to the conversation, and to her surroundings as she listened. Or she could re-create in her notebook with more detail than Clara had provided what it must have been like to live with the gambler man; what he looked like, close up, and the sound of his laugh, and the sullen anger with which he more and more frequently had threatened her, and frightened her; and the grief she must have felt when he was gone; and the joy.

But these last things were beyond her, thought Emily, jiggling the pen between her fingers. If she were capable of giving authorship to her imaginings, she'd be writing mystery stories instead of reading them.

She bent to her notebook, intent on authenticity.

CHAPTER 11

They moved into Marion's sitting room, where the tree was, for Christmas cake and coffee.

Leona was the first to leave for home, and then Clara departed, standing abruptly and stooping to rub her thighs which she said ached from all this sitting. She stood at the door leading to the hall and said goodbye to each of them by name, her hands clasped in front of her, nodding slightly to each of the people in the room, her farewells restrained and shyly dignified.

"Let me walk you to your door, Clara," said Marion's other tenant, David Bermas. "And tuck you into your bed," he said, smiling down at her.

"Does he do a lot of that, Marion?" asked Vern Palmer from a chair across the room. "Does he go around tucking everybody into bed around here?"

Emily didn't like Vern any better than she had the first time she'd met him, the day almost a year ago that Marion had moved. Yet she had to admit that his bumbling jocularity had helped dilute the heavy gloom which was Henry's contribution to this Christmas celebration.

Clara turned away from David, frowning, her hands flapping the air in front of her. "Such a thing," she muttered, and left.

"You embarrassed her, David," said Marion. She sat near the tree, just out of reach of the light from the lamp beside the sofa, and for the first time that day Emily thought she looked relaxed. Her hands rested on the arms of the chair, her ankles were crossed, and the shape of her legs was outlined by the folds of her long green dress. Emily realized that Marion had been standing and sitting very straight all day. It was a relief to see her resting, her head back against the stuffed chair.

"Oh no," said David. He thrust his hands into his pockets and walked over to Marion. "I don't think I embarrassed her," he said, looking at her. Emily saw Marion's face grow cautious. "May I sit down here?" He took his hands from his pockets and arranged himself on the floor at Marion's feet, resting against her legs.

"He's drunk," said Vern. "Needs someone to take him up to his room. Otherwise he's going to fall asleep right there. I'll do it for you," he said, grinning. "I volunteer to get rid of him for you."

"He isn't going to fall asleep," said Marion.

Emily thought she should offer Vern a ride home. Then she would take Henry to his house. He was sitting on the edge of his chair, elbows on his knees, looking down at the floor. She would go inside with him; make him some coffee and let him talk for a while, if it would make him feel any better, about Harriet.

Emily had been surprised to find herself missing Harriet from time to time, this Christmas day, especially when she made her long-delayed announcement about being without a job. She wouldn't have gotten any sympathy from Harriet, or even any suggestions as to how best to keep herself occupied. But there would have been a brisk stringency in Harriet's reaction which Emily thought might have been good for her.

It was a relief to finally blurt it out. She'd felt quite giddy and carefree at first; but then, disappointed. Nothing useful had come of her confession. She didn't regard Henry's offer of a trip to Hawaii as useful. It was a place she wasn't fond of, and she certainly didn't want to go there with a brother who was as yet unwilling to let anyone pry him from his suffering.

She had a flash of them there; Emily was dabbing patiently at his leaky eyes, empty Kleenex boxes piling up on the beach beside them, while the sun burned her back.

"I think it's time we were going, Henry," she said now. But she was reluctant to leave the sitting room. She liked it in there, one side kitchen, messy with the remains of dinner but almost in darkness, the other side cluttered with sleepy people and a Christmas tree. She liked, too, the clutter of emotions in the air. There was lots of trouble there, she thought vaguely, what with one thing and another, but generosity and affection, too.

Emily stood and stretched. All that wine, she thought, it's made me sleepy; I'll sleep well tonight. "Don't get up, Marion. I'm just going to get our coats."

She left the room wishing she could go straight home, straight to bed. She had enjoyed the day, but was glad it was over. Christmas demanded so much of people, it was unrealistic, some things couldn't be put aside, docilely, just because the twenty-fifth of December had come around again . . . she half turned back to the kitchen door, to close it, and felt a swift stroke of cold air against her legs, a painless but alarming blow; somebody's left the front door open, she thought, and looked down the hall . . .

It was the reality of what she saw that shocked her almost senseless. Imagination, however frightening, was an interior thing—but this was exterior, three-dimensional, appallingly physical. Seeing him, having believed him only a product of her mind, was like a sudden accident, a windshield in the face, precipitate and astonishing, smashing bones and spilling blood. She looked down the hall and saw the psychopath, and her acknowledgment of his reality was violence done upon her.

he stood facing her arrogant and undeniable and his head was enormous and black and he had no eyes no eyes she heard the creaking of his leather and screamed, and clung to the wall, and at the other end of the hall he moved, and she screamed again

Vern Palmer burst through the door behind her. At the same moment the man in black whipped off his head, revealing a normal one beneath, and Emily opened her mouth to scream again but didn't.

"I'm terribly sorry," said the man in the helmet, which was now clutched under one black leather arm.

Marion rushed into the hall.

"I've frightened her," said the motorcycle man. "I'm terribly sorry, ma'am," he said to Emily.

"Jesus, man," said Vern.

"It's all right, Mike," said Marion, putting an arm around Emily's shoulders. "Emily, let me introduce you."

But Emily, swallowing again and again, shook her head vigorously and pushed past them into the sitting room, and with one hand over her mouth and the other stretched out in front of her she hurried to Marion's bathroom, where she vomited.

CHAPTER 12

The family New Year's Day dinner was held at Olive's house. Henry was absent, which Olive seemed to find insulting. "Christmas was hard on him," Emily told her. "He wants to be by himself."

"If he's recovered enough to be planning a trip to Hawaii," said Olive, "then he's recovered enough to be here, with his family, where he belongs, on New Year's Day."

She was serving baked ham, with carrot pudding for dessert. She said it was their mother's recipe, and that it was traditional that they eat carrot pudding on January 1. She said this every year, and every year Emily searched her memory and couldn't recall having eaten carrot pudding as a child on New Year's Day. She was sure that was what their mother had served as Christmas Day dessert. But she never argued with Olive, whose grip on tradition was like a bulldog's on a bone.

Olive, unlike Grace, expected to be helped in the kitchen, but with two other women to do it, Emily didn't feel the need to volunteer. She sat rocking in the living room, occasionally touching her cheek, where a tic had developed. She wished someone else could have joined them for dinner. But Nelson was busy with his girlfriend in Toronto, Grace didn't have any children, Olive's only daughter was spending the holidays with her in-laws in Medicine Hat, Polly's son and his family couldn't afford to come out from Vancouver, and her engaged daughter was in Saskatoon.

"When's the wedding?" Emily asked, as Polly and Olive came into the living room.

Polly sat on a straight-backed chair near the doorway to the hall. "In July."

"You must be getting excited," said Grace from the sofa. "I love weddings. Is it going to be in a church?"

"It's going to be in Saskatoon," said Polly, her hands in her lap.

"That's where he comes from, isn't it?" said Grace, and Polly nodded.

"He's Catholic," said Olive reprovingly. "They might as well know," she said to Polly. "They'll have to know sometime." She looked at Emily and Grace. "She's going to turn," she announced stentoriously.

Emily burst out laughing. Her hand went to her cheek.

Grace, glancing at her uneasily, said, "Well that's not so bad, is it? What does it matter, Polly? I mean, at least she'll still be religious."

"It matters to me," said Polly grimly. Her face had become a dull red. Olive nodded, gloomy.

"Oh my God," said Emily, resting her head against the back of the rocking chair.

"We're all God's children, after all," said Grace hesitatingly.

Polly refused to respond. Her small hands remained folded in the lap of her black-and-green pleated skirt. Above the collar of her white blouse her face looked weary, and her hooded eyes miserable.

"It's all very well for you, Emily," said Olive. "These things aren't important to you. One day you're going to need God, Emily, oh yes you are, and then you won't find it so hard to understand the devotion other people have had all these years."

"But will it really matter, Olive, whose God I get devoted to?"

Maybe I should get a crucifix to ward off my psychopath, she thought, and smiled to herself, imagining the uselessness of that confrontation.

"I sent a Christmas card to Mrs. Cruikshank this year, as usual," said Olive, helping herself from a bowl of mashed sweet potatoes. "You remember old Mrs. Cruikshank, don't you Polly? Ninety-two if she's a day, and smart as a whip. But the card came back. Turns out she's in a home now, poor soul, lost her faculties, doesn't even know her own daughter. That's Mabel Henderson, you remember. She's up in her seventies now herself, I guess. Pass the ham, will you Emily?"

Olive's small house didn't have a dining room, so they were eating at the kitchen table. Winter sunlight flooded the room, since Olive liked to have the main meal of the day at one o'clock; it flashed from the silver, and Emily tried to blink it away.

"Mabel's sister Hettie," Olive went on, "I met her downtown the other day, she's doing some volunteer work at an extended-care hospital. Here, Grace, have some more ham," she said, passing on the platter. "She asked me if I'd make some afghans for the old folks in there. I was thinking I might." She looked up, and caught Emily's eye across the table. "The winter's long sometimes," she said, and bent industriously back to her plate. "I might as well make good use of my time, while I've got it."

"What do you do with your days?" said Emily later, driving Grace home.

Grace didn't look at her. For a moment Emily thought she hadn't heard. "Why haven't you ever married again, Emily?"

Emily remembered a tour to Europe she had taken ten years earlier. It was the first time she'd been outside North America, and she came back wanting to tell everyone she knew about the green-gold haze of spring in France, the downy-soft meadows, the blue sea, the cobblestones, and a well she had seen in the middle of an ancient courtyard. There had been a gloomy, brooding fellow of about her own age on the tour, who held himself aloof from the rest of them. One day he sat next to her on the bus and held her hand and talked to her quite magically. The last night of the tour he had come to the door of her hotel room, and she had let him in. She thought now that that was probably the last time she would ever make love. She wondered if Grace ever lay in the bathtub, mounds of bubbles covering her up to her chin, and touched herself with friendly loving hands, coaxing from her body a brief but passionate admission that there were some things you never lost your taste for.

"The world's running out of men, Grace," she said. "Haven't you noticed?"

"Men are too bossy, anyway," said Grace. "Don't you think? If a man lived with me he'd be constantly going on about having the furnace checked because it's August, or the eaves troughs cleaned out because it's April, or the lawns fertilized because it's May."

Emily liked to think about Grace in her house, which seemed to keep peace within it like a fragrance. There was lots of space in it; you were never bumping yourself against the furniture. There was a glow in Grace's house. Emily imagined her humming softly to herself while slowly, lovingly burnishing things all alone, in private. She saw Grace in her mind playing the piano, or watering her plants, or cleaning her windows slowly, voluptuously; or picking up a ringing telephone and saying hello with expectation on her face, and never being disappointed.

"What do I do with myself, you ask me," said Grace, looking out the window as they drove down Ninth Avenue, past the post office, and the Palliser, and the Calgary Tower. "I have routines. I have a lot of routines." She looked over at Emily and smiled. "It sounds silly, doesn't it?"

Emily felt precarious, at risk; she shook her head.

"I can abandon them in a minute if something better comes along. But that doesn't happen very often. I have rules, too. I don't allow myself to stay in bed a minute later than eight o'clock on weekdays or nine on weekends. I wash dishes as soon as I've finished eating. I don't watch television or read while I eat. I have only one glass of wine or sherry a day, except when I have guests. And I always have a useful project of some kind under way. Sorting my slides, cleaning out the closets, things like that."

"Grace," said Emily.

"No, I think you should know all this." She went on smoothly. "That's not all there is to my life, of course. In the summer I have the garden to look after, and I play tennis once a week. I can usually count on somebody inviting me to dinner once or twice a month. And I go to movies, or plays. And out of the blue, Emily, I get so sad sometimes I think for a minute I've got the flu."

"What do you do then? When you get sad?"

Grace was silent. Emily, glancing at her, saw her profile as a cardboard cutout.

"A lot of people I know belong to the Old Age Pensioners' club," said Grace. "They go off dancing all the time. That's fine if you like that sort of thing, but I've never been one for dancing. You probably remember. I'm a terrible dancer." She leaned forward as far as the seat belt would permit, looking through the windshield. They were now in her neighborhood, approaching her block. "Sometimes I get in my car and drive somewhere," she said, more rapidly. "Toward the mountains usually, unless it's winter. And sometimes I say to hell with the rules and I just pour myself a good stiff drink and go to bed early."

Emily pulled up in front of her house. "I'll wait here until you get inside."

Grace looked at her closely. "You've got a tic, Emily. Right there," she said, placing a suede finger lightly beneath Emily's left eye. She undid her seat belt and leaned close to kiss Emily's cheek; Emily was aware of her perfume. "You take care," said Grace. She got out of the car and bent down to say with a brilliant smile, "And if you're bored some night, give me a call."

Emily waited until lights had come on in Grace's front hall, and in the living room, before she drove away, through the dusk of late afternoon.

She felt tears on her face before she got to her apartment building. She shook her head hard, to make them fly from her cheeks, and laughed at herself.

When she had parked her car and traveled up fourteen floors and unlocked her apartment door she wasn't entirely sure for a minute whether it was she herself who had left the lights on and the stereo playing; and if not, who, precisely, she expected to find in her living room.

CHAPTER 13

Spring had come, and Emily was writing a letter to her son.

It was an April Friday. She had sat down at her typewriter, loaded it with paper, and switched on the motor. It sat there, busily humming at her, waiting. She had typed "Dear Nelson" but was unable to decide whether to follow this with a comma, a semicolon or a dash. A dash would be best. It was brisk and authoritative, without the impersonality of a semicolon. But it was hard to make proper dashes on a typewriter. A comma would be easiest, but there was something hesitant about a comma. So she sat there, looking at "Dear Nelson," unable to proceed.

Emily's letters to her son were more dutiful than affectionate. It was a struggle, now, trying to create in his mind an image of an Emily comfortable, and outgoing, and sought after, and busy—very, very busy. She told herself that she did it because she didn't want him to worry about her, but she knew this was unlikely. More honestly, she admitted that she wanted him to know that she didn't need him, especially since he had announced in January his intention to be married in the fall to his Toronto girlfriend, a young lawyer named Merle whom Emily didn't look forward to meeting.

She turned off the typewriter and sat back, sifting through the things in her life it would be satisfying to share with him, looking for humorous little events or observations to chat away about. It was always easier to chat to him in letters than in person. Speaking to him face to face she always felt that things were more serious than she might have imagined; even casual, inconsequential happenings were heavy with significance. It made her wonder what implications, what portents she had missed in all the conversations she had had with other people throughout her life.

She switched on the typewriter and after "Dear Nelson" put a series of dots. She looked at it, dissatisfied. It wasn't casual, and it wasn't apologetic, but it did seem a little absentminded, as though having written the salutation she now couldn't remember who this Nelson person was.

She brought the carriage down two spaces, ready to begin the body of the letter.

But first, for inspiration, she picked up the slim vase which sat on her desk and sniffed the two red roses which it held. She had bought them several days earlier, they were now in the blowsy, droopy extravagance of full bloom, disconcertingly exotic in the dry warmth of a Calgary apartment in early spring. She set the vase down carefully, and decided to tell Nelson about the final papers she had recently typed for three English students.

But this didn't seem very interesting. She could imagine him ripping open the envelope and letting his eyes skim over the page, or pages, maybe; if she ever did finally get going there might be more than one of them. Having absorbed the surface of things he would let the letter drop onto his kitchen table and she knew, she absolutely knew, that the whole thing would fly promptly from his head. Nothing of whatever she might eventually write him would make the slightest impression upon his brain. It wouldn't even be in there long enough to register; in through his eyes and out, zap, just like that.

She lifted a heavy hand and again switched off the typewriter, and combed her hair with her fingers. Her eyes caught a movement and her ears a soft sound; she turned her head and saw that one of her roses had dropped several petals and as she watched more of them fell, a satiny red pool had formed at the base of the slim white vase. She moved her chair so that she was closer to the flowers, and waited, but no more petals fell. She could hardly tell, looking at the rose, that it had lost any at all, so rich with petals it was still, so full and lush—but its head was drooping. She picked up a handful of petals and closed her fingers around them, and opened her hand. The petals were slightly creased, but as she watched them, they slowly uncreased; they didn't seem to realize that they were detached from their flower, and close to death. Emily brought her hand to her face and rubbed the petals against her skin. They seemed to caress her with an eager, curious touch which felt like satin, and the fragrance of the rose was incorporated in its petals. She dropped them onto the desk and this imperceptible impact released another cascade. She watched as the rose lost itself, until all that was left was the exhausted center, withered around the edges, some tiny yellow stamens in the middle, and clinging to the outside a few small crinkled petals which even when she flicked them with her finger again and again refused to fall. She picked up another handful of petals. They were a much brighter, clearer red now than when she had bought the roses. They were soft and slightly sticky in her hands, and perfumed. Finally she dropped them into the wastebasket and the rose from which they had fallen, as well, and turned to the vase and pressed her face against the flower which was still luxuriously whole.

"Dear Nelson . . ." she read out loud.

For the first time she wished she had permitted herself to make close friends of people she had worked with over the years. She could be corresponding with them now, those who had moved away. But it was one of Emily's principles that work should be separate from the rest of one's life, otherwise things could get unpleasantly tangled. She had made this rule for herself after becoming briefly involved with one of the architects at the firm where she'd worked for two years after her husband's death. Remembering this, Emily experienced a painful sensation of time being simultaneously expanded and contracted. It seemed no time at all since she had been involved with that man. She could still feel the rough texture of his Harris tweed jacket under her hand, the warmth of his breath upon her throat, the pressure of his thick body against hers; yet she knew this had happened almost twenty years ago.

The complete lack of sound in her apartment caught her attention, and made the skin prickle at the back of her neck. She reached up and rubbed it, and the dry, somewhat rasping noise this made caused her to freeze as though by rubbing her neck she had revealed her presence. The room was filled with light, yet fear crept close to her on rubber-soled shoes. She sat unmoving, breathing fast and shallow, trying to focus her mind. She didn't actually imagine someone sneaking up behind her with a knife in his upraised hand; she knew she was alone in her apartment; it was the aloneness, though, which seemed to hold the knife. Her back arched inadvertently, a quiver of a movement. She wrenched herself around and stood up; in the kitchen the refrigerator began to hum, and Emily tried to laugh.

"A knife in the back," she said aloud, marveling. "Me, found right here," she said, gesturing, looking down, "lying dead on my living room floor with a knife sticking out of my back. Now that," she said with conviction, "that would be a mystery."

And as she went into the kitchen to get an apple and a cup of tea, she cast herself in the role of detective assigned to solve the murder of Murdoch, Emily, age sixty, found dead on her living room floor in a pool of rose petals.

CHAPTER 14

One evening in early summertime, in the middle of June, Emily put her notebook and her pen in her coat pocket and went out onto the streets of Calgary to look for her psychopath. Her fear was too heavy to carry any longer, and she thought that she preferred to die by violence than from timidity and exhaustion.

She walked in the park first, beneath the rustling trees, upon the green grass. The golden shadows lengthened into oncoming dusk.

She left the park and walked the streets, under looming cranes, along construction fences, over the rubble of building. There were other people on the streets, most of them in groups hurrying from parking lots to movie theaters and restaurants.

She wouldn't find him yet.

She heard a patient voice, amplified and easy, issuing from a rapid transit car which had pulled up to the stop she was passing: "Please remember, folks, there's eight doors on the train, not just the one." It sounded old-fashioned, like a voice from another time and place. She wrote down the words in her notebook.

She walked on, down Seventh Avenue toward the library. On the cool green lawn of the Anglican church, some people sat leaning against its sandstone walls. There was a tablet of stone sitting upright in a shabby garden and Emily went closer to read the words carved on it: "The love of Christ constraineth us." Next to the stone tablet an empty wine bottle had been plunged into the dirt, upside down. Emily couldn't make sense of the words, but she thought they must be significant, so she wrote them down, and also described the wine bottle angled neck-down into the dirt.

She turned down Centre Street and saw people slouched drinking on the sidewalks outside hotels, lurching expressionless people fumbling with one another and going into broken-down hotels in dreary heartsick pairs. Sometimes eyes would meet Emily's and slip away, wiping her from their minds. Where do you live? she wanted to say. Show me where you live. Is there room in this city for you?

Then there was a lot of noise and yelling, and a woman staggered along the sidewalk, shouting at a man ahead of her. "Bastard," she yelled, loud but hopeless, and the man approaching Emily was muttering, "Bitch. Go away, bitch." He didn't look at Emily. The woman, as she followed him up the street, clutched a big worn handbag which was slung over one shoulder. She wore jeans and a denim jacket and had long black unkempt hair. Her face was screwed up in fury and she was crying. She saw Emily and stopped and looked at her and was quiet for a minute. Emily thought she might say something, but the woman just stood still on the sidewalk and watched her until she'd passed, and in a few seconds Emily heard her start again. "Bastard. Bastard," the woman shouted, and Emily looked back to see that she had taken up her drunken pursuit of the man, who was nowhere in sight. Emily reached for her notebook and paused for a couple of minutes, writing.

She walked and walked and didn't find him, and finally she reached First Street, and walked under an overpass, and eventually came to the entrance to the lane where she had seen the old man asleep with his bottle.

She looked up and down the street, but nobody was walking toward her, and there were few cars going by. She took some steps into the lane. Nobody lay dead and bleeding upon the ground, and she was glad of that, but he wasn't lying there sleeping, either. She looked for bloodstains on the blank surface of the lane, and on the brick wall, too, in case it had spattered, but could see nothing. It was a year ago, she told herself, a lot of rain and snow has fallen; yet still she thought there ought to have been signs of what had occurred there but could see none. The lane was quiet, deserted, apparently serene.

Emily stayed there for several minutes, searching, and waiting. But she realized that there was nothing there for her to find, and that it was not a place the psychopath would return to.

Sometimes she strived to make him more than he was, wanting to imbue this struggle with some dignity, and thought of him as Zarathustra's Pale Criminal, thirsting for the happiness of the knife. Usually, though, she recognized him for what he was—a cold and witless hoodlum.

Emily turned from the lane and walked heavily back to the street.

She looked left and right. Nothing significant revealed itself to her. She was very tired, and filled with despair.

She began walking toward her apartment building, and the blocks flowed grayly one into another, and the notebook lay impotent in her coat pocket, and the empty rooms of her home loomed closer . . .

. . . and then she heard him behind her, not quite soundless, the pads of his leather boots striking the sidewalk with a quick even thudding, like thick laughter. She walked fast and faster but felt his arm rise, heard the creaking of his jacket: His leathered limbs were made of springed steel and his glittering knife was in his hand. Emily was almost running now, moving awkwardly, hands stretched before her, sobs clotting her throat. But he was right behind; she felt him pressing against her; and then she felt his knife sweep delicately down her back from nape to waist, felt the fabric of her coat separate, felt a long red crack open in her skin, and she stopped, and was not breathless, and felt blood gush from the fissure in her, and waited, upright, for all the life to be gone from her . . .

"Emily."

she searched with her eyes but couldn't see him

but he was there, she heard him breathe

she stretched out a hand to hold him there, to deflect his knife; she was pulled into light

"Are you all right?"

She saw Leona, her face flushed and glistening through a thin layer of sweat.

he was gone, then

She saw Leona's disheveled hair, the damp T-shirt. She felt Leona's small hands clutching one of hers, and looked down.

She wasn't standing in blood, of course.

She looked again at Leona's face, and pulled back as the girl moved to embrace her.

"I'm fine," said Emily, and her voice was one she knew. "Just fine, thank you."

CHAPTER 15

Two weeks passed. Emily didn't leave her apartment or answer her telephone or respond when, once, her doorbell rang. She ate from cans and bathed and slept now and then, but didn't think. She tried to stay alert; watchful.

One day she found herself moving restlessly around her living room. Her fingers briefly, uneasily touched her television set, the leaves of plants, the back of an easy chair, books in bookshelves. The light had shifted in her living room. She tried to guess the time—guessed one o'clock. She looked at her watch. It was ten minutes to five. She realized that she didn't know what day of the week, or the month, she was living.

Her throat closed, and her skin became cold.

She sat down carefully, and looked into her mind, and saw only splinters there. Gently she gathered in its scattered bits and pieces, visualizing herself doing it, talking to them in a croon, urging them to reunite. Gradually she built an uncertain, tottering structure, an assemblage of shreds. The cracks in it made it unreliable, she knew. But it would have to do.

It was June, she remembered.

She went to the phone and dialed Marion's number. There was no answer.

She picked up her handbag and her notebook and opened the door. On the floor outside in the hall lay a long white florist's box.

It's my birthday then, thought Emily.

She imagined the roses withered and dead inside their white cardboard coffin. She stepped over it, and closed the door behind her.

Emily parked in front of Marion's house and rested her hands on the wheel, looking straight out the windshield down Marion's street, green and drowsy and deserted in the summer afternoon. When she turned finally to look at the house, she saw immediately that there was nobody inside except Spot, who sat in the bay window watching her car, his ears up.

The house looked closed, like a shop whose owners have gone on vacation, forgetting about their watchdog.

Emily got out of her car and went through the gate and up to the door. Spot peered out at her, hunched over in the window seat, his tongue hanging out as though he were grinning at her.

She wondered if she had been followed. She looked back at her car, which sat on the street directly in front of Marion's house, advertising her presence. But there was nothing she could do about that now.

She opened the screen door and touched the knob on the inner door, and it turned in her hand. The door opened, and Emily went through into Marion's front hall.

It was quiet in the house, except for Spot's tail thumping against a chair in the living room, where he stood looking at her with interest through the glass door.

Marion's house seemed to admit her reluctantly. She didn't forget my roses this year, Emily told herself, trying to believe that the disapproval she felt was imaginary.

Finally she began walking toward Marion's kitchen. She had no choice now anyway. She had used up all her courage to get here, and had none left to get her out.

MARION

CHAPTER 1

Marion first saw the house on a cold November Monday, in the company of her real estate agent, and she wasn't much impressed. It was in a somewhat run-down section of Calgary. Her parents, she knew, would not approve.

She put her hands on her hips and looked the old house up and down intently, calling upon her instincts. When you came right down to it, it was much like setting out to get yourself a dog or a cat, this house-hunting business. Marion's search for a dog had concerned itself not at all with breeds and backgrounds, certainly not with pedigree, and only marginally with health. She had looked the beasts intently in the eye and waited for a sign of mutual recognition, and if there was none, she turned away. It had worked well; she was extremely pleased with her dog, Spot. She saw no reason why it shouldn't work equally well when looking for a house to buy.

There was, she realized, something naïve in this point of view, and as an intelligent career person she probably ought to develop a more businesslike approach to house buying. But it was new to her, and she tended in new situations to rely heavily upon coping mechanisms which, however unsuitable to the occasion, at least had the advantage of comfortable familiarity.

After rejecting several houses about which the real estate agent was unaccountably enthusiastic, Marion had decided she'd better explain her theory, but that had been a mistake. The agent had become agitated and dismayed.

"You can't buy a house with, say, faulty wiring, Marion," she had said, "just because you like the look of the place."

This irritated Marion, who had no intention of buying a house with faulty wiring. And why was it, she wondered, that nowadays a mere introduction was enough to encourage people to call you by your first name? She didn't argue. She just told the woman to keep on looking.

It was late afternoon, and the November sun was sinking fast, but it glinted from the bay window to the right of the front door, and sheened the glass with gold. Marion felt weightless, looking at it. She had to lift her face to the sky to see the roof of the house, three stories up, and when she did so a breeze passed across her skin, cold, and smelling of winter.

She thought that her abrupt desire to own a house perhaps had something to do with security, and she would accept this about herself, but it didn't please her. Marion, at thirty-seven, was impatient with preoccupations with security. She lived her life from day to day, calmly, except for occasional explosive intrusions of her instincts. There flitted into her mind now and then tentative wonderings about her future, but she usually managed to swat these away as dispassionately and conclusively as she would have dealt with a fly. It seemed she had taken to heart an adage first heard at the age of ten from her Aunt Emily: "Look after the present, and the future will take care of itself." It hadn't occurred to her at the time that Emily, then in her mid-thirties, was saddled with a husband, a full-time job, and a two-year-old child, and the immediate present was just about all she was capable of dealing with.

If she looked at her current situation from a slightly different angle, thought Marion, she could interpret it not as an uncharacteristic interest in real estate as an investment but simply as a desire no longer to live in buildings owned by other people. And it would be good for Spot, too. As the manager of her building frequently pointed out, an apartment was no place for a dog that size.

From the sidewalk she inspected the houses on either side of the one she had come to see. The one to her right, situated on a corner lot, was a duplex, and both it and its yard were in good repair. She could see no obvious signs of children there, although she supposed that no children in the immediate vicinity was too much to hope for. The house on the other side was a small two-story structure placed smack in the middle of its double-wide lot, and it was badly in need of paint, and its yard was scruffy. Marion looked again at the house under consideration, and went up to the low iron fence to inspect the front yard. It was small, because the house was set back only fifteen feet from the sidewalk, but neat, and there were flower beds on each side of the front door, the earth in them cleaned of dead plants and waiting to freeze.

She raised her head to look up at the roof, which seemed even farther away now that she had advanced upon the house. "It's awfully big," she said to the real estate agent.

"There's something you should know before we go in, Marion. It may not be the kind of thing you want to get into."

Marion turned to face her. "I knew it. It's too much money, isn't it?" She shook her head. "What a waste of time. Really. You know perfectly well what I can afford."

"It's not that, Marion. It's a revenue house."

Marion was bewildered. She thought immediately of stills.

"There are four suites, including the ground floor, which would be yours."

"Suites?"

"The three rents would just about cover your mortgage payments. I think you can afford it, all right. Assuming that you have the down payment. Or can get it."

Marion walked closer to her. "You're out of your mind, my dear." She looked up at the house, a narrow building with a small balcony jutting out from the middle of the third floor. The top two thirds of the house was painted white, the bottom was brown. "I couldn't possibly live in a house with a bunch of strangers. It's out of the question." She turned back to the agent. "I have an aversion to strangers at the best of times. I certainly don't want them cluttering up my private house." Marion lived among her fellow creatures warily, checking them out on her personal rating system over a long period of time, and only after they had passed certain tests of which they remained forever ignorant were they permitted easy access to her life.

It was almost dark, and the cold breeze had become a cold wind.

Marion gloomily agreed to look through the house. She told herself this was because of the real estate agent's discomfort. She was not suitably dressed for the outdoors and her shivering had become audible. She obviously needed to get warmed up before climbing back into Marion's five-year-old car, a 1976 Renault station wagon whose seats were made of vinyl.

She expected to find within the house countless flaws, and looked for them almost eagerly. She found them, too, but they were superficial imperfections, nothing worth rejecting the place for, she thought, as the elderly couple who owned the house chanted confidently of new roof, new wiring, new carpeting throughout. Finally, on the ground floor, she trudged after them through a long narrow living room and an enormous kitchen into a tiny hall which led to a large bedroom.

As Marion stood in the doorway looking into the bedroom, her mind became extremely active. She stood there quietly, thinking. She saw the room swept clean of the double bed, the two substantial night tables, the chest of drawers, the chiffonier, the dressing table and the heavy drapes at the windows. She imagined a small bed, a small table next to it, and across the room a long work surface with bookshelves above it and beside it and things on top like a typewriter and a telephone and baskets marked FILING and TO DO and WORK IN PROGRESS.

She didn't know where this had come from, but she didn't question it. Her instincts, she knew, were sometimes devious. She nodded meditatively, awarding them a delicate, courteous respect.

She turned and looked past the owners of the house to where the real estate agent stood, at the end of the hallway, in the kitchen. "This may have possibilities after all," she said, in her firm, clear voice.

States of excitement, for Marion, were not joyous moments to be gloried in for their own sake. She used excitement, when it came to her, as a kind of fuel for necessary action.

"If you're right about the rents covering the mortgage payments," she said to the real estate agent when they were once more on the sidewalk in front of the house, "then I will buy this house, and I will leave the *Star* and become a freelancer." She watched the real estate agent with interest.

"Oh my God, Marion," the woman said, staring at her in dismay.

Marion turned away, satisfied. When she was a child she had visualized the human race as being composed of three distinct groups. She had called the largest group the Mass, and into it she put most of the people she knew; probably, she thought, most of the people on the face of the earth would fit there, too. She didn't bother to define this group but if she had, she might have said it was composed of people with no instincts at all. A smaller number—including for a while her father—fell into the group she called the Thinkers. And the smallest number of all were the elite bunch she referred to as the Skyscrapers; among their characteristics was a calm acceptance of Marion, and an assumption that she usually knew how to handle her own life and that if she sometimes made mistakes, that didn't make her wrong. Some people had gotten moved from one group to another, either as she got to know them better or because they had changed. She knew her child self would at first meeting have shelved this real estate agent among the Mass.

"Quit your job? Freelance? But why, Marion?"

And her child self would have been right.

"Isn't that what you do?" said Marion. "You don't get a salary, you get commissions. What's the difference?"

"But I've got a husband! We're a two-income family!"

Marion lifted her eyebrows, and the agent looked away.

Marion stood looking at the house she had decided to buy. Her white quilted jacket glowed in the light from a streetlamp twenty feet away, and so did her shoulder-length hair. Marion tended to walk through life like something arrogant, and some people thought her green eyes were cold. But others saw mainly the translucency of her white skin, and thought what a fragile covering it was.

"Whoever lives there now," she said firmly, watching as the blinds were lowered over the three windows that made up the bay, "has got to go. I insist on selecting my own strangers. And they'll have to do their own cleaning. They had better do it, too, I won't live in a dirty house. I'll provide all the supplies, but . . ." She turned suddenly to the agent. "Good heavens. They don't get any meals from me, do they?"

"No, Marion. It's not a boardinghouse. Didn't you see the stoves and the fridges and the sinks and the cupboards? Each suite is completely self-sufficient."

"Not quite. They have to share a bathroom. At least I'll have my own bathroom. I won't let any of them into my part of the house at all," she said resolutely. "Yes. That's final." She looked up at the third floor balcony. "Yes. I will buy this house. And then I will quit my job."

"Just make sure you don't breathe a word about quitting the paper until you've got your mortgage," said the real estate agent. "You will never, ever get a mortgage, Marion, without a job. Your job is the single only thing that's going to get you that mortgage, do you understand?" She was positively clattering on the sidewalk, in her gray suit and black kid gloves and black pumps, but she certainly did look like somebody's idea of a successful businesswoman, even to the slim briefcase she carried. Marion took mental notes, and then walked to her car.

"Get in," she said. "We'd better talk about money. How much of a mortgage will I have to get? What do they want for this house, anyway?" She laughed at the black sky, silvery laughter aimed at invisible stars. "I haven't even asked you how much it costs."

CHAPTER 2

Marion was an efficient packer, a well-organized mover. On the day her friends and Emily helped transfer her things to the house she was up three hours before the first of them arrived but there were no last-minute things to be done, just coffee to make and cups to put out, along with a box of sugar cubes, another of plastic stir-sticks, and a jar of powdered cream. This took her less than five minutes, when she got back from delivering Spot to the kennel.

She walked around her apartment in a state of great excitement, trying to calm herself. She felt no wistful attachments to the rooms she paced, although she had lived in them for four years. She saw in the bathroom mirror that her green eyes were bright, and her pale face was flushed, and she felt commotion in herself.

She checked her belongings, wondering how many trips it would take to get them all to the house. In the living room there was a sofa, an end table, a coffee table, a battered maroon easy chair, two table lamps and a floor lamp. In the bedroom waited a single bed, a chest of drawers, a night table, a dressing table with a mirror, and a chair. Apart from three dozen boxes filled with china, cutlery, linens, clothes, books, and other assorted odds and ends, that was it. She had sold everything else, planning to buy whatever she needed and have it delivered later to the house. The furniture in the tenants' rooms came with the house, and some other pieces, too, which she might or might not keep.

When Emily arrived, Marion let her in eagerly, relieved to have something to do other than walk around impatiently, rubbing her hands. Bruce was next, and then Leona, who had Vern in tow because he didn't have a car. Marion found this exasperating, and often scolded him for stubbornly insisting on not owning an automobile. "Hell, I don't think I even remember how to drive any more," he'd said cheerfully the last time she mentioned it. She understood that some principle was at stake here, but didn't approve of principles unless they had a practical application, which this one of Vern's certainly didn't, since he ended up being driven around by his friends. Marion would have admired him if he refused even for inexplicable reasons ever to get into a car; to refuse merely to own or drive one was only irritating.

It was Bruce who got things organized, as Marion had expected. It wouldn't occur to him that she might prefer to issue the necessary instructions herself. Because he was doing her a favor, though, by helping her move, she didn't protest, and even thanked everyone for coming, before anybody had actually done anything at all. Marion didn't like to be beholden to anyone, and their offers of assistance had surprised her, but it would have been foolish to turn them down—to do so, she had realized, would actually have hurt them.

She and Emily loaded Marion's station wagon while it was still in the basement parking garage, so that when it was time to leave it would still be warm. When she got into it she pulled her tuque down over her ears, and pressed her gloved hands against wool-covered ears, and closed her eyes, suspending herself in silence, looking briefly for peace. She looked for it dispassionately, because it was something she didn't think she believed in and was contemptuous of herself for seeking, even casually. Then she sat up straight and started the motor, put the car in gear and drove out of the parking lot.

The brightness outside was almost blinding for a moment; the ice fog had begun to dissolve under the harsh attack of the winter sun. There was no traffic on Marion's street—only Emily's yellow Volkswagen and Bruce's pickup truck and Leona's red Honda, belching clouds of exhaust into the cold white morning. Marion didn't watch for them to follow her. My house has a garage at the back of it, she thought, how nice, and a place to plug in the block heater of my car.

As she drove toward her house Marion expressed again her fervent thanks to the wayward, willful gods who this time had come through for her. She hadn't realized how important the house had become to her until her bank told her they wouldn't lend her five thousand dollars for the down payment. She shivered in her car, the heater on full blast, remembering that. But she had refused to admit defeat, and had been encouraged by Emily, who reminded her that banks were there to serve their customers and the town was filled with banks. So Marion had thought about it and had gone to her bank and withdrawn all the money from her savings account and opened a new savings account at the bank down the street.

Two days later, with a vision in her head of her real estate agent, she dressed for work in a tailored suit and a fake fur jacket, and spent an uncomfortable morning ignoring the comments this produced among her colleagues. At noon she hurried to the hairdresser. At one-thirty, she was seated across the desk of the loans manager at her new bank. She asked him for five thousand dollars. But this time she didn't say that she needed the money to use as a down payment on a house. She told him she wanted to buy a color television set for her mother, and also to take the poor woman to California for what, Marion implied, might well turn out to be her last vacation. Since her mother disapproved of television, and wasn't fond of California either, this gave Marion considerable private satisfaction. Then she announced to the loans manager, smoothing her gloves, that she was an editorial writer with the Calgary *Star,* an institution of some substance in the community for which she had worked steadily for fifteen years.

Marion knew that the favorable impression she made on the loans manager was due not only to her intelligence, her capabilities as a professional person, and her credit rating; it also owed something to her blond hair, green eyes, and fair complexion. But she wanted the house very badly by then, and when he let her have the money, she felt only relief that her stratagems had worked.

She did remind herself now, however, on her way to move in, not to patronize that loan manager's bank in the future. People in his position ought to be much more careful about lending out their depositors' funds.

As she turned onto Memorial Drive, she realized that Emily's car was still out of sight. She slowed down, and by the time she reached the turnoff she thought she saw it about half a dozen cars behind. She drove two blocks and turned left, onto a street parallel with Memorial, where the snow was much less trampled. Her hands were gripping the steering wheel harder than was necessary; her whole body had tensed. She thought not of moving into her house but of embracing it, enfolding it roughly in her arms, taking possession of all that it was, all that it ever had been, and cultivating it, making it grow into she didn't know quite what.

She drove more slowly along the street, where snow lay heavy upon invisible lawns and sidewalks and the sun shot needles of light from it. People were out shoveling their driveways, and she heard muffled sounds of metal on concrete.

She saw her house, and watched it get slowly bigger as she approached, and pulled up in front of it and bent to look at it through the window on the passenger side of the car. Its front porch and steps and sidewalks were blanketed with snow.

Marion glanced behind her and saw Emily's Volkswagen turning cautiously onto her street two blocks away. She hurried out of her car and up to the gate in the low iron fence. She paused there, then pulled open the gate and stood for a minute looking at her house.

It was very quiet. All she could hear was the sound of Emily's car approaching and behind it the pickup truck and close behind the truck, Leona's car—the sounds of the motors were muted by the cold; she heard the crunching of tires on snow. Her breath appeared before her face in small white clouds.

She stepped ceremoniously through the gate. If I make perfect footprints all the way to my door, she thought, looking at the snow, a thick smooth carpet laid over porch and steps and walk, then this house will bring me good fortune. With great care she stepped along the short walk leading to the steps, lifting her feet high; she felt like a horse in slow motion. Each step made a soft cushiony sound as her boot broke the surface of the snow, then a smothered creak as her full weight compacted it against the concrete beneath. She heard car doors open and close.

"Christ, it's huge," said Vern.

"Stay where you are!" Marion called out, not turning around. "Don't move!"

She was up to the steps now. They would be tricky, because the snow was deep, and careless about outlines; it hadn't tucked itself neatly around each step. Marion judged, put her foot down precisely; and got the first step right, got the next one right, took the final step up to her front door. She began to turn her head, to look back over her shoulder at her perfect footprints.

"Come on, Marion," said Vern, crashing through the gate, "get a move on, open the door."

"You idiot!" Marion heard herself shriek. "Look what you've done!" The snow was in ruins. "Idiot! Damn fool idiot! I can't see them! You've wrecked them!" Tears in her eyes, they might freeze, crystal shards in her eyes. She shook her head in pain.

"She swore at me," said Vern. "What did I do?"

"What did he do?" said Bruce.

Leona's mouth was half open in shock. Bruce was glaring at Vern, angry but uncertain. Vern shivered visibly. Marion caught Emily's eye and felt suddenly like a fool.

She threw up her hands. "Ah well," she said. "It's nothing. He didn't do anything."

She pulled open the glass door and unlocked the inner door and opened it. The house seemed to breathe into her face. "Come on," she said to her friends, who hadn't moved. She turned, holding the door open, and smiled down at them. "Come into my house," she said, and the burst of celebration in her chest made the words shake.

CHAPTER 3

Several weeks later, Marion was awaiting her parents' first visit to her new home. She had finally finished the redecorating, with Emily's help, and was now comfortable in her house. She had lived in it long enough to have become acquainted with its sighings and settlings; knew at what time of day sunlight, if there was any, came through which windows; and through stripping and sanding and oiling and painting knew most of its walls and most of its passed-down furniture intimately. The tips of her fingers tingled from the rough touch of her house upon them; her spirit, she thought, had expanded to fill all of its corners.

She awaited her parents with a certain amount of tension, which was natural enough, but without trepidation.

She had, however, deliberately chosen to get this visit over with before the upstairs rooms were occupied, because she knew with what horror her parents regarded the idea of Marion's becoming a landlady.

And when the doorbell rang, she hastily put Spot outside.

"Happy new house, Marion," said her mother, smiling, when Marion opened the door. She held out a large, oddly shaped parcel.

Marion took it from her and said, "Thank you, Mother. Come in." And they entered her house and stood in the middle of the hall looking around.

"What a lot of work you've done, Marion," said her father, who had been to the house before the previous owners moved out, to check the foundations and the wiring and the roof. He gazed at the wallpaper and the mirror tiles. "This was all painted brown, I think it was, Harriet. Very gloomy." He looked more closely at the wallpaper.

"Come down the hall and into the kitchen," said Marion hastily. "I'll show you around."

"I'll just take my boots off first," said her mother. "Where would you like me to put them?" She stood with her boots dangling from her fingertips, dripping melted snow onto the hardwood floor.

"I guess I'd better buy a boot tray," said Marion. "Just put them anywhere, Mother."

In the kitchen in the weak March sunshine she unwrapped the parcel, which was heavy only at the bottom and turned out to be a fern. She put it on the kitchen table in the middle of the room, and regarded it thoughtfully. She didn't like plants much. Neither did her mother. There wasn't a plant in her mother's entire house.

"Where do you suggest I put this?" she said, as her parents entered the kitchen.

"I like what you've done with this room," said her father approvingly. "You've made good use of the space here. Turned it into a little sitting room. Very nice."

"Well, I don't know exactly, dear," said her mother, looking speculatively at the fern. "Where it will get good light," she said decisively, after a minute.

"Would you like coffee?" said Marion. "Or shall I show you the house first?"

"Oh, by all means let's see the house," said her mother. "Do you plan to replace this linoleum? Cushioned tiles are wonderful, so easy to keep clean."

"Eventually perhaps, Mother. Now down here is my bedroom and workroom." She went down the tiny hallway to her bedroom and was immediately soothed.

"This is a nice cozy bathroom," said her mother, down the hall. She backed out of the bathroom and joined Marion. "Good heavens. No curtains?"

"Well, there are blinds, you see," said Marion, pulling one of them down. "Roman shades, they're called."

"I see."

"Well now, this is very nice," said her father. "Got your work place all organized."

"What's that above the desk?" said her mother.

"That's a bulletin board, currently empty, but soon to be covered with things that will help me keep track of all the work I'm going to get," said Marion firmly.

"Another hardwood floor," said her mother, looking down.

"Yes, it is."

"Rolling that typewriter chair across it is going to mark it."

"I bought a secondhand floor polisher through the Buy and Sell."

Harriet looked around the room. The single bed was covered with an ivory bedspread. There was a large green cushion on it. The night table held a clock radio and a book; there were more books on the shelf below. On the other side of the bed was a chest of drawers, with a mirror on the wall above. Across the room, two long worktops were held up by a set of drawers at either end and a cupboard in the middle. On the work surfaces were Marion's portable electric typewriter, a telephone, a hollow plastic cube containing loose square pieces of paper, a long set of orange dividers for holding file folders, and numerous containers for pens and pencils, thumbtacks, elastic bands, and paper clips. With the exception of the orange dividers, and the cushion on the bed, and the books, which also filled shelves reaching from floor to ceiling on either side of the window at the far end of the room, everything in the room was white.

Marion watched her mother, aware of the scent of floor wax. The room purred to itself, turning a frank and open face to Harriet, who was frowning, her eyes darting here and there, seeking clues. They caught for a moment on Marion, who smiled at her mother, giving her nothing.

"There's nothing quite as lovely when the sun shines on it," said Harriet after a minute, "as a good hardwood floor."

"I know," said Marion. "Let's go upstairs now."

"You're going to have trouble renting this room," said Henry uneasily, on the third floor.

"It's absolutely freezing up here," said Harriet, rubbing her arms.

"I know," said Marion. "I'm going to get one of those baseboard heaters that has a thermostat control on it."

"The electricity bill," said Harriet, "will be astounding."

Marion marched onto the tiny landing and stood with one hand on the doorknob until her parents had followed her out.

"But it's nice in there," said Henry, "with the french doors, and the balcony. Somebody," he said heartily, "is going to be very happy in that room."

On the second floor they inspected the bathroom.

"It's quite large," said Harriet. "And these shutters on the window are very attractive." She turned to Marion. "You must have had to spend a great deal of money to put this house in proper shape."

"I did the work myself. Emily helped with the tenants' rooms," said Marion. She led them to the small room at the end of the hall.

"A nice bright room," said Henry, looking inside. "I wonder who's going to end up living in these rooms. Hard to imagine you sharing a house with people you don't even know."

"I don't approve of it at all," said Harriet, "as you know, Marion."

"Close the door after you, will you, Dad?" Marion was now heading down the hall. "This is my favorite suite," she said, opening the door, "probably because it's the first one we redid."

"You will have absolutely no way of making sure these people aren't thieves, or worse," said Harriet. "Yes, I see, it's very nice, lots of cupboard space in the kitchen."

"Okay, that's it up here, let's go down and I'll show you my living room."

"Better make sure there are locks on all the doors between you and them," said Henry as they went down the stairs.

"Good heavens, yes," said Harriet.

In the living room Marion said, "Do you remember what color these walls were, Dad?"

"Sort of a sickly green, I think. Oh yes, this is nice, Marion. Much brighter, with that off-white on the walls. Yes, this is a very nice room. See, Harriet, the bay window? And there at the other end, where she's got the dining room suite, see the fireplace behind it? Those tiles are original, Harriet. Very nice. Yes, Marion," he said, turning to smile at her, "you've done a good job with this house. Very nice."

In the kitchen she made coffee.

"I must say, the whole place is spick-and-span," said Harriet. "Quite frankly, I'm amazed."

"I'm sure it won't stay this way, Mother."

"Please remember to have those locks installed," said Harriet, wandering to the window. "Oh you have a garage, that's good. And a fenced yard for your dog, too. Is that your dog? My God, he's large. Does he sleep in the garage?"

"No, Mother, he sleeps in here. He couldn't do his guard duty very well from the garage, now could he?"

"There must be dog hair all over the house," said Harriet, glancing over her shoulder at the chair she had sat in earlier. "I've never been able to understand where you get this fondness for domesticated animals." She lowered herself carefully onto the arm of the stuffed chair.

Henry was inspecting the books in the shelves to the right of the window, and whistling softly to himself. The coffee dripped into the pot. Marion clattered china as she got out mugs and cream and sugar.

"I'm really very glad to see you in a house of your own," said Harriet. "There's no reason to wait for marriage necessarily before buying a house."

"If I had waited for that, Mother, I'd still be waiting on my deathbed."

"Oh, it will happen, all right," said her father with an encouraging grin. "A girl as pretty as you—I've no doubt about it at all."

"But what about her security in the meantime?" said Harriet. "No job any more, no pension plan. I'll never understand that, Marion, leaving that good job. I'll tell you, you'd better get married eventually. You'd better set your mind to it, Marion."

"Good heavens, Mother." She turned her back, took two slow, deep breaths. "I'm not totally stupid, you know," she said, putting things on a tray. "I've got a pension plan. Monthly contributions are in my budget. I do not intend to get married. I thought you had accepted that by now." She took the tray to a table near her mother's chair and went back for the coffee pot. She saw her parents glance at one another. "Do you know how many marriages end in divorce? Almost one in two, Mother. Almost half. I plan to support myself for my entire life."

"Well, it's your decision, of course," said Harriet distantly.

"Just wait till the right man comes along," said her father. "You'll change your tune then."

"Dad," said Marion. "I am thirty-seven years old. I have encountered a great many men in my life. There is no right one. I will undoubtedly encounter a great many more," she said, noticing that Harriet's face announced she had withdrawn from the conversation, "but I am never, ever going to get married. And if you'll forgive me, I am getting extremely weary of telling you this." She sat down.

"I don't understand what you've got against marriage," said Henry unhappily.

Marion looked from one of her parents to the other, and would have laughed, except that she felt exhausted.

"But we won't bring it up again," said Henry, after a pause. "Will we, Harriet?"

Harriet raised her eyebrows questioningly, summoning the confusion of one who has been daydreaming. "Do you have an aspirin, Marion?" she said. "I've got the most dreadful headache."

CHAPTER 4

Marion had done all she could think of, for the moment, to find work. She knew that something was bound to come of the visits she'd made to editors, the story ideas she'd submitted. She had confidence and faith. But sometimes she worried. It was another new experience, having to look ahead and calculate how much longer her money supply would last. She supposed it was something she'd have to get used to, but it was difficult at first, when she had no idea how that supply would be replenished. It was quite amusing, actually, she thought. But when Leona called and asked if she might come over, Marion saw this as a welcome respite.

She had crackers and cheese and scotch for dinner, while Spot slurped dog food from his big blue plastic dish. As she ate, she mulled over her empty rooms. It was already a day past the middle of March. She had no excuse for continuing to live in the house all by herself. Take yourself in hand, she thought sternly, pouring more scotch in an effort to dampen flickers of panic.

The next morning she would call once more every editor she had approached, and she would phone the *Star* with her rooms-to-let ad, too. Meanwhile, she thought she might allow herself to become just slightly smashed.

When Leona arrived, obviously excited about the prospect of working on the city desk, Marion was happily distracted. "We must immediately drink a toast to your new career," she said, hauling Spot down the hall from the front door into the kitchen.

"I haven't decided whether I should do it or not," Leona called out as she hung up her jacket in the hall closet, but Marion ignored her and fixed them drinks.

"Congratulations," she said, lifting her glass, when they were settled in the sitting room.

"You think I should take it, then," said Leona.

Marion liked the look of her sitting there on the sofa, her hair dark against her cheeks, her small, slight body looking almost like a child's in its navy blue sweatshirt and faded, scruffy jeans. She was in her sock feet, having left her boots at Marion's front door. None of Leona's layers was shadowy, thought Marion. The sun shone through all of them, like a rainbow. She didn't try to hide anything from anybody but herself, and she didn't even let herself do that for very long.

"Of course," said Marion. "You're a very capable person."

"Good," said Leona decisively. She stood up suddenly, and walked back and forth across the sitting room with a quick, awkward stride. She looked as though she was about to give a speech, but couldn't remember how it began.

"What on earth are you doing?" said Marion.

"I have no idea," said Leona, and laughed. She sat down again, and stared at the floor. "My apartment's got something strange in it."

Marion came back from the kitchen with a fresh drink. "What? Bugs?" she said distastefully.

"It's a kind of—moribund expectation," said Leona.

"I don't like the sound of that," said Marion, out of politeness, but she was exasperated and wary, and sure enough, Leona went on to talk about the impermanence of life, and Marion finally had to tell her that she wasn't interested in having morbid conversations. It was true that aloneness and death were the only certainties the future had to offer, but this was so self-evident that Marion saw no point in even thinking about it, much less discussing it.

"You could buy a house, too, you know," said Marion finally, since Leona's unease seemed to be concentrated on her apartment.

"I don't think I want to own a house, though," said Leona. "I don't think that would help."

Once she starts her new job, thought Marion, studying her, she'll be too busy to let herself get depressed. She got up to put on a record and refill their glasses.

"You see," said Leona, "I've been thinking quite a lot lately about Peter."

Marion deliberately finished putting ice and scotch in their glasses, and returned to the sitting room, and handed Leona her drink, and sat down and put her feet up before she said a word. The sound of the man's name was in itself enough to infuriate her.

"He took care of me," said Leona.

Marion almost flicked Leona out of her life, right then and there.

"Took care of you," said Marion, trying to sound thoughtful. But her irritation was too enormous. "Took care of you," she said again, furious, remembering Leona's pain, and her self-abasing tears, and the degrading dependence which even his eventual absence had not, apparently, eradicated. "My great aunt Fanny, Leona," she said contemptuously, "you have an enormous ability to deceive yourself."

Leona, to Marion's surprise, broke into laughter.

"He probably wasn't even any good in bed," said Marion. He was physically attractive all right, she wouldn't deny it, but he was also too much aware of his charms, and this Marion couldn't abide. But most of all she condemned him for his unfaithfulness. Marion would not have wanted faithfulness herself, but she knew it was important to Leona. And Peter knew it, too. He had had no right, therefore, to move in with Leona and then continue to go off with other women whenever the urge struck him. No control over his appetites, no consideration of his live-in lover, and an overweening appreciation of his own attractiveness; a real winner, that one, thought Marion.

"He said he wanted to have children someday," said Leona, wiping tears of laughter from her face.

"I'm not at all surprised," said Marion. It seemed to her that most of the people in the world who wanted children were men.

"Oh, Marion," said Leona after a while. "I have so much exhilaration these days. I don't understand where the despair comes from."

She got up to go, and Marion went to the door with her. When she stood up, her head was buzzing from the liquor.

"I don't have any despair in my life," said Marion at the door. "I don't have a great deal of exhilaration, either." She said this in self-congratulation, because she didn't want either hills or valleys in her own personal landscape; the rolling sweep of the prairie she found eminently satisfying. But Leona looked at her sharply, and before Marion had a chance to explain had dropped her purse on the floor and moved to embrace her.

Oh dear, thought Marion.

As Leona's arms went around her there was a spilling of something inside her, and she felt warm all over, and had inadvertently summoned tears. Her head was light and buzzing and her body was filled with rushing warmth, and she hugged Leona back, and kissed her hair. Leona pulled away, to look up at her, and Marion's lips touched her cheek. Marion felt at that moment both protector and protected, and was appalled.

CHAPTER 5

It was the end of March, and Marion was finally working on her first freelance assignment. It was a story for the inflight magazine of a regional airline, for which she was to be paid three hundred dollars. At three hundred dollars a shot, she thought, she'd have to write a lot of stories in order to survive. She had discovered that there were quite a number of freelance writers in Calgary. She hoped there was enough work for all of them.

She didn't really know how good a journalist she was. But she did know that she worked harder than most people. She believed firmly that hard work and applying oneself to tasks with complete dedication led to success, and that although talent may also get you there, it can't do it alone, whereas sometimes hard work can. So she didn't bother much about whether or not she was good, or how good she was, or whether someone else was better. She saw a lot of good writing in the magazines and newspapers she devoured every week, but she saw a lot of sloppiness, too.

She sat in her bedroom office, alone with her notes and her typewriter, the sun shooting golden arrows through her window. The story was about some consulting psychologists who hired themselves out to companies. Marion thought the world had come to a pretty pass when employers referred their employees to consulting psychologists in the course of a business day. She would write the piece in a slightly detached manner, she decided; make sure that despite all the approving quotes she had to use, nobody who read the thing would think the writer was personally enthusiastic. The lead would say something about Medicare and Denticare and now psychological care as employee benefits. She was certainly glad the *Star* hadn't had psychological care as an employee benefit. She thought of calm and quiet Ziggy, or flint-eyed Jack Hiller, calling somebody into his office and telling him he should take advantage of the new psycho-care package available to him as a *Star* employee. She began to smile, imagining the reaction of Leona, or Bruce, or Vern. Then she frowned, because really such a thing would be terrible, it would make a person feel dreadfully uncertain about herself, and in some places in Calgary it was actually happening.

Marion lectured herself. She was going to get paid story by story. She couldn't afford to pick and choose. And if she didn't write the things briskly and accurately, she would starve. She wasn't the keeper of the world, after all. It was hard enough just to try to help a friend now and then, and if some people were stupid enough to work for employers who sent them off to psychologists, well that was their problem. Besides, they didn't have to go.

She rolled a sheet of yellow paper into her typewriter and, hands poised over the keys, looked through the window for inspiration, but all she saw was the back of her garage, a still leafless tree of some kind, and the top part of her fence.

Marion heard the doorbell and pushed herself away from her desk.

By the front door Spot waited expectantly, his tail wagging. At first Marion had tried to keep a vase filled with tall dried weeds and flowers on the hall table, under the small rectangular stained glass window. But the dog's tail striking the table legs had caused the table to shudder and the vase to rock, and one day it fell over and broke.

The dog trumpeted once or twice. Marion opened the door. "Harrumph, harrumph," bellowed Spot dutifully, and, suddenly agile, he sprang at the stranger to sniff his crotch.

The man shuffled back quickly on the small porch, pushing at the dog's head and glancing behind him in terror of falling down the steps. "Shit," he said.

"Spot!" snapped Marion, grabbing the dog's collar and yarding back on it. "I'm sorry," she said to the man.

"Spot?" he said, amazed, looking at the animal, which was, after all, totally black.

"He's got a spot on his tongue," said Marion, and heaved the dog back into the hall. "What do you want? I'm working."

"Probably nothing," said the man, looking at Spot. "Maybe a room."

"Oh, goodness," said Marion, and tried to struggle into her landlady persona. "Well, I've got one. Actually I've got three. But how did you know? The ad's not going in until tomorrow."

"A guy at the *Star* told me. I'm going to work there. I don't need it for long. Just until I find an apartment."

"This isn't a hotel, you know," said Marion.

"What kind of a dog is that?" said the man, still on the porch.

"He's a mixture. Black Lab and Newfoundland."

"Jesus he's big."

"Do you want to look at the room or not?"

He hesitated. He was about thirty-five, no more than medium height, thin, with brown curly hair and ginger-colored eyes. "Yeah, okay," he said, and went into the house.

She took him up the stairs to the second floor.

"Nice wallpaper," he said, and she turned to see him running his hand over it. Trying to find bubbles, she thought. But he looked at her and smiled. "Stripes. I like that."

Marion continued up to the second-floor hall. She wasn't even going to show him the room on the top floor, because she hadn't yet bought the wall heater—she had planned to do it that afternoon.

"This is the biggest suite," she said, opening the door into the tiny entrance hall. There was a small kitchen straight ahead, and a large room on the left. "It's a bachelor suite," she said stiffly, as though speaking a line from a play.

He nodded and went past her into the large room.

"Eggshell," she muttered, waving at the walls. There was dark brown wall-to-wall carpeting, a sofa and chair and table and lamp on one side of the room, and a divan piled with cushions on the other.

"This the bed?" he said, pointing to the divan.

"Yes," said Marion.

Under the window facing the street were a desk and a chair. There was another window behind the sofa, and in the other wall a large closet with a chest of drawers inside.

"Where's the bathroom?" he said, looking around.

"Down the hall," said Marion. "There's only one bathroom. For the tenants, I mean. When I get them."

"When you get them. Hey, wait a minute. I'd be the first guy to move in here?"

"Well, somebody's got to be first," said Marion.

"I don't like the idea of sharing a bathroom."

"I know how you feel. But that's the way it is."

He sighed, and wandered over to the window behind the desk and looked out. "There's a window box," he said.

"Yes."

"I might want to plant things in it."

"Be my guest. But it would be months before you could plant anything in it."

"I better take a look at the kitchen," he said.

It contained a small table and two chairs, a half-sized refrigerator and a small gas stove. There was also a glass-fronted cabinet, and several cupboards. Marion opened the tiny broom closet, which was stocked with cleaning supplies. "You'd have to do your own cleaning," she said.

He peered out the window. "No window box."

"No," said Marion, who thought she was being very patient.

They stood in the kitchen, looking around. "It's very quiet," he said. "Is this a quiet neighborhood?"

"Pretty quiet."

"Not that it matters." He sighed again. "Can I see the bathroom?"

She took him into the hall and pointed out the door. He disappeared into the bathroom, and she wondered whether to close the door to the suite or leave it open or what. She didn't know anything about being a landlady. The only thing that had finally gotten her to place the ad was her undeniable financial need. It was all very well to figure that the tenants would cover her mortgage payments—but first she had to get the tenants. In the ten days since Leona's visit, Marion had gotten three assignments and was feeling pretty good about that. But the empty house rebuked her and brought thoughts of things like bankruptcy, and sheriffs coming to board up the doors and windows, and Dickensian flashes of her being dragged off to prison in chains. So finally she wrote out the ad and called it in to the *Star*'s classified people and now here she was having to pretend she was a landlady—no, she corrected herself, she was not pretending, she *was* a landlady, no point in denying it, just get the rooms rented and stop moaning.

He emerged from the bathroom. "Nice," he said. "Big. I like the shutters."

Marion nodded, and closed the door to the suite firmly. "If you're going to consider taking the room, I should show you the storage space in the basement."

"Don't have anything to store. I'd like to see the backyard, though."

"Why?" said Marion, startled.

"I don't know. Aren't you going to let people sit out there in the summer?"

This had never occurred to her. "I guess so," she said, reluctantly.

She went downstairs, and he followed. In the kitchen the dog was lying on the rug in front of the television set. He thumped the floor with his tail a couple of times but didn't get up.

"He's friendly, is he?" said the man.

"Oh yes," said Marion, opening the back door. To the left, the addition containing her bedroom-office and bathroom jutted from the house. The yard was long and narrow, the garage at the back. A sidewalk hugged the fence on the right, and led to a gate. Except for a young tree planted at the end of the addition, the yard contained nothing but brown grass and heaps of discolored, bedraggled snow. Marion reminded herself to get out there and clean up the dog leavings again, before a spring snowfall buried them.

"Hmmm," said the man, as Marion shivered. "Not much room for a vegetable garden."

"I have absolutely no intention," said Marion, "of having a vegetable garden." She stalked back into the kitchen, rubbing her arms. He followed.

"Is that coffee?" he said hopefully. The drip pot was half full and the light was on.

"Are you interested in the suite or not?" said Marion. "Because if you're not, I've got to get back to work."

"If I am, will you give me a cup of coffee?" He had a radiant smile which Marion figured he saw as part of his arsenal. "Yeah, I'm interested in the suite," he said hastily.

"Sit down," said Marion.

He hovered in the middle of the room before sitting at the kitchen table, away from the dog.

"Nice fern," he said, looking up. It hung by the window over the sink, because Leona had told Marion that it liked humidity.

Marion poured coffee into two mugs.

"Might do better over there, though," he said, pointing to the opposite side of the room, where there were two windows. "More light."

"I know nothing at all about plants," said Marion. She looked up at the fern and saw that more of its fronds were turning brown. She put the mugs onto the table with a little more force than necessary, and went back to the counter for cream and sugar.

"I've never lived in a boardinghouse," said the man, taking three spoonfuls of sugar.

"This isn't a boardinghouse," said Marion quickly. "In boardinghouses you get meals. You don't get any meals here."

He looked at her curiously, studying her for the first time. She thought how pleasant it was to have known people for a long time, so that when they looked at you it was you they saw, and not your irrelevant façade.

"You sure don't look like a landlady," he said, grinning.

"Oh well," said Marion distantly, "I don't feel like one, either."

"I'd like to take the room," he said. "My name's David Bermas."

He reached across the table, his hand outstretched, and Marion automatically stretched out hers. It was a moment of peculiar intimacy; sunlight on the kitchen floor, steam from two mugs of coffee in the air, the touch of a stranger's hand.

"Marion Tyler," she said, shaking his hand firmly.

"I know. They told me at the *Star*."

"Where are you from?" she asked politely.

And then it wasn't just politeness, and she almost gasped, leaped to her feet, and ordered him out, as it fell upon her that this man was actually going to come to live in her house. It was an unbelievable situation. She knew absolutely nothing about him; thank heaven he was at least wary of her dog. They would be alone in her house together, she thought, the two of them; horrified, she stared at him.

"London. Ontario. The London *Free Press*." He smiled. "I'm seeing the world. Gotta tell you," he said, leaning toward her, "I may not be here too long. In Calgary."

"I don't allow drugs," she blurted, and flushed.

He looked at her disbelievingly. "What have they been telling you about London, Ontario?"

"No, I mean, I just don't want any drugs in my house," she said, and flushed redder.

"What about booze?" he said. "Are you some kind of religious person?"

"No," said Marion. "Booze is okay."

"Well, booze is all I do," he said. "Can I move in today?"

"Today?" She'd had the last night alone in her own house, and hadn't even known it. "Sure. I guess so."

"I'd better get going, and let you get back to work." He stood up, and so did the dog.

"Stay," said Marion sternly. The dog looked at her, wagging his tail. "Down," said Marion. After a few seconds he lay down.

"Pretty good," said David.

She walked to the front door with him. "What are you going to be doing at the *Star?*"

"Desk. Wire desk. I gotta get myself a car." At the front steps he turned. "I left my stuff there. I'll go back and get it and move in tonight. I'll give you a check when I get back." He started down the steps.

"Do you want to call a cab?" said Marion.

"Nah, I want to walk around for a while. See what this town looks like close up." He waved, and sauntered off down the slushy sidewalk.

Marion, closing the door, thought it hadn't been the way she had imagined it, renting her first room. Heaven only knew what kind of a person he was. She went back to her typewriter. The *Star* wouldn't send anybody who wasn't okay, she assured herself. And made a mental note to speak to them; she couldn't have the *Star* dumping itinerant deskmen on her doorstep.

She stared at the blank sheet of paper in the typewriter. What if he appears at my door one evening wanting to borrow some soap? But she had provided soap up there, so he wouldn't do that. What, then, if he appeared just wanting to talk? She'd have to work out a speech for these tenant people, outline for them right from the start what sort of situation they'd gotten themselves into. No fraternizing with the land-lady, she'd tell them.

But that's presumptuous, she scolded herself. Probably they would move in with uneasiness a twin to her own, wondering if she was likely to tiptoe up the stairs and tap softly on their doors, seeking company.

She turned to her notebook, to refresh her memory, and applied herself once more to the psychologists.

He returned shortly after dinner, bearing a large suitcase and some-thing she guessed was a portable typewriter. She gave him a key and he gave her a check. When he started up the stairs to his room, she went back to the kitchen and looked at the check and marveled at it—money earned for her by her house. And a good thing, too. The house had to pay its way, just as she had to pay hers.

A little later she heard him go out. It was distracting, someone else's comings and goings in her own house, but she supposed she would get used to it. There was no need for her to have anything to do with her tenants, she reminded herself. There were doors between her and them —her and him, now—doors that closed, if they didn't lock. She should probably put locks on them, all right. But she should have done that before she started renting out the rooms. What was that fellow going to think if he came home from work one day and found somebody energetically installing locks on the two doors which separated Marion from the rest of the house? He was bound to feel personally insulted.

Oh for heaven's sake, she told herself angrily. It's my house, I'm going to be here a great deal longer than he is; he'll probably be gone in a month; he's probably out looking around for an apartment with its own bathroom this very minute. She made a note in her Day-Timer to call a locksmith the next day.

One room rented, two more to go, she thought. And the first story was written, retyped, neatly enclosed in a manila envelope ready for mailing in the morning. It would get there two days before the deadline, even allowing for Canada Post's habitual mishandling of her mail. She would call the editor Monday to tell him it was on its way. And then she'd get down to work on the other two assignments. And she'd better spend some time on her finances, as well.

I am living life a day at a time, thought Marion; flying by the seat of my pants. She was well pleased.

She didn't hear him come in, but late in the evening she became aware of sound; she strained to hear, and finally decided it was a typewriter. She wondered whom he was writing to and, if it was a woman, why he had left her.

CHAPTER 6

Emily called on her unexpectedly on a Thursday evening in late June. This was unlike Emily. Marion was surprised to see her there when she answered the door. But she had discovered by then that operating a revenue house had altered people's images of her. They were more casual with her now, as though she had flung open her doors to strangers because of a previously unsuspected strain of generosity and not simply a need to pay the mortgage. She found, though, that she didn't mind this as much as she might have expected. She thought it must be working alone which had increased her pleasure in other people's company.

"I'm so glad I didn't get you out of bed," said Emily.

Marion smiled as she pushed Spot into the kitchen. She had far too much to do these days to spend more than six or seven hours a night in bed. She had gotten a spate of work, and was enjoying the challenge of meeting several almost simultaneous deadlines.

"I'm astonished to see you here at this hour, Aunt Emily," she said, knowing that her aunt liked to be in bed by ten o'clock, since she had to leave for work early in the morning. "Do you mind if I go on with this?" She was making a casserole that she would serve the next day to Leona and David Bermas.

Emily had nothing to say, and Marion looked at her curiously; she was staring at the wall with a peculiar intensity. Marion began to feel uneasy. "I do hope you aren't the bearer of bad tidings," she said, wondering if something had happened to Emily's son, Nelson.

But she hadn't even finished her sentence before Emily whirled to face her, then turned away and announced, apparently to Spot, "It's very bad news indeed. I can't think of a way to say it except just to say it. Harriet is ill. Henry says the doctors have said she doesn't have more than six months."

Marion looked at her dog. He seemed undismayed. Then she looked uncomprehendingly into the mixture she was stirring, which was thick and heavy and kept sticking to the spoon.

"What's wrong with her?" said Marion. She shivered, although it was really very warm in her house, which was reluctant each evening to release the day-long heat of the summer sun.

"It's cancer," said Emily.

That's fitting, thought Marion.

It looked as if Emily might be there for a while, so she sat in her maroon chair.

"When did you find out?" she said.

"This evening. Just before I came over here. Henry called me."

That's fitting, too, thought Marion. She wondered what might happen if she pretended Emily had never trotted over here to spread the news. How long would it take her parents to inform her? The woman would probably be in the ground, thought Marion, before he noticed I hadn't stopped by to offer condolences.

"She must be furious," said Marion. Emily finally stopped staring at Spot and looked at her. "I mean, good heavens, she thinks to be ill is to be careless; to be dying must be the height of imprudence." Emily looked distraught, and her eyes were dangerously shiny. Marion went back to the kitchen and spooned the casserole into a Dutch oven, even though it wasn't mixed together well enough. "My father must be quite overcome." She returned to her stuffed chair. "Well, this is going to take some getting used to," she said briskly, hoping Emily would take this as a sign that she could go.

"I'm terribly sorry, Marion," said Emily. She started to get up, but Marion saw that she planned not to leave, but to deliver a comforting embrace. Alarmed, she waved her hand vigorously, and Emily subsided.

"What can I do for you?" said Emily.

"Oh, I'm absolutely fine," said Marion. "Surely you can see that." She was surprised to find that she was angry. It's because this is bound to affect my life, she thought, my schedules are sure to suffer from this, my entire existence is going to be thrown into turmoil by this woman and her dying.

"I'm certainly not going to burst into tears," she said to Emily, but even as she spoke, she was heavy with unexpected tears. "Come here, Spot." The dog plodded over and rested his head in her lap. "There is nothing to be done, Emily." She looked steadily at her aunt, her hands gripping the thick black fur of the dog's neck. "Nothing."

CHAPTER 7

"I have never been a strong woman," said Harriet. "No, it's true, Henry," she said, a hand up to stop him speaking. "In some ways, why yes, if that's what you were going to say. But not physically, Henry. Not physically."

"Is it going to be painful for you, Mother?" said Marion from her parents' kitchen counter, where she was making coffee.

"I'm sure it will be, Marion. Dying isn't easy. I don't have the faintest hope, therefore, that it can be accomplished without pain."

If only she weren't so theatrical, thought Marion, measuring coffee, perhaps I could feel at least some superficial sympathy.

"I'm glad to know that it isn't cancer," said Marion. She had decided to participate in their charade.

"Cancer is a vulgar disease," said her mother. "I never worried about getting cancer."

"Will you be—incapacitated?" said Marion, turning, the coffeepot in her hand.

"I can't stand this," said her father, getting up from the table.

Marion put down the pot and went to him. "I'm sorry, Dad," she said, putting her arms around him. She felt him trembling.

"We won't let this thing beat us, Harriet," said Henry, turning from Marion's embrace. "We'll find another specialist. We'll go to Vancouver—or Toronto, or New York. Wherever the best men are."

He looked haggard and desperate. Marion, watching them, saw that their faces were absolutely bare, that they were anguished and stricken and couldn't hide it. If she were to wave energetically between them, or jump up and down upon the kitchen's tiled floor, she doubted they would notice. She went to the cupboard to get cups and saucers. Maybe I should have taken her to California, thought Marion, remembering the lie she'd told to get her bank loan. But this almost made her smile, because she wasn't a superstitious person. She wondered, though, putting cups carefully upon saucers, what she would have done if by taking Harriet to California she could have prevented her mother's illness; she let the third cup hang by its handle from her middle finger and idly sway back and forth as she thought about it.

Her parents' home had been lovingly created. It was full of things—some precious, some not—collected in the course of years of travel. There were few things in it which Marion remembered from her childhood; that had been a time when they had had to make do, and the objects they had suffered then they had gotten rid of later, when they could afford more expensive replacements.

The house itself was one Marion had never lived in—not that she would ever want to—God forbid. It had one luxuriously huge bedroom which still, after all these years, contained but one huge bed, and this was something Marion found difficult to comprehend. Whenever she had thought, from adolescence onward, about her parents making love, she had imagined her mother lying there stiff as a board with her eyes scrunched closed and her teeth gritted, because who was to know, the condom might have a tiny hole in it or the pills might be defective, and then, my God, pregnancy, it would arrive as the clap of doom, so to speak . . . Marion really would have expected her mother to forsake whatever joys she might have found in the marriage bed in favor of safety, but apparently she still had not done so. Although now, of course, and for some long time past, she had had no need to worry about pregnancy. Over the hill she was, Marion's old mom; maybe all they did in bed was cuddle . . .

Also in this house there was a spacious living room. It had no fireplace, but there were paintings on the walls. Marion's mother had in recent years taken up Canadian art, and had made the acquaintance of gallery owners in Calgary and Edmonton. Now they called her every so often to tell her confidentially of good buys. Marion hadn't been able to determine how much her mother actually enjoyed looking at these paintings, but she was certainly proud of them. Too well-mannered to discuss prices, she still managed to imply that the current worth of several of them was considerably more than their purchase price. Sometimes, now, the galleries called Marion's mother to ask if they could borrow back one of her paintings for a show. Harriet responded to these invitations gracefully, and reported them to family and friends with great satisfaction. Whenever Marion admired one of them (for there were some which she would like to have lived with herself), her mother provided her promptly with an exhausting amount of information about both the painting and its creator.

These instructive sessions also took place on the few occasions when Marion's aunts were invited to Harriet's house. It was then Marion's habit to make critical comments about the paintings of which she was personally not fond, and to enjoy Harriet's irritated but spirited defense of her investments. Grace was the only one of the sisters who seemed to get any real pleasure from Harriet's declamations, or from the paintings, either. Olive peered at them incredulously from above her half-glasses, and Polly seemed to find them personally insulting. Emily was polite, but Marion knew she didn't think much of Harriet's taste in art.

Marion had a favorite among her mother's collection. It was not representational, but every time she looked at it, it became a painting of an orange sun sinking behind a wheatfield. She felt the heat of the sun, heard the rustle of the wheat in a late summer breeze. Perhaps she'll leave it to me in her will, thought Marion hopefully, pouring coffee.

"What are you taking in your coffee these days, Mother?"

"It's probably too strong, so I'll have a spoon of sugar, please."

Marion brought the coffee to the table and sat down. "I think it's an excellent idea to find another specialist, Dad. It's certainly hard to believe that the one you've got knows what he's talking about," she said, looking intently at Harriet. "I don't think I've ever seen you looking better, Mother."

"It's the weight I've lost, Marion. Which happens to be one of the symptoms."

Her hand was a bit shaky, lifting the cup to her lips. And there was a pallor spread across her skin, like the dust from butterflies' wings. She sat erect. Her hair was a still-golden cap—no girlish curls for Harriet. Her figure was trim in its bottle-green suit. But the lace on her blouse half hid a neck gaunt and corded, her hazel eyes were slightly sunken, and, yes, her hand was shaky.

"They have been known to make mistakes, doctors," said Marion's father heavily. "I want you to let me find another man. I'll inquire around," he said, and stopped, and waved a hand vaguely in the air.

"Henry," said his wife. Marion looked at her quickly. "Please," said Harriet, a private word filled with slow and tender regret. "I'm so tired," she said.

Henry reached across the table and took her hand. "Oh," he said, an expelling of breath.

"Let's just take our trip, Henry, and not think about it."

Marion looked back and forth between them, as she often had, and chugged her mind into its observer mode. She allowed herself to wonder what on earth her father would do without her mother. She, Marion, would have to visit him frequently, that was obvious. She thought that wouldn't necessarily be unpleasant—assuming, of course, that he gradually found new interests and didn't constantly reminisce.

"All right, Harriet," said Henry finally, and had to stop to clear his throat. "We'll go on our trip, and talk about this again when we get back."

Harriet turned to Marion. "We're going to Europe again, Marion," she said.

"That's nice, Mother," said Marion politely.

"We expect to be gone—oh, what, Henry, about six weeks? Two months? Something like that. We'll give you a key again, and we'd like you to check the house every now and then."

Oh my goodness, thought Marion suddenly. It's the twenty-seventh, and I've forgotten Aunt Emily's birthday roses.

"Certainly, Mother," she said, and smothered without difficulty a small surge of anger.

CHAPTER 8

On a cold, heavy-clouded day in October, Marion went to the hospital to see her mother.

Her parents hadn't been able to go to Europe after all. Harriet's illness had moved quickly, gained on her rapidly. Now it was breathing over her shoulder. They put her in the hospital for tests, to see precisely how far the disease had progressed, and Marion found it necessary to go to visit her there.

It was inconvenient, because Marion had a lot of work to do. She had recently been getting assignments from a couple of national magazines, and it was important that they be done as well as she was capable of doing them, to make sure she'd get more.

Still, there you are, she thought, putting on a skirt and sweater. For some reason she felt it was more important to visit her mother than work today, and she knew that if she tried to deny this she would spend an irritating, frustrating afternoon at her typewriter.

She decided to go whole hog and wear an entire suit. It might have been out of respect for Harriet; she was perfectly willing to admit that possibility. People approaching the end of life ought to be respected, for who knew what glimmers and glimpses they got while contemplating their situation. But the suit was also out of respect for herself for actually going to the hospital, a thing she didn't want to do at all but which her instincts told her was essential.

Harriet had a private room, of course. She had flatly refused to enter the hospital unless she could be assured of suffering and doing whatever else she might be called upon to do absolutely in private.

The door was half open. Marion stepped around it. She hadn't decided which of the several opening sentences she had been practicing would be the best one to use; she had counted upon Harriet's reaction to her presence to help her make up her mind. But her mother seemed to be asleep.

Marion went closer, looking up at the ceiling, clearing her throat to give Harriet a chance to open her eyes if she happened just to be resting. Harriet didn't open her eyes, though, and Marion didn't know what to do. If she woke her mother, Harriet would immediately wonder how long Marion had been observing her, and would be irritated at having been watched for however short a time while she slept.

It was very quiet. A heavy silence clung to the walls and the furniture and was not budged from its insistent occupation of the room by the small sounds which crept in from the half-open door; an almost noise-less wheeled object of some sort passing by, the brisk whispering of nurses' shoes, even an occasional voice could be heard. But these made no impact upon the silence of her mother's room. The blinds were drawn and the light was soft and sooty, except for a brilliant flash like a knife-edge down each side of the blind.

Marion took another step closer to the bed, on tiptoe. She bent over, head averted, one hand outstretched. Should she touch Harriet's shoulder? Should she try to awaken her? God knows I don't want to come back here again if I don't have to, thought Marion.

She saw her mother's arms and hands lying on top of the covers. The nails were medium long and manicured and covered with pink polish. The skin of the hands had a few spots of brown. The arms were quite thin, but still the skin up near where the sleeves of the hospital gown ended was loose, and there was loose skin around Harriet's thin neck, too. Her hair was mussed but clean. Marion sighed, and looked straight at her mother's face, expecting the worst. She was uncertain about what that would be, but she expected it.

Her eyes went back and forth across her mother's face like a flash-light or a laser beam—all business they were, looking, checking, absorb-ing. But the more information they gathered and stored away, the more astonished she became. She had never seen her mother's face so young. It was very pale, but completely without lines or wrinkles. Good heav-ens, thought Marion, did she come in here for cosmetic surgery? But she knew that wasn't the case, otherwise they would have done her neck as well, and probably her arms, too; her mother never did anything by halves. Maybe, like her elegant thinness, this youthfulness was one of her symptoms. But Marion had never heard of a symptom like that. Her mother's face looked as though it had been ironed. It was completely smooth. If she kept her eyes on the face and didn't let them wander, she could have believed that Harriet was a teenager, or even a child. It was as though she was dreaming about her youth, and the dream had transformed her. It had never before occurred to Marion to wonder if dreams painted themselves upon people's faces as they slept.

She backed quietly away from the bed and stood by the half-open door, her purse dangling from her hands in front of her, looking at her mother's face with awe. And then Harriet's eyes were open, and she was looking right at Marion.

"Mother," said Marion. Harriet didn't say anything, just kept looking at her. Maybe she's still asleep, thought Marion. "Are you asleep, Mother?" She watched as her mother's mouth opened slowly.

Harriet began to speak and stopped to laboriously lick her lips. "How can I be asleep," she said slowly, her voice rough and oilless, "when my eyes are open."

"How are you feeling?"

"Quite dreadful, thank you. How's your father? Where is he?"

"I really don't know, Mother, where he is. He seems fine when I talk to him on the phone." Harriet hadn't moved at all, except for her mouth; not even her head or her hands had moved. Marion felt awkward and big-footed in her pumps. "Can I get you anything?"

There was a tap on the door and her father came in. "Marion," he said, surprised. "You should have told me you were coming. I'd have picked you up." He turned to Harriet. "How are you, sweetheart?" He walked to the bed and leaned down to kiss her forehead.

Harriet's eyes closed and Marion thought that somehow she must have disturbed the equilibrium of her dream, because her face shook a little, like water struck by a pebble, and rapidly took on the familiar lines and wrinkles. Marion watched, fascinated. Henry wound the bed up and helped Harriet get comfortable in a half-sitting position. Her face now looked to Marion even older, more lined and wrinkled than usual, and certainly more pale. If that's what you pay, thought Marion, for a few minutes or even hours of youth, then those dreams are not for me.

Marion had thought for a while in her childhood that Harriet was superhuman. Later she had read in books and magazines about somebody's ideal woman, referred to as Supermom. Marion gathered that this creature was supposed to be admirable, one of those people with large laps for soothing in, and large arms for enfolding, and competent hands for making cookies and painlessly applying Band-Aids. But every time Marion saw or heard that word, Supermom, she shivered.

Harriet had always seemed able to do anything, anything at all. But this had not comforted Marion as a child; it had terrified her. She knew instinctively that there would always be many things that she, Marion, wouldn't be able to do, and she knew that her father couldn't do everything, either, but her mother was ferociously capable of doing anything at all. Except things which she said bored her, and of course she didn't do them out of choice.

Marion thought of her as an ice queen, as immortal, as evil, as possessed of magic powers. She was also possessed of anger so strong it seemed to Marion to shake the walls. It was quite capable of bringing down the ceiling, she knew it. But Harriet would make sure it never got free enough to do that; not because this would injure Marion (Harriet didn't care much about that, she could always get another little girl if she wanted one, they were plentiful enough, and besides, she would be happier without a little girl), and not because the ceiling falling in would hurt Harriet, either, because of course it wouldn't—it would fall on her head and break in pieces around her; she wouldn't let it happen, thought Marion, because putting it up again would be an awful lot of trouble.

The anger placed an immense distance between Marion and her mother. Marion lived for a while in the absolute certainty that she would never grow up, that her mother's anger would kill her. Once grown up, she had laughed at herself for this, and sometimes mused about it, protective in her mind toward that small quiet child; then her own adult anger would stir and she would wish it had been born in her earlier.

So here she was now, a not terribly sympathetic observer of her mother's final illness, not knowing at all what was expected of her. Was she supposed to try to manufacture grief? And tears? All she could come up with was polite regret.

She decided not to reproach herself. Her attitudes had developed all on their own over her lifetime and there wasn't much she could do about them now. Besides, she knew that none of this would bother Harriet, assuming she ever gave it a thought. It might bother her father a bit, though, and she thought about that as she drove home from the hospital and decided that if he felt anything at all about this subject, it was far too late.

She parked her car in front of her house instead of in the garage, which she used only in the winter, when snow clogged things up and cold froze things up and the garage kept her car dry and clean and the plug-in kept it warm enough to start. As she got out and locked the car, she saw Clara turning the corner at the duplex.

Clara wore a scarf tied around her head and a heavy thigh-length jacket over a skirt that fell almost to her ankles; on her feet were sneakers and knee socks of a dark purple color. Marion, watching her approach, was amazed that she had let a room to a woman at first glance so disreputable. But Clara defied categorizing.

She wore loose-fitting clothes because her work required her to move around a lot. She wore her working skirts long because she knelt a lot to scrub floors and dust under bookcases with a feather duster. (If a new client didn't own a feather duster, Clara would buy one for her and then present her with a neatly printed bill with the cash register receipt stapled to it.) But she didn't need to wear sneakers and knee socks; that was for show; and she didn't need to select clothes in purple, lime green, and hot pink, either; that was for show, too. The knee socks concealed misshapen feet with toenails carefully manicured and painted red. Marion had seen them one day when Clara came down to pay the rent wearing open-toed sandals, which she favored when indoors and not at work. Marion's eyes had been riveted to those red toenails.

"It's not possible to do nice things with my fingernails, you know?" Clara had explained. "Because of work. So I do nice things with my toes instead."

She wore her scarf loosely knotted beneath her chin so as not to disarrange her bright red hair, which she set in rollers every night. She put on makeup each morning before going off to the first of her customers. Marion, smiling as Clara came nearer, saw that, as usual, the mascara had lumped itself at the ends of her lashes, and that during the day specks of it had fallen off and lodged on the upper parts of her cheeks.

"Marion, hello," she said as she approached. "Such a day I've had, that stupid woman, jam all over the top of the piano, can you believe it?" She waved a hand in disgust as Marion opened the gate for her. "Those kids, I don't know, they're wild like animals, jam on the top of the piano and nobody tried to get any of it off. 'We'll just leave it for Clara,' that's what they say to themselves, I can hear it in my brain."

"Do you want a cup of coffee, Clara?" said Marion when they were in the house.

Clara turned in surprise, her right hand on the banister, her left clutching a big black battered handbag. "Oh, yes?" she said, suddenly shy. Then, scoffingly, "No, it's too much trouble for you."

"No, really. I'd like it," said Marion. "You know me well enough by now, Clara, to know that I never say a thing unless I mean it."

Clara looked at her sharply, then smiled. "Well, maybe, that could be true. If you're sure, then," she said, turning away from the stairs.

Marion let Spot out into the backyard. She didn't care at the moment about David's garden. Besides, there was nothing left out there except a few failing flowers. They'd eaten all the peas and beans and lettuce long ago, and the brussels sprouts and the potatoes, too, and everybody she knew was sick to death of his zucchini. Still there were those puny flowers. "Ah, good grief," she muttered, and opened the back door to call Spot inside.

Clara was at the window, looking out into the yard. "He's a fine gardener, that man," she said. "It could be he's in the wrong business." She turned around and stood in the middle of the kitchen-sitting room, holding her handbag.

"Sit down, Clara," said Marion, wondering now what impulse had been in operation when she suggested this. What on earth would they have to talk about, for heaven's sake, even over a small cup of coffee? And in fact she got cups and saucers from the cupboards, instead of two of her big mugs. "Do you have any children?" she asked, putting cream and sugar on a tray.

"Of course," said Clara. "Three children."

"Do they live here? In Calgary?"

"One lives in Winnipeg and one lives in Edmonton and the other just moved to Vancouver. I have three grandchildren, too, all from the same daughter, the one that moved to Vancouver."

"You must miss them," said Marion, and she turned quickly to look at Clara, because of course it wasn't necessarily true at all that she missed them, and Marion wanted to see whether she would pretend.

Clara's eyes were brimming with tears. "Ah, so stupid," she muttered, and picked up her bag from the floor to rummage around in it. Marion handed her a Kleenex from the box on the kitchen counter, but Clara waved it away and with head bent continued to poke around among the great quantity of objects in her bag until she fished out a pocket package of tissues. She dabbed beneath her eyes, smudging the dots of mascara there. "They are fantastic kids, those grandchildren, you wouldn't believe it," she said.

Marion wondered if she ought to tell Clara about the black streaks she'd caused to appear on the tops of her cheeks. It seemed an improper intimacy. "Will you go to visit them?"

"Ah, who knows. They say I will, yes, but who knows." She accepted her coffee with a nod of thanks and picked up her handbag.

"What are you looking for?" asked Marion, watching her ransack the interior of the bag.

"My saccharin, I can never find it. I know it's here." She finally began taking things out, so as to see better. She removed a plastic eyeglass case with a pair of sunglasses in it, a large circular makeup mirror of the kind which magnifies on one side, an address book stuffed with pieces of paper and what might have been letters, a wallet, a change purse, and an enormous plastic flowered makeup case with a zipper in the front. Then she pulled a small vial from the depths of the bag and held it up triumphantly. "I knew it was here, the stupid thing," she said, and packed everything back in the bag, willy-nilly. There was great loveliness in her face, Marion thought.

"How often do you see your children?" said Marion.

"We have Christmas, and they visit me sometimes, and sometimes I visit them." Clara stirred saccharin into her coffee. "My daughter Annabel, I used to see her every week, oh more than that, and the children, oh you wouldn't believe it." She shook her head, almost disapprovingly, so overcome was she by the gifts of her grandchildren. "Their father is a professor," she admitted reluctantly, "so of course they're smart."

"Do you like him?"

Clara shrugged. "He's a good man. I guess he's a good man."

"My mother," said Marion, putting down her coffee cup, "is very sick, you know."

Clara made an exclamation of dismay. "What's wrong with her?"

"Cancer. She won't admit it, but that's what it is." She linked her hands around her knees. "She's going to die of it, of course. Pretty soon now, I think."

"Ahhh," said Clara, slowly shaking her head. "Such a thing, it's terrible, terrible. How old is she, your mother?"

"I'm not exactly sure. Sixty-four or sixty-five, I think."

"That's not old," said Clara. "Such a shame. It's hard for you. It's very hard when a mother dies. I remember, oh, I remember."

"It doesn't seem to be affecting me at all, actually," said Marion. She noticed some stains on the braided oval rug. Luckily it was black and beige, and they didn't show much.

"Don't you like your mother, then?" she heard Clara ask, cautiously.

"I can't imagine why I'm telling you this," said Marion. "After all, you're a mother yourself. I'm sure it isn't very pleasant to hear that some people don't care for their mothers."

"A lot of things aren't pleasant," said Clara.

"It would be easier for me, I think, if I did like her," said Marion, examining the shiny toes of her brown pumps.

"Don't pretend to cry for her," said Clara suddenly. Marion looked at her. "Ah, what do I know," said Clara.

"No, that's all right," said Marion. They heard the front door open, because Marion had left the door to the hall ajar. Spot sat up, listening.

"It's that motorcycle man," said Clara disdainfully. "Ah, he's not a bad man, I guess," she said, pushing herself up from her chair.

Marion stood up, too. Spot cocked his great head, but still didn't hear or see anything worth getting up for. He was used to people coming and going; all their sounds were now familiar to him. With a sigh he laid his huge black body down to sleep.

Clara reached down to pick up her bag. "Thank you for the coffee," she said.

"You're welcome."

Clara stopped at the door to the hall and turned back to Marion. "Don't mind telling me these things," she said. "Someday maybe I tell you some things. Then we'll be even."

She disappeared down the hall.

Marion closed the door and began collecting their cups and saucers. Her pumps pinched her feet, and her suit skirt was riding up at the waist. She put the china in the sink and went to her bedroom to change.

Her mother was such a small person, really, thought Marion, taking a turtleneck sweater from a drawer. And she had looked even smaller, lying in a hospital gown, under hospital sheets. It was hard to believe they were related, she and Harriet.

The sweater got stuck as she pulled it over her head. She tugged at it, but for a moment it wouldn't move. Her eyes flew open; her lashes brushed the wool of the sweater; she couldn't see anything but a dark blue haze.

She heard a noise at her bedroom door, the soft scuff of a slipper. She turned, unseeing, toward the sound. She pulled hard, and harder, and finally the sweater slipped over her head. She blinked rapidly and her vision cleared. There was nobody standing, slight and slippered, in the doorway to her room.

CHAPTER 9

"Have another drink," said Vern, pouring more brandy into Marion's glass. "Are you going to spend the night?"

"If I spend the night, it will be because I have become too drunk to drive myself home. I do not intend, however, to spend the night." She looked distastefully around his living room. "I can't imagine not spending the night in my own house." She was sitting on the floor, on some pillows, wearing a long dark blue skirt and a low-cut white blouse. She had agreed to go out with Vern because it was expedient; she needed to be distracted from her mother's dying. He asked her regularly once a month or so, but she had never before said yes.

"Come on over here, why don't you?" he said from the sofa. He tried to leer at her, keeping it light, but she heard his hesitancy.

"I'm perfectly happy where I am," said Marion, sipping her brandy.

It had been a peculiar evening. She'd had to pick him up, since he didn't have a car. He had insisted on filling her gas tank and when she pulled into a self-serve station he got out to operate the pump, which surprised her. She had assumed that anyone who didn't drive didn't know anything about cars at all. She watched him operate the pump and wished she found him even the slightest bit physically attractive. She decided to try to be attracted to him, and did, during dinner at La Caille, but by the time she'd driven them back to his apartment she knew it was a lost cause.

"My sex drive is low," said Marion, and felt laughter bubbling in her throat. She put down her brandy glass and folded her hands in her lap. She felt regal, and her neck as she turned to look at him felt long and supple.

Vern leaned forward, his hands on his knees, to see her better. She couldn't imagine getting into bed with a man who was wider at the hips than across the shoulders. She sighed a little, and with the tips of her fingers pushed her glass farther away from her on the coffee table.

"I'm not interested in sex right now," Marion continued. "You're the most recent in a very long line of men whom I don't find at all appealing. Physically. I enjoy your company, of course, or I wouldn't be here."

"Oh," said Vern. "Well, I'm glad it isn't just me. Or are you trying to be polite?"

"Oh no," said Marion. "I haven't been interested in sex for quite a while now."

"How long is quite a while?"

She calculated, narrowing her green eyes and noticing the curtains on his living room window, which were brown, with great swoopings of white upon them, looking like the result of some sort of accident. "Thirteen months," she said.

Vern's mouth fell open. He let himself drop back into the sofa. "Thirteen months. Jesus."

Marion wondered how much of his amazement was pretense. "Has that never happened to you?" she asked, as humbly as possible. From her pillows on the floor she saw his head shake slowly back and forth, and laughter threatened again. She frowned, to get rid of it.

He sprang to his feet, picked up the bottle of brandy and his glass and got down on the floor next to her. She smelled his aftershave, or perhaps it was cologne, and turned slightly away from him.

"If you won't come to me, I'll come to you," he said. "It's help and advice you need, my friend." He wriggled around, trying to get comfortable, and finally plopped a pillow against a chair and leaned back. "How many times have you been in love?" he said.

His balding head shone in the light; his smooth face was too young for the rest of him. He was eagerly curious, but anxious to help, too. Eventually, of course, he would offer himself as her salvation. I'm perfectly sober, thought Marion. Thank heaven.

"Well?" said Vern. "How many times? When was the first time you . . . fell in love?"

Marion thought his choice of words quaint and rather touching.

She stretched her legs out in front of her and propped herself up on her hands. She arched her back, to ease some tension there, and watched her breasts strain against the fabric of her blouse.

"How many times?" she said. "Dozens of times. When was the first time? When I was thirteen." She turned to smile at him, and this time the laughter when it began deep inside tumbled right out of her mouth, and she liked the feeling so much that she let her head fall back a little so that it could come out more easily; she loved the sound of her laughter, chiming clear in Vern's living room. "Don't you have any records?" she said, when the laughter had gone away.

"My stereo's on the fritz," he said, watching her.

"What do you play on it, when it isn't on the fritz?" said Marion, crossing her ankles.

"I play a lot of jazz, and some rock. What do you play on yours?" He touched her hand. "We're getting off the subject, don't you think?"

"I was never seriously on it, Vern," said Marion, withdrawing her hand. She pulled up her knees and looked at her watch. "I went out with you because since I began freelancing I've gotten out of the habit of going places. It takes an effort now to go somewhere. This is something which just recently occurred to me."

"You can go out with me any old time your heart desires," he said, grinning. She saw his hand reach out, then change direction. He drank some more brandy.

"Thank you," said Marion. She got to her feet.

"Don't go," said Vern, scrambling up.

"Oh, I must," said Marion, reaching for her evening bag. "It's time for me to go."

"But I haven't helped you with your problem." He put his arms around her.

Marion stood still for several seconds, looking over his left shoulder at an empty space on a shelf beside the window which must be where he kept his stereo. There was nothing wrong with the room. It was a perfectly ordinary room, except for the curtains; tasteful, pleasant, even welcoming. The scent of his cologne was stronger, as she stood pressed to him, his belly pushing against hers. She thought idly that if they were to go to bed in the dark she might not even notice his paunch, and perhaps his thighs were thick and muscled, and the skin at the base of his spine would be soft, and she could hold his testicles in her hand and rub her lips against them.

She put her hands on his shoulders and pushed him gently away. "I didn't come here to have you help me with my problems. I came here for your company." She thought about kissing his cheek, just to see what he tasted like, but changed her mind.

He went to the door with her. "Hey, look," he said sturdily, helping her on with her coat. "What's thirteen months? Thirteen months is nothing, right?"

She opened the door and stepped out into the hall. "Thank you, Vern," she said, trying to sound warm, yet aloof. "I've had a very pleasant evening."

"Hey, listen," he called after her. "I'm going to work on it. As soon as I get a theory, I'll call you, okay?"

From halfway to the elevator Marion turned and waved and sent him a smile and her silvery laugh.

CHAPTER 10

Marion drove reluctantly to Leona's apartment one sunny Saturday morning in November, feeling irritable. All this fuss over a four-day absence from work, when Bruce had been on the wagon for months now. Some people had no faith at all, she thought, disapprovingly, as she pulled up in front of the building where Leona lived.

She ought to drop in to see Emily on her way home, she thought, peering through the passenger window toward the lobby, but the sun striking the glass made it impossible to see if anyone was in there.

She drummed her fingers on the steering wheel, waiting. She had to admit it was most unusual for him to be sick.

She noticed as soon as Leona got into the station wagon that her friend was different. Subdued, yet twitchy. It made Marion feel awkward in her company.

She was going to ask her about it but hadn't decided how to phrase the question, when Leona asked about Harriet.

It was tempting, actually, to talk about Harriet, but what was there to say, after all? Everything was quite clear-cut. The woman was dying, and Marion didn't yet understand what she felt about that. A lengthy conversation on the topic, with Leona or anyone else, wouldn't help at all, and would quite possibly result in her feelings becoming more muddled than ever.

"Oh, let's not talk about my mother," said Marion airily. "Look at the mountains, Leona, they're Alp-like, all covered with snow."

Leona huddled in the corner of the car like an abandoned puppy. Marion decided she had no real desire to drag her friend's problems out for discussion either. It was, after all, impossible for people to advise one another. It was Marion's experience that discussing things, if they were important things, frequently made them seem even bigger and more important than they really were. Unless she'd had a couple of drinks first, she became alarmed when people approached her, bearing their problems in their outstretched arms. Did they really believe that giving their problems to her was going to make them disappear? When slightly looped, however, she gathered them in willingly, quite prepared to take the responsibility for dumping them cheerfully over the nearest cliff, without even studying them first.

Yet she didn't like seeing Leona miserable. It made her uneasy.

"Is there something wrong, Leona?" she said finally, when they were almost at Bruce's house.

"What? How do you mean?"

"You look a little strained, I thought. That's all. Not your normal ebullient self."

"I'm just thoughtful today, I guess," said Leona.

"You probably aren't getting enough exercise. That's probably what it is." She nodded to herself, satisfied. "Why don't you get a dog?"

Leona burst into laughter, and Marion, after a moment, had to join her, since she knew that Leona wasn't all that fond of dogs.

They bumped through the potholes in the driveway up to Bruce's door, parked the car, and got out. Marion looked around her, unable to comprehend why people chose to live in the country when they weren't even farmers. All Bruce and Norma did with their three acres was plant a huge vegetable garden, which seemed to Marion a monumental waste of perfectly good land. The least they could do, she thought, climbing the steps with Leona, was get some chickens or pigs or cows or horses or something. The silence, broken only by birds, was unnerving, and so was the enormous sweep of empty land all around the house. Marion didn't like the sight of the city in the distance, either. She liked to feel the city, active and preoccupied, surrounding her, heedless but protective.

She didn't enjoy their brief visit. Norma's direct gaze made her uncomfortable.

"How about some coffee?" said Norma, having reported on Bruce's apparently legitimate illness, and Marion was relieved when Leona said no, they didn't have time.

"Thanks for coming," said Norma at the door. "You can report that he's alive, and getting well."

When on the way home Leona suddenly told Marion to stop the car, Marion thought she just wanted to look at the mountains. But as soon as she pulled over Leona flung open the door and stumbled dizzily along the edge of the road, and Marion became extremely alarmed.

She got out of the car and went to Leona.

"I'm all right, really," said Leona, as Marion put an arm around her shoulders.

"What is it? What's wrong with you?"

Leona didn't actually look sick. She looked wiry, as usual, but strong. Her hair blown back from her face by the wind was thick and shiny. Her face had some color in it, too. And when she turned to face Marion her eyes seemed brighter, and Marion relaxed, but then Leona said, "Oh, Marion. I'm so fucking scared."

Looking down at her, Marion had an unpleasant urge to march back to her car and drive away, leaving Leona stranded by the side of the road.

"My heart keeps doing this jeezly pounding," said Leona. "It scares the shit out of me. The doctor says there's nothing wrong with it, but then why is it happening to me, Marion, for Christ's sake?"

I don't think I can stand this, thought Marion distractedly, patting her friend's shoulder. Not on top of my mother. A wave of panic surged through her, gone in an instant, but it left her feeling weak and uncertain. She dredged up some counterfeit confidence and led Leona firmly back to the car. There she questioned her thoroughly, seeking loopholes through which her unwilling sympathy might escape, transformed into practical advice.

As they drove back into the city Leona dozed, and Marion wondered in dismay how she had managed to become so stickily enmeshed in other people's problems. It seemed to her that she was surrounded by a plethora of illnesses, although there were only two, and that never again would her own life be the single thing absorbing her attentions. Why is it, she thought, that they think I care?

CHAPTER 11

Marion's mother was brought tenderly home from the hospital by Henry later that month, on a Wednesday morning, under a November sky of pewter and cream.

"I'll never see another spring, Henry," she said, probably not believing it. He was too busy bundling her indoors to respond, but Marion knew her mother's words would stick in his brain like spiny things, and that what they meant to him was that there would never be another spring.

She stood in the doorway of their house, waiting, intending to be helpful. Her mother nodded to her as she walked slowly past, leaning heavily on Henry's arm and shoulder. She wore less makeup than usual, but what struck Marion was that she wore any at all.

Henry took her straight into the living room, where he had rearranged the furniture slightly. The reclining chair now faced the window, and a small table had been cleared of decorative paraphernalia and sat next to the chair. There was a floor lamp behind it, positioned so the light must fall exactly over Harriet's left shoulder when she sat in the chair, properly illumining whatever she might be trying to read. The only thing on the table was a small brass bell. "That's so you can summon me, Harriet, wherever I may be," he said as he helped her off with her fur coat.

"My voice carries as far as that bell does, Henry," she said, but she gave his hand a squeeze.

Henry settled her in the chair and took off her boots. He sent Marion to the bedroom to collect her slippers. Marion found them neatly side by side in the closet, and picked them up, her skin prickling. She hadn't thought until that moment about contagion: how dreadful, she thought, to catch death from one's mother.

Back in the living room, Harriet lay in the reclining chair, her eyes closed, dark shadows beneath them, aging rapidly as Marion watched. It was frightening to see on the exterior of Harriet the interior transmutation sketch itself, and Marion struggled against curiosity about her own inner workings.

She knelt in front of Harriet and nudged her small feet into the furry slippers, restraining herself from patting the calf of her mother's leg comfortingly, as though she were a child. But when she stood up she discovered an immense weariness, and was sure it was the kind of weariness mothers feel, up and down up and down all day long, adjusting their gigantic height to the smallness of their needful offspring.

She sat on the sofa and studied the painting of the wheat field, not sure how long she ought to stay in that house.

"Leave your eyebrows alone, Marion," said Harriet sharply. "You're going to rub them right off your head."

Marion became instantly aware of the fingertips of her right hand, and removed them from her brow. Her mother was the only person who had ever drawn Marion's attention to this mannerism. She caught herself doing it sometimes and knew therefore that it wasn't her mother who precipitated it, but nobody else in the world seemed to find it worthy of notice. She resented Harriet for finding it annoying.

Harriet studied her from the reclining chair.

"Do you have to go back to the hospital, Mother?"

"I don't have to do anything. Dying people have a few rights, I've decided, and I don't intend to do anything just because it's been recommended to me."

"Have the doctors recommended that you go back to the hospital?"

Harriet closed her eyes for a minute. When she opened them again she looked straight at Marion, and studied her some more. "You've turned out well, Marion," she said, to Marion's utter surprise.

She felt a brief flash of gratitude, of burgeoning joy, and quickly crushed it. "And do you take credit for that, Mother?" She watched her mother's face closely, looking for guilt or just unease, but all she spotted there was a small smile.

"Some credit," said Harriet. "Certainly."

Marion stood up slowly, wanting to feel she towered over this woman in the reclining chair, but instead she felt more like a lady-in-waiting wishing to take leave of a queen. And as Marion stood, Harriet nodded slowly and solemnly, as though knowing this and accepting it as her due.

"I hope you'll call me, Mother, if there's anything I can do." She had to stop herself from bowing and backing out the door into the hall.

She went into the kitchen, where Henry was standing at the stove, watching some soup in a pan. On the table was a wicker tray with a bowl, a plate for buttered toast, and a mug made of English china with roses on it, all ready for Harriet's tea. Marion knew that he would have warmed the mug under the hot water tap, and that the water in the kettle, just beginning to whistle, would have been fresh.

"I'm going now, Dad."

He looked up and smiled. "Okay, Marion. I'll call you."

"Okay."

The whole business was very distracting, she thought in exasperation, on the way back to her house. She really couldn't allow it to distract her anymore. She had stories to write, and columns for the *Star*, now, money to earn; the bills weren't going to pay themselves; deadlines had to be met. The world didn't care that Harriet was dying. Marion's editors might be politely sympathetic if they knew, but if Harriet's dying interfered with their deadlines they'd simply get themselves another writer.

As she pulled up in front of her house she hesitated; should she park in the garage? It was going to freeze. But surely not hard enough to require her to plug in her car. Besides, she didn't know how much room there was in her garage. Maybe Mike had taken over the whole place with his motorcycle and his black Plexiglas helmet and all the rest.

She got out of her car, slammed the door, and stalked around the house, through the gate, down the sidewalk and along the fence to the small door in the garage. She flung open the door. She'd evict him on the spot, she would, taking advantage of her generosity like that. She switched on the lights.

The motorcycle was parked along the side of the garage. There was plenty of room between it and the opposite wall for Marion's car. And he had used only one shelf of the set of six which occupied the wall at the end of the garage. There were cans of oil and a pair of heavy gauntlets and the black helmet, all lined up neatly. She saw that the other shelves had been recently dusted, and the garage floor had been swept. A long extension cord was plugged into the electrical outlet below the shelves and looped around a hook sticking out from the far wall; it waited, out of the way but conveniently near, for her car to need it.

Marion stood still, thinking about her tenants; the kindness of strangers, she thought. She closed her eyes and leaned her forehead against the wall and let it seep into her for a moment—the dispassionate kindness of strangers who planted things in her garden and listened to some of her sorrow and kept her garage clean. How had it come to this? Yet she saw no other path she might have taken.

She left the garage and went toward her house, where Spot waited at the kitchen window, his nose pressed anxiously against the glass. She was wearing a woolen hat and boots and gloves, and in her kitchen, with Spot thrusting his big head at her thighs and making woofing noises, she wondered what to do. It wasn't the right time of day for anything specific. Too late to settle down to work, too early for dinner. She could have a glass of wine and read the paper, but she was too restless for that.

She put Spot on his leash; as soon as she took it from its hook on the wall behind the refrigerator, he went into paroxysms of gratitude and glee, galompfing from one door to the other, not knowing which way she wanted to go out.

She didn't want to see anyone, so she took him out the kitchen door and down the walk. When she opened the gate he erupted joyfully into the lane. As long as she stood by the gate where he could see her, she could depend upon him to confine his galloping to the alley, which he did. At first he didn't even stop to sniff garbage bags put out for the morning collection, or to respond to the frantic barking of dogs who lived in backyards at the other end of the lane. When he began to slow down and take more interest in what there was to see and smell and urinate on, Marion called him, and put him on the leash. He heeled, docile, not even panting much after all that running. I should take him out to Bruce's, she thought, and wondered how far and fast he would run before finally tiring himself out.

They turned right at the end of the lane and walked to Marion's corner, then down a block to walk back and forth along another street much like the one her house was on. She'd have liked to walk him along the riverbank, but it was impossible to get across the heavy traffic on Memorial Drive.

It could go on for months, her mother's dying, thought Marion; even over Christmas, for heaven's sake. Her parents were frequently away for Christmas, spending it in a warm place somewhere; this year, though, they would stay home.

She thought suddenly of a summer afternoon in her childhood. She couldn't remember exactly how old she'd been; old enough to go to school, she thought, but not much more. She felt socks wrinkled around her legs and imagined she could smell the sweet child sweat. She was probably grubby. She thought she'd been wearing a dress, or at least something with a skirt. Her hair was long, past her shoulders. Her scalp felt sticky with the heat and in the kitchen, standing on the linoleum floor, she'd asked her mother a question having to do with sex.

She couldn't remember what the question was, but it must have been specific. Her mother was ironing. It occurred to Marion, remembering, that if it had been a hot day, as she thought it had, her mother must have been in one of her grim and long-suffering moods; otherwise she wouldn't have been ironing. This ought to have warned Marion off, because these moods could flash suddenly, unexpectedly, into rage. But there was something in Marion's head which gave her courage, as though she knew her question would put her mother off her stride.

She stopped walking, to concentrate. Spot stopped, too, and looked up at her, his tail wagging inquiringly. What was the question anyway? But it wouldn't come to her, and neither would her mother's reply.

All she could remember was that her sense of challenge had been dissipated and she'd been filled with embarrassment. She couldn't look her mother in the face as she spoke, and in her imagination now Harriet stood headless at the ironing board while her hands continued to operate the iron. She could feel the soft, relentless, rhythmic banging of the iron on the board. This was another sign of Harriet's anger. She wasn't angry this day, but Marion watched the iron with great care. Any increase in the speed with which Harriet wielded it would signal the building of her rage. Maybe that was why she couldn't now recall what her mother had said; maybe she had been mesmerized by that iron, waiting for it to start banging down upon the pillowcase more quickly. If it had, Marion would have backed softly toward the kitchen door, ready to run around the corner if the iron should get whisked high enough for her to fear that her mother would fling it at her.

It didn't, though. It continued to bang heavily but slowly upon the pillowcase, over and over again, and behind this noise was her mother's voice droning an answer, an explanation. It seemed endless, this lecture, if lecture it had been, and Marion couldn't remember a word of it.

She walked again, Spot heeling obediently, and tried to remember other conversations she must have had with Harriet about sex. One more came back to her. Again it was Marion who broached the subject. At least this time she'd chosen a more auspicious moment. Harriet was sitting up in bed, reading the morning paper, a cup of coffee on the table beside her. Marion knocked at the door and was told to come in. Her mother smiled at her, and Marion had asked her question—it was enormously frustrating, she reproached her child self, not to have any memories of these questions. But she did remember Harriet's expression; amazement, then irritation, and then a grim, reluctant, facing-the-problem kind of look. She opened her mouth and began to say something and then, still talking, she threw back the covers and got out of bed. She kept on talking while she thrust her feet into slippers and wrapped her robe around her. Then, still not finished saying whatever it was she thought it necessary to say, she glanced quickly at Marion and began making the bed.

It didn't occur to Marion to help her. She usually offered to help do absolutely everything, thinking this was expected of her, but on this occasion she stood by the door, feeling respectful of herself. She had managed without even trying to turn her mother's attention to certain of Marion's needs which even Harriet couldn't deny. This created an avid interest in Marion; there were some things, then, about being a mother which even Harriet accepted, if not with grace, at least without question.

Marion thought for a while she might be able to turn this to her permanent advantage. She thought up a whole bunch of questions which seemed to her to be related to the ones which had caught Harriet's attention. But either she thought up the wrong questions, or Harriet had become quickly bored, because never again did she get this kind of reaction; never again did she feel that there was honor in her innocence, that the breathless excitement in being a growing, learning person was something that adults might recognize and respect.

She reached down to let Spot off his leash. He didn't run free, just stood looking about him, leaning part of his enormous weight with thoughtful delicacy against her leg. She knelt down to hug him and felt against her cheek the quick beat-beating of his heart. If only a dog's heartbeat could be slowed, if only his heart could be persuaded to work less hard, then she could count on having him with her for the rest of her life. His tongue reached out and lapped her cheek consolingly.

They started for home. Marion saw herself ten years hence taking this same walk, with Spot at her heel. His muzzle would be gray by then, and so would Marion's hair, probably. She'd have different tenants ten years from now. Where would they have gone, her motorcycle man and her cleaning lady, and David; and who would be occupying their rooms?

She lifted her face to the darkening sky and considered her mother. She should have another sex talk with her, before she died. Marion laughed soundlessly, imagining it. This time she would talk, and Harriet would listen.

CHAPTER 12

The basement of Marion's house was cool and dry and possessed that special fragrance which belongs only to the basements of old, well-kept houses. It smelled to Marion as a root cellar ought to smell. A root cellar was a thing she'd never seen, but only heard about; a place with earthen walls, cool, in which foods were stored for the winter.

It pleased her to go down the steep wooden stairs which had no risers, into the cool dry depths of her fragrant basement, which seemed to gather calm into itself. She thought of it as the heart of her house, and liked to go down there and lean against one of its walls and listen to her house breathe. She felt then that she was snuggled inside the center of something which gave her strength. This symbiotic relationship with her house, in which she felt one moment comforted and another briskly protective, gave her great satisfaction.

She sought its soothing ambience on the day that her mother died.

Marion tried to tell herself, making her way down the somewhat shaky stairs, that she was surprised to find herself affected by this death. But it was an effort she soon abandoned. She'd come to realize during the months of her mother's dying that these proceedings were in fact having a profound effect upon her, a thing which didn't please her, but which she had reluctantly accepted. She was confused, now, standing in her basement. She felt no grief, had embarked upon no sentimentalizing, didn't struggle to produce tears, wasn't even the slightest bit sad, exactly; but she didn't feel normal either. A kind of undelineated wistfulness had encompassed her. She had a story to write, and a column; yet these things didn't interest her. She felt breathless, standing in her basement, as though waiting for something to happen.

She looked around, commanding herself to take notice of things. The smooth surface of the wall at the bottom of the stairs had crumbled away in places, revealing naked stones beneath. Nearby stood a pile of things belonging to Clara—two old steamer trunks, several cardboard cartons tied up with heavy string, even some pieces of furniture, including a purple plastic hassock which looked brand-new, a tall skinny floor lamp with a gush of protuberances at the top, meant to hold light bulbs, and a wood and canvas director's chair with a broken arm. Clara's pile of possessions, huddled against the basement wall, struck Marion for the first time as singularly lonely.

She looked away, at the coal bin empty of everything but black dust, at the almost new oil furnace: There had once been a different furnace down here, a big old fat black one with a door and a fire blazing behind it.

She didn't have to worry about her father. His voice on the phone, granted, had been a shattered thing, tears breaking through it like the relentless ocean through a shipwrecked vessel, but he was surrounded by sisters and would muffle his sobs in their aprons. She herself had no sobs to muffle but, gripped by a profound bewilderment, had asked her father to put Emily on the phone, and had requested her company. She hadn't been able to wait quietly upstairs for Emily, though, hands clasped on the desk at which she sat, looking curiously through the window at the cold and steely sky. She'd stood up after a few minutes, irritated by the sound of her own breathing, and without thinking had gone down into her basement.

It was cool and dry and fragrant and held calm within itself, but Marion's mind was skipping like a pebble across the surface of still water.

She's gone, she thought. She said it aloud, "My mother is gone," articulating clearly. But she didn't believe it.

She climbed the stairs to the kitchen and closed the basement door. She heard Spot lumbering down the hall to the front door, and she could see the outline of somebody standing on the front porch. At the door the dog waited, his tail wagging.

Marion opened the door and stood looking at her aunt.

"Goodness me, Emily," said Marion, "my old mother's gone and died . . ."

Emily stepped inside and closed the door. She came close to Marion and put her arms around her.

". . . and I hardly know what to think," said Marion, blinking hard. She stood quietly, looking from Emily's embrace through the half-open door into her living room. Emily felt slight against her; she'd lost some weight. There was a great and terrible pain in Marion's chest. I don't want this, she thought angrily. I don't want it at all.

CHAPTER 13

Marion dived quickly into meaningful activity.

She prepared long lists of story ideas for every magazine she'd written for and she got back many no's and some yesses, which, when coupled with the column she wrote weekly for the *Star*, swamped her with work.

She ignored the magazines' deadlines and set one single early deadline of her own, December 15. If she made it, all her stories and columns would be done well before they were due and she'd have ten days in which to prepare for Christmas. She had invited her father and Emily for dinner, and also Leona and Vern.

She worked twelve and fifteen hours a day for two weeks and thought she had never worked more efficiently or with more imagination. She went to every interview fully prepared, wasted not a minute of the time spent in the *Star*'s library, didn't hesitate before starting to write but leaped right in there. I can always make it better the second time around, she thought, but usually she was surprised to discover that the pieces came out sounding strong and sure the very first time.

Late in the evening of December 15, she typed the last thing on her list, which was her *Star* column for the first week in January. As she put it away in the file marked "Star" she was overcome by a dreadful weariness, and lowered her head onto her arms, and fell asleep at her desk.

A little while later Spot woke her by thrusting his head against her. She took him to the front door and let him out and sat in the bay window, keeping herself awake until he should reappear. She could see that the night was very cold. There was a lot of old snow, and though the streets had been plowed and sanded, they would be as slippery as glass. Up above, the stars were burning small cold holes in the black sky.

Soon she saw the dog come loping along the sidewalk toward the house, his ears flapping, a swift-moving graceful black shadow against the snow. She got up to let him in. As he stood in the hall, panting, shaking snow from his coat, she became aware of the sound of the typewriter upstairs, and as she became aware of it, it stopped.

She put Spot in the kitchen and closed the door. Holding onto the banister, because she was very tired, she went softly upstairs and knocked at the door to David's room.

He opened it and looked at her quizzically. His curly hair was uncombed and his shirt was creased. "Hi," he said.

Marion, realizing that she had never before in the nine months he'd lived there come up to knock on his door, was embarrassed. "I don't think I thought about the time," she said, "and it must be very late, but I heard your typewriter."

"I've been hearing yours, too. You've been going at it full blast lately, haven't you?"

"Yes, but I'm all done now, until after Christmas. I just finished a few minutes ago."

"Then come in and have a drink." He opened the door wide and stepped back to let her past.

She thought that a drink sounded like a very good idea.

She went in and sat on his divan, which she was relieved to see he hadn't yet made up into his bed. On the desk sat a portable typewriter and piles of yellow paper, some clean with all the edges neatly aligned, and some typed upon and messy. The messy pile was higher.

"I don't have much," he said. "Just beer and wine."

"I'll have a glass of wine, please," said Marion. Clearly he didn't spend all his time writing letters. Nobody wrote letters that long. "Are you doing some freelancing?" she called to him.

He came in with a can of beer and a glass of red wine. "Didn't ask if you'd prefer white," he said, handing her the glass, "because red's all I've got." He glanced over at the desk and sat in a chair near the window. "No, that's a play."

"A play?" said Marion, astonished.

"Yeah. Maybe a television play. I don't know. I'm just fooling around with it."

"My goodness," said Marion. "I had no idea." She looked with respect at the weary pile of yellow paper. "What's it about?"

"People," said David, and grinned at her. He rested his head against the back of his chair and stretched out his legs. "It's very quiet in the house, isn't it, with both our typewriters silent."

She listened to the silence and heard within it the sounds of her house—furnace and hot water heater and refrigerators and clocks.

"I came to ask if you've made any plans for Christmas," said Marion, and crossed her legs serenely.

"I haven't even thought about Christmas," said David.

"Are you going back to London, or will you be here?"

"Oh, I'll be here," he said, and drank some beer.

"Then why don't you plan to have dinner downstairs? There'll be some other people there, too."

"You don't have to invite your tenants to your parties, you know, Marion. Landladies are supposed to remain aloof, remember?"

"Oh, I'm quite aloof. I'm not inviting Mike, for instance. Or Clara."

He nodded. "Why?"

Slightly flustered, she debated with herself and then admitted, "Because Mike's working on Christmas Day and Clara's going to Vancouver."

David laughed. "You want to make sure we're all properly taken care of, right? You don't want to think that anybody in your house is going to be lonely on Christmas, right?"

"Yes, right," she said, irritated. "Actually it's quite selfish of me. I could always go someplace else for Christmas, you know. That way I wouldn't have to give any of you a single thought, would I?"

He watched her for a while. She felt herself become beautiful, a process always astonishing and not always gratifying. She finished her wine and held out her glass imperiously, not looking at him, and, holding it, was suddenly languorous. "My goodness, I am tired," she said, and stretched slightly from the waist to ease the ache in her back and dipped her head slightly, feeling the arch in her neck and strands of hair caress her cheeks.

David stood up and took her glass and as she turned to look at him, smiling, he kissed her fingertips. "I take it," he said, "that you'd like just a little more wine."

For a minute she was certain he would pull her to her feet and wrap his arms around her and kiss her on the mouth. She looked at him, her lips apart, extremely curious to discover whether she would enjoy kissing him, aware that it was a thing she'd wondered about before.

He let go of her hand and went into the kitchen, and came back with her glass refilled. "You're very tempting, Marion," he said as he gave her the wine. "Most unlandladylike." He sat down again just as far away from her as ever.

"I'm sure I don't go around trying to be tempting," she said. As she spoke, that persona which both intrigued and frightened her, that Marion of pliant sexuality, of confidence and grace, retreated, deserted her, and she blushed. She drank quickly, wanting to be rid of the glass, and stood up, smoothing her jeans over her thighs. "I'm just tired. That's all."

"If you really mean it," said David, walking with her to the door, "I'd like to have Christmas dinner with you."

"There'll be a lot of other people there, too," she said hurriedly, keeping her body away from his.

"Can I help cook?"

She stopped in the hallway. "I don't know. I don't usually like to be helped in the kitchen."

"Why don't I just wander down there and peel potatoes or something. If I get in the way just tell me, and I'll take Spot out for a walk."

"Okay," she said. "Sure. Thanks for the wine." She turned at the top of the stairs and saw him smiling at her from the doorway to his room.

CHAPTER 14

"I've had quite enough coffee," said Marion to her assembled guests on Christmas afternoon, "and I'm off to get myself an alcoholic beverage."

She went through the dining room into the kitchen. David and Spot went with her.

"I'm going to put him out on the back porch for a while, okay?" said David.

She went to the kitchen cupboard and opened it, looking for a glass, but there didn't seem to be any glasses. All she could see were rows and rows of canned things, enough, she thought, to feed her for weeks in case of a nuclear holocaust. But of course she probably wouldn't live through one of those; except maybe if she happened to be in her basement. Maybe I should move this stuff into my basement, she thought. She stood there, frowning into the cupboard, and when she felt David's hands on her shoulders she closed her eyes and turned around and slowly laid her cheek against his shoulder, letting her arms and hands hang limp at her sides. He put his arms around her and held her tightly and began to sway gently back and forth. She felt she could comfortably go to sleep there. Her legs were loosening at the knees, where she thought they had gotten themselves locked.

She felt his breath upon her hair as he spoke. "This is one peculiar mixture of people you've got gathered here together."

"Well, now, isn't this a pretty sight," said Vern from the doorway.

Marion opened her eyes and over David's shoulder saw his face for an instant drawn and grim. Then a wide smile was there. He came toward them, his hands in his pockets.

"I thought I might cadge a drink, if you're getting one for yourself," said Vern. "But I can always come back another time."

Marion withdrew from David, whose arms didn't relax around her until she began to move. She reached up and ran her fingers through her hair. From the living room she heard the second cut on Pavarotti's Christmas album begin to play, a sweet and stately melody which she didn't recognize. She stepped around David and touched Vern's purple tie. "I hadn't realized until this minute that you've come to my Christmas dinner all dressed up."

"What did you expect?" said Vern. "It's Christmas. You're all dressed up, aren't you?"

Marion raised her hands and turned slowly around, looking down at her floor-length dress, long-sleeved, décolleté, made of dark green velvet. "Why yes," she said, smiling at him. "I guess I am."

She was flushed from the heat of the kitchen when they sat down to dinner, and filled with benevolence and good cheer. As her guests helped themselves from bowls and platters, she surveyed them with affection only occasionally tainted by contempt. She didn't expect to see much improvement in her father's state of mind until the end of May, six months after Harriet's death; she thought six months ought to do it. She had decided to be firm but patient with him until then, recognizing and respecting his grief but refusing to allow it to inundate him while he was in her presence.

Emily looked very attractive today, thought Marion approvingly, and seemed to be enjoying Clara's company, which Marion wouldn't have expected. She'd had to invite Clara after all, the poor woman, when her plans to visit her daughter in Vancouver fell through.

Leona was irritable, which apparently was usual in one who had quit smoking, although Marion would have thought she'd be over it by now, having quit more than two months ago. Of course, she thought, sending Leona a sharp look, it could be that her heart was banging again. She would turn her attention to Leona, now, thought Marion, and make sure she got to a specialist if she had to drag her there by the hair.

David, she noticed, was quiet; Marion looked at him, suddenly suspicious. Sitting there smiling and hardly saying anything, he's probably putting everything down in his head to use in his play, she thought. It was a disconcerting notion.

"I may go away for a while after the new year, Marion," said Henry.

He sounded so exhausted that Marion doubted he'd find the energy, but she said politely, "Where, Dad?"

"Maybe to Hawaii for a week of so."

Marion looked at him with interest. It hadn't occurred to her until now that deprived of his wife he might actually change for the better.

"By yourself, Henry?" said Emily.

"I thought so, yes. Unless you'd care to come with me, Emily? Of course, there's your job," he added, staring at his food.

"Well, actually there isn't," said Emily. "I don't have a job anymore, Henry. I've been laid off."

Marion felt stricken. "Emily! When did this happen? Why didn't you tell me? That dreadful Grebbs, it's typical, laying somebody off at Christmastime."

Emily smiled. "There's no need to worry, Marion. I'm certainly not destitute, and I've been doing some work at home, to keep myself busy."

Marion was amazed that she had kept it to herself for so long. It was this which she most admired about Emily; her ability to remain serene, her talent for grappling with her life and causing order to be created out of disorder. Whatever happened, Emily just got on with things, without complaining. She looked fondly at her aunt, glad that her own strength had come from this side of her family.

"I think it's time we went home, Henry," said Emily later in the sitting room.

Leona had already left, and Clara had just gone upstairs. Marion felt David's body warm and solid where he leaned against her legs. She wondered how she was going to get rid of Vern, who had refused a ride with Leona, saying he'd take a cab.

"Don't move, Marion," said her aunt, already on her way to the door.

Marion closed her eyes. It's time that everybody went home, she thought, and let me get to bed.

"I might stay for one more drink," said Vern.

Marion ignored him. At a certain point, she thought, I will announce in clarion tones that the party is over.

"It's hard to get a taxi on Christmas night, I bet," said David.

"Maybe I'll walk," said Vern.

From the hall Emily screamed, a sound so unexpected, yet so unquestionably real, that for a moment they froze where they were. She screamed again, and everybody moved at once, but it was Vern who reached her first.

They found her clinging to the wall, facing Mike at the front door.

"I'm terribly sorry," said Mike, his black helmet under his arm. He still had a hand on the doorknob, ready to flee back into the night.

"Jesus, man," said Vern.

Marion put an arm around Emily's shoulder and attempted to introduce her to Mike, but she realized how ludicrous this was; Emily's body was being whipped by uncontrollable shivering, her face was white and her hand was clapped over her mouth. She shook her head, pulled away from Marion and rushed back into the sitting room.

Marion stayed for another minute to reassure Mike, then left her other guests to finish the job and went to find Emily.

Her aunt was in the bathroom, vomiting. Marion rested her head against the wall next to the bathroom door and waited. Finally Emily came out. She was still very pale; the color seemed to have faded even from her eyes. But she looked composed.

"I'm sorry, Marion. I don't know what got into me. He took me by surprise." She gave Marion's hand a squeeze. "I hate to admit it, but it's possible that I had a bit too much wine."

David offered to drive her and Henry home, but Emily, apparently quite back to normal, refused, and when she and Henry left, she insisted that Vern go with them.

"It's the least I can do," she said to him, "after startling you so."

"Why don't you just put those plates down on the floor and let Spot clean them off?" said David.

Marion stopped in the middle of the kitchen, her hands full, and stared at him. "What a sickening idea," she said, and put the plates on the counter. She went back to the dining room.

"I'm not going to help you with that, you know," said David, linking his hands behind his head.

"Who asked you to?" said Marion, returning with more plates. She was followed back and forth closely by a plodding, patient Spot. "In fact, why are you still here, anyway?" She opened the cupboard below the sink and began scraping plates into the plastic garbage bag attached to the door. Spot sat and panted, watching her, and occasionally he moaned.

"Are you sending me to my room?" said David.

Marion shrugged, still scraping. "I'm not particularly enjoying your presence."

"That's because I'm sitting here watching you work."

"Well then, why don't you leave?"

"I feel like having a conversation."

"Oh, for heaven's sake." She crashed the plate down upon the counter.

"Come and sit down for a minute." He got up and went over to her, took her by the hand and led her to the sofa. "Sit down there. Just for a few minutes."

"I'm not much good at frivolous conversation."

"Who said it's going to be frivolous? It could be very important stuff. You never know until you start talking."

Marion sighed. "Do you want a glass of wine or some coffee or something?"

"No. I just want you to sit here beside me for a while." He got up to turn off the overhead light, and the lamp. He also went to the dining room for a candle, which he lit and put on the coffee table in front of them. "There. Now isn't that nice? Very calming."

"I'm actually perfectly calm, David."

They looked at the tree for a while. Marion had planned to decorate it in nothing but silver, with only white lights, but at the last minute had decided it looked like something in a department store. Now she was glad. It would have been too sophisticated a tree for the sitting room, which was also part of the kitchen. She liked the multicolored lights. They made it look comfortable and friendly.

"I don't think I ever said so," said David, "but I'm sorry that your mother died."

"It's quite a relief, actually," said Marion. Her voice seemed to come from a long distance away. "What's your mother like?" she said suddenly, and turned to look at him. They were sitting at opposite ends of the sofa, which wasn't long, but still permitted two feet of empty space between them.

He was looking at the tree. "She's thin and anxious. She worries a lot."

"Does she worry about you?"

He smiled. "What's to worry about?"

"Are you going to go back there? To London?"

"Oh, I don't know. I don't make plans."

"But you came out here."

"Yeah. One day I just felt like it. I got restless. I might go to Vancouver next. Never been there before, either."

She felt an ache in her house, like the ache from an extracted tooth.

"Oh dear, oh dear," she said, shaking her head. She gritted her teeth and clenched her hands but it was no good, he came close to her anyway, and put his arms around her, and her hands flew open and reached behind him to stroke the back of his neck. "Oh dear oh dear," said Marion, closing her eyes as his mouth drew closer and she opened her lips for him, and soon and in a great hurry they took off their clothes.

He had a thin hard body and his face so near to hers looked older, more strained. She felt lush and succulent, gripped him with limbs rounded and voluptuous, felt herself to be all flesh, as delicious as a nectarine. When his hands tried to stroke her for too long she pulled him close so that his mouth would touch her skin. She hurt, waiting for his mouth, and moved beneath him, and finally finally his lips and tongue suckling between her legs his hands full of her breasts she overflowed, exploded, made sounds in her throat and reached down for him to guide him into her a sweet hot arrow and gripped him tight and sweaty, felt him loose himself within her, and collapse upon her.

"Good Christ," said David into her throat.

She closed her eyes tightly and turned her head away from him. Maybe if she lay still and silent as though asleep he would get up and collect his clothing and tiptoe away up the stairs to his room.

He got up and sat on the edge of the sofa. With both hands he turned her head toward him. "Marion. Open your eyes."

She shook her head and felt tears slide down her cheeks. She pressed her lips together hard. He kissed them, and kissed the tears.

"You're magnificent, Marion. You're a magnificent woman."

Her eyes shot open and she struggled to sit up, folding her arms in front of her. "I'm salacious. That's all. It comes over me sometimes. Please go away."

He sat back and pulled at her until her head was leaning against his shoulder. After a while some of the stiffness went out of her body. That useless dog, she thought, her eyes on Spot, who was lying on the kitchen floor watching them politely.

"You're beautiful in the candlelight," said David. He picked up his shirt from the floor and wiped the stickiness first from Marion's body, then from his own. "There. That's neater." He put his arm around her again. "Are you comfortable?"

Marion didn't answer. If she turned her head just slightly to the left her lips would touch his skin; it would taste salty, like the sea. He bent his head and she looked up at him. He kissed her, first pleasantly, then a gentle full-lipped sucking. She lifted her hand to touch his cheek and he stopped, and kissed her forehead and her temples.

"My Christ but you're delicious," he said.

"I've got to go and get my robe on," said Marion.

He let her stand up. She felt him watching her as she walked across the kitchen to the door leading to her hall. She could imagine just what he saw, too, in the soft witchy light from the candle and the Christmas tree: her long legs and resplendent buttocks and the sweep of her naked back. At the door she looked at him over her shoulder. He was still sitting on the sofa, his hard narrow body motionless and expectant, his face enigmatic. Marion stood still, a whole room between them, invulnerable with her back to him, showing him only part of her face, a few strands of disheveled hair in her mouth; she felt wanton but for the moment safe. A sudden smile lit his face, but she was implacable. She went to her room to brush her hair and wrap her robe around her.

CHAPTER 15

Her father's house was, after all, a very modest one, thought Marion, pulling up in front of it. It seemed flatter than the last time she'd seen it, like a partially deflated balloon. And though its coating of white paint was as smooth and clean as ever, it looked duller to Marion. She didn't like the look of the windows either, blinds sloppily drawn, neither open nor closed. It was feeling Harriet's absence, this house. Marion dreaded the mess she might find inside.

But there wasn't any mess. Perhaps an unusual quantity of dust, but that was all.

Her father sat in the living room with a large trunk in front of him, a blue metal trunk with silver-colored strappings. The first thing that caught Marion's eye was a small pile of books which she immediately recognized.

"Were these in Mother's trunk?" She picked up the top one on the pile, a large old green book whose covers had been mended with electrician's tape. She opened it and saw crayoned scrawlings, and on the title page, right above *The Wizard of Oz*, her own name printed large and laborious. "These are my books," she said, looking at the others in the pile—*Lassie Come Home, Anne of Green Gables, Ozma of Oz* and *Lad, A Dog*. "What was Mother doing with them?"

"I didn't know she had them," said Henry. "Maybe she was keeping them for your children."

Marion sat down, cradling them in her lap. "I'd like to have them back."

"Do you see this?" said her father, holding up a ring whose large green stone was made of glass. "This was her first engagement ring." He turned it in his fingers. "I wanted to buy her an emerald ring, so we went to Birks and asked to look at them. They were beautiful, exactly right for your mother. She didn't like diamonds. She never liked diamonds. But we didn't have any idea how much emeralds cost. When they told us, I couldn't believe my ears. If I'd sold everything we both owned, there still wouldn't have been enough money to buy one of those rings." He handed Marion the piece of green glass, rectangular, set into a cheap metal band which had once been the color of gold. "So your mother said we could get one just as pretty somewhere else. She took me to Woolworth's. We bought this one for thirty-five cents, or maybe less. She wore it for a long time. Not every day, but often."

"I've never seen it before," said Marion, and gave it back to him.

"No, well, she put it away when I got her the real one. It's nice that she didn't throw it out, though." He opened a small metal box with an embossed lid and put the ring inside. "There are other things in here, see? What's this thing?"

"I think that's a Brownie pin. I think it was mine."

"And this, this is an Eastern Star pin. I remember she told me it was her mother's." He closed the box and looked around, then held it out to Marion.

"No, I don't want it, thank you, Dad."

"I don't know what to do with it," said Henry. He put it on the table. "It's hard to know what to do with all these things." He reached into the trunk to pull out a pile of photograph albums with leather covers. "I guess I can keep these. I might like to glance through them now and then." He put them on the floor. "Emily's going to help me with her clothes. When I get back from Hawaii. If I go. She's going to put them into boxes and take them to the Salvation Army. Except for her fur coat." He sat back on the sofa. "The books and the paintings, they're all right. I'll keep them; I want to keep them."

Marion pulled a long cardboard tube from the trunk.

"That's diplomas in there," said Henry.

Marion took them out, several rolled up together. The paper was brittle and resisted being straightened. There were three Royal Conservatory of Music diplomas, for grades six, seven, and eight, and a smaller document which announced that her mother had graduated from a secretarial school in Saskatoon.

"Why didn't we ever have a piano?" said Marion.

"Your mother didn't really enjoy playing. She took lessons because her parents wanted her to."

Marion's memories of her maternal grandparents were dim and uncertain. She remembered a gray-haired grandmother with a back like a ramrod, saw her sitting in a chair with her hands crossed in her lap and her feet crossed at the ankles. She wore black shoes with laces and was so short that when she sat down, her feet didn't touch the floor. She never slumped in a chair or even leaned back into it; there were always a couple of inches between her body and the back of whatever chair she sat in. Marion's grandfather had been a tall, angular man with broad shoulders and long arms. He wore round eyeglasses and a shapeless gray cardigan over a white shirt, and suspenders instead of a belt, and he didn't talk much. In their presence Marion hadn't had a great deal to say, either.

"Didn't she like her parents much?" said Marion.

Henry sat up and rested his elbows on his knees. "She resented them. They weren't unkind people, but I think they were harsh."

"You'd think she'd have learned something from that."

Henry looked at her sharply. "She did. She wanted you to have all the important things she didn't have."

Marion shrugged, careless.

"They had two children," said Henry. "The oldest was your Uncle Ron, and he was the one they sent to college. Harriet wanted to go to college too, but they told her it was her duty to get trained in something quickly, so she could support herself until she got married. You didn't argue much with your parents in those days."

"What did she want to go to college for?" Marion's own choice of occupation had been based on what she would have to leave Calgary to learn to do. She remembered wavering between veterinary medicine and journalism, because for either of these she would have to leave home. She hadn't wanted a confrontation, just a smooth passage to freedom. Although she liked animals, she loathed sickness; but she liked to read, and she liked to write, and so she left home to become a journalist. When she returned, her parents had sold their house and bought this smaller one, anticipating that she would no longer want to live with them. It had all been much easier than she had expected.

"She wanted to be a lawyer," said Henry. "She would've been a good one, too."

Marion ran blind fingers over the cover of *The Wizard of Oz*, seeking to read with them the letters of the title. It was the first book she remembered being given, a present from her Aunt Emily, though it was her mother who had read it to her. It had seemed to Marion at the age of five a veritable tome, but she had lugged it with her everywhere and pored over the illustrations and eventually learned to read it to herself.

"Doesn't it seem odd to you, Dad, that Mother never mentioned these things to me? Parents usually tell their children important things from their pasts, don't they? But not Mother. And not you, much, either."

Henry moved things slowly from one side of the trunk to the other. "We like to put things behind us, I guess." He looked up at her. "I'm telling you now, aren't I?"

Marion stood up with her armful of books. "I'm going to pull up those blinds. Let some sun in here." My mother the lawyer, she thought. Her hand shook with anger as she yanked on the blind. It shot to the top of the window with a sound like the crack of a gun. What *use* was she to me? thought Marion. With her lips clamped tight on life and secrets, and anger the only thing she gave me; none of her thoughts she offered me, none of her history she shared with me, who was she, anyway, that useless useless woman? "Just dump all that stuff, Dad." Marion stood with her back to the window, and she knew he couldn't see her furious, childish tears. "Throw it into a big green plastic garbage bag and put it out with the trash. Get rid of it."

"I probably will," said Henry. He squinted against the sun.

"It's ridiculous to sit there pawing through that meaningless collection of memorabilia," said Marion. "I'm amazed that she didn't chuck it herself." She shifted her books from one arm to the other. She wanted to ask her father a sly crude question about his sex life. "I'm going home now." She moved quickly to the hall closet where she'd left her coat and boots. When she had put them on, she went back to the living room.

Her father was still motionless on the sofa, hands resting on his knees. As she watched, he reached into the trunk and took out a pile of scrapbooks. "This top one," he said, opening it, "is from when she was in high school."

"Goodbye, Dad." Marion turned and went to the hall and outside, slamming the door behind her.

CHAPTER 16

It was a working day in late January. Marion was already tinkering in her head for a lead, absorbed in a story even as she let Spot outside into the winter-gripped backyard and dumped her breakfast plate and knife into the sink. When the phone rang, she reached for it without thinking, reminding herself to turn on the answering device as soon as she hung up.

"I think you've been avoiding me," said David.

"That's entirely possible," said Marion, leaning against the counter.

"I was going to swoop down in the dead of night and bang on your door. But I figured that if Spot didn't get me, Mike or Clara would."

"Yes, it's a good thing you didn't do that." She twisted the thick brown telephone cord between her fingers and waited. She hadn't the faintest idea what to say to him, but he had initiated the conversation and therefore he ought to be able to keep it going.

"I plan to do it tonight, though."

Marion's stomach shot upward and she swallowed hard to shove it back down where it belonged.

"Not exactly in the dead of it," he said. "I thought somewhere around eight or so."

"I may be going out," said Marion quickly.

"What time?"

"About seven." She could always call Leona and suggest that they see an early movie. It would be good for Leona to go out, Marion told herself; she was getting nervous about her upcoming visit to the cardiologist.

"I'll be there about six-thirty," said David, and hung up.

She plugged in the answering device immediately, although it was now too late. When Spot scratched at the door she let him in, and that glimpse of the backyard, layered in months of snow, exasperated her. She banged the door closed, marched into her room, and sat at her desk. She marshaled her concentration and focused it on the story, and then on a column, stopping only for a sandwich in the early afternoon.

At four o'clock she finished the column and covered her typewriter. She stood up and stretched and stripped off her jeans and sweatshirt. She would put on a wool dress, the dark pink one, and do up her hair, and if Leona couldn't go out for dinner and a movie then she would go by herself. She would take along the current *Maclean's* and read it while she ate, she thought, pulling the dress over her shoulders.

She pinned up her hair in something that resembled a Gibson girl style and applied makeup, and sprayed herself with perfume. By now it was almost five o'clock.

She got her fake fur jacket from the closet and pulled on her knee-high boots and collected her gloves. She was at the kitchen door, ready to go out through the backyard to the garage, when there was a knock on the door to the hall. She watched the knob turn and lifted her eyes calmly to look into David's face as he opened the door.

"I knew it," he said. "You're trying to escape."

Marion took off her jacket slowly and threw it over the back of the sofa. She pulled off first one boot and then the other, and then she straightened and stood quietly, her hands clasped in front of her. "I was, yes," she said.

"May I come in?"

"I believe you're in already."

"May I sit down?"

"Certainly."

"That's a very pretty dress."

"Thank you."

"It makes your cheeks look pink."

"Thank you."

"Why don't you sit down, too?"

Marion sat in a chair opposite him, her hands on the arms, her feet crossed at the ankles.

"Where were you off to?" said David.

"I was going to have dinner somewhere and then go to a movie."

"By yourself?"

"Maybe by myself, maybe with Leona." At the moment, though, this felt like too much of an effort. Exhaustion swept through her with the unexpected strength of a summer storm. She grieved, suddenly, for hot sun and blue skies and a garden full of flowers.

"We have a problem here, I think, Marion."

He was watching her, relaxed and oddly respectful. At once she was aware of her legs, and her full breasts, and her mouth, pink with lipstick to match her dress. She leaned her head back and felt herself melt into the chair. She wouldn't move, she decided, no matter what.

"We're strongly attracted to each other," he said. "But also skittish."

Marion smiled to herself; she didn't think he could see.

"Are you going to plant things again this year?" she said. "If the winter ends?" Behind her closed eyes she imagined it—zucchini growing monstrously big, peas fattening within their sun-pierced pods, hollyhocks exploding into blossom.

"Did you like my garden? I thought you were just being kind, letting me plant it."

She opened her eyes. At first she had tolerated his garden, and then she accepted it, and eventually she liked it. She wondered if he'd put a garden in his play. Her body was purring patiently. "I've never been particularly fond of growing things," she said, moving her green eyes across his face, "and it came as a surprise to me, but I did like having it out there. Of course I wouldn't have one of my own," she said dreamily, "but it was extremely pleasant, after a while, to enjoy one which, although it was in my own backyard, was someone else's responsibility." Her fingers stroked the arm of the chair, as though it were a live thing. "Clara says you may be in the wrong business."

He smiled at her. "Marion, let's get it over with. We can't go on living in the same house without getting it straightened out."

Marion recrossed her legs. "Without getting what straightened out?"

"I can't possibly tell you," he said, "what a delight it was to discover how much you love to make love."

Blood rushed to her face; she stared at him, furious.

"You'd be surprised how many people can't enjoy it like you can. You're very lucky." He got up and walked across the room and knelt in front of her chair. "What do you like to eat?" he said. "Strawberries? Do you like the red juice of strawberries in your mouth? Or tomatoes, hot from the sun, with salt on them? What do you like to eat?" he said, not touching her.

She looked at his face, at his ginger-colored eyes, and kept her hands on the arms of her chair. "White chocolate," she said. "I like to eat white chocolate."

"I love white chocolate," said David. "I'd like to lick it from your lips."

Marion willed herself to hang onto the chair, and to keep her legs crossed; she could feel the warmth of his body against her thigh.

"It's simple, you know, Marion. Lust is very simple, right? And it's good, too. It's a good thing, sex is. You know that."

She watched her hands rise, and move through the air, and bracket his face. She looked at him intently, trying to see something important in the moment she had left. "You're going to go away," she said.

"Sure. Eventually. If I didn't, you'd throw me out yourself."

His hands moved up to her breasts and she let her hands drop from his face, and her head fall back, and her eyes close. He knew her, now, and he was nothing permanent, no threat, and yes, she could throw him out, and yes his hands were on her breast and inside her thighs this time she would let him lead, for a little while anyway, she would see how detached he was, how skillful . . .

CHAPTER 17

Late one April night the phone in Marion's bedroom-workroom rang. Her eyes shot open and stared straight toward the ceiling. The phone gave another insistent purr and she looked quickly at the digital clock on top of her chest of drawers. It was 3:17, and it changed to 3:18 as she looked at it. She got out of bed and went to the phone.

"Hello?"

"Marion? It's Emily."

"Emily? Aunt Emily?" Emily was whispering, so Marion whispered, too. "What's the matter?"

"This is absolutely ridiculous," said Emily out loud. "Calling you in the middle of the night."

Marion privately agreed. "What's wrong, Emily?"

"Oh, Marion, I'm such a fool. It's nothing. I just suddenly got nervous. It's ridiculous, waking you at this hour."

"What made you nervous? Are you still nervous?"

"I was sitting in bed, reading, and suddenly I thought I heard something, that's all."

"What did you think you heard?" Marion had been standing in the dark. Now she sat at her desk and turned on the lamp. The surface of the desk was littered with files, stories torn from newspapers and magazines, scraps of paper bearing notes scrawled during telephone conversations.

"Oh, Marion, it was nothing. I thought I heard him trying to break in. I *know* nobody's trying to break in, but I imagined somebody was. Don't ever let anybody tell you, Marion, that imagination is a good thing."

"Did you hear bangings and thumpings," asked Marion curiously, "or what?"

"I thought I heard someone trying to pick the lock."

"I don't think you'd be able to hear that from your bedroom, Emily." Marion picked up a pen and began doodling on the inside cover of an open file folder.

"I know. That's what I mean. I must have imagined it. Marion—do you ever get nervous in your house?"

"Oh, Emily, how could I be nervous with Spot around?" He lay on the floor at the end of her bed, a huge black shadow. She could hear him softly panting. "You should get yourself a dog. Dogs are wonderful. But in the meantime, go and check the door. I'll stay on the phone. Just put the receiver down, go and check the door, and come right back to the phone."

She waited, doodling. She had drawn a clothesline with sheets hanging from it, some of them blown into sails by the wind. She looked at this with some interest. She hadn't hung anything outside on a line to dry since she was a child.

Emily came back to the phone. "I checked. Everything seems fine."

"I was going to give you five minutes," said Marion, studying her drawing, "and then I was going to call the police."

"Nelson's getting married," said Emily. "Did I tell you that?"

"Yes, you did. High time, too." Marion threw down the pen, stretched, and stood up. "Maybe you'll be a grandmother soon, Emily. That'll be a new experience for you."

"I was writing to him, earlier today, but I couldn't think of much to tell him . . ."

"You know, Emily," said Marion, closing the file folder, "I don't think anybody could pick your lock if they tried. Not with that deadbolt you've got on it."

"I know, Marion," said Emily. "I'm an idiot." She sounded almost cheerful.

"Are you going to be okay now?"

"Of course I am. I'm truly sorry to have called so late. I couldn't think of anybody else. Thank you for being so patient."

"Good heavens, it's nothing. Sleep well."

Marion hung up the receiver and turned off the desk lamp. She climbed back into bed and lay looking up at darkness.

It always surprised her when people did unexpected things, but it shouldn't have. People were, after all, extremely erratic. It was their chief characteristic.

She would call Leona on Monday, when she got back from Vancouver, and ask her to keep an eye on Emily. At least Leona was healthy again, thank heaven, that was one less thing chipping away at her concentration.

Marion turned on her side and composed herself for sleep.

It was very quiet in her house, except for the breathing of her dog.

CHAPTER 18

Her bed wasn't big enough for two people to sleep together in, but it was big enough for sex, because when they were having sex two bodies didn't need much space, all wound up together, legs and arms interlaced.

They lay now side by side, she and David, on an evening in June, cooling off. Already Marion felt smeared and sticky, disheveled and disarranged; and irritable, too. Men never seemed to feel this way after sex, she thought, perhaps because their hair wasn't usually long enough to get very mussed, and they didn't wear makeup. Still, you'd think they would be bothered by sweat and the untidy spilling of their sperm, but no, it was always Marion who had to restrain herself from leaping off the bed and going immediately into the shower.

Despite this, she was dismayed, maybe even unhappy, at the thought of not having sex with him much longer. But six months was six months, and six months was her limit. It was necessary to cut off relationships before she became emotionally embroiled.

Quite frankly, she said to herself, regretfully, I've become very fond of the man. She could say it now, immediately after sex, because this was the nadir of things. It was the moment at which Marion was most clinical, most dispassionate. Very fond of him indeed, she thought, her hands loosely clasped upon her stomach, beneath the sheet which covered her but did not cover David.

He was first of all extremely useful, helping her exercise Spot and planting gardens and changing light bulbs and fixing the fence and putting new washers in leaky faucets. He was also pleasant company, quite apart from his sexual attractiveness; detached but not cold, recondite but not secretive, with a sunniness of manner which she found soothing. He was a good tenant, too, got along well with the others and always did his share of the cleaning in the bathroom and the upstairs hall. He was able to talk easily with Marion without being irritatingly inquisitive; he never gossiped; she had never seen him lose his temper

. . . she sighed to herself, inventorying his good points, and when lying next to her in bed he heard her sigh and didn't comment, she added another; he didn't get into conversations immediately after having sex.

It was really too bad that she would soon have to call it off. On the other hand, it was a very good thing that she knew herself so well, and had accepted what she knew, and ordered her life around it. It was the only way to guarantee oneself a certain amount of contentment.

"I have to take a shower now," she said.

"Okay," said David.

She got up and put on her robe and slippers and was about to go down the hall to the bathroom when she realized he hadn't moved. He was still lying on her bed, his hands behind his head and his knees drawn up. He seemed to be absorbed in a study of her ceiling. She paused, looking at him and the mussed-up bed. She would have to change the sheets when she got out of the shower. She didn't like to leave him there, but it seemed uncivil to say anything. And what would she say, anyway? "Get out of my bed"? "How long are you going to lie there?" She couldn't think of anything that wouldn't sound either rude or too intimate. Dissatisfied, she went off to the shower.

She stood under the hot water for a long time, soaping herself and rinsing, soaping and rinsing, washing with particular care between her legs and under her arms, and while in the shower decided to wash her hair as well. Steam filled the bathroom, and behind the shower curtain Marion felt every smidgen of external dirt remove itself from her, washed away from her body and down the drain by hot soothing water. She held up her face and felt all her pores open to the heat, to the sheeting water.

When she turned off the taps, the rushing sound of the shower was replaced by dripping. She clattered the curtain back on its rod and stepped onto the mat, wrapping a white towel around her head and a bigger one around her body. She rubbed her hair and patted her skin dry and put deodorant under her arms and lotion all over her body, except for her breasts and inner thighs, which she powdered. She slipped on her robe and slippers, and combed her hair. She wiped the steam from the mirror with a towel and saw that the shower had smudged her mascara without removing it. She wiped her eyes carefully with oil and then a tissue, and washed her face with soap and water and rubbed cream into it.

She got sheets and pillowcases from the cupboard in the bathroom and went down the hall.

David still lay upon her bed. He'd propped himself up against her pillows and covered himself with the sheet.

"What are you doing?" said Marion from the doorway, holding the clean linen. She felt more exposed, with wet hair and a clean body and a clean face, than when she had lain with him naked. "Why are you still here?"

"I'm waiting for you."

She was furious. She clutched the clean sheets tightly to her chest and stayed in the doorway.

"I'd like to talk to you," said David. "I thought you'd rather have your shower first."

"I'd rather talk to you tomorrow."

"It's kind of hard to get to see you sometimes. And this is pretty important."

"Why didn't you do your talking before?"

David grinned. "That's hard, too."

"Well, what do you want, anyway?"

"Come and sit down here," he said, patting the bed.

Marion was stiff with rage. "I would prefer," she said, "that you get up from there, and that if you have anything to say, you say it in my sitting room." She tossed the sheets on top of her desk and stalked off down the hall.

She poured herself a drink. He came in a few minutes later, fully dressed and with his hair combed. She looked at him stonily and didn't offer him a beer.

"I'm sorry, Marion. I didn't mean to trespass."

"What do you want to talk about?"

"I'll be leaving soon. I wanted to tell you. That's all."

He was wearing jeans and a white shirt with the sleeves rolled up. There was probably a button missing from one of his cuffs, thought Marion. He was a neat person, and a clean one, but not concerned about things like missing buttons. She thought he must shop quite absentmindedly, too, because sometimes he wore shirts that were far too big for him. Not jeans, though. They fit him snugly, making her want to put her hands on him as he stood there in front of her. She could see his thighs tight under the denim.

"When? Leaving where?"

"I gave the *Star* my notice today. I'm going at the end of the month."

"Where?"

"I haven't decided. Maybe Vancouver. It sounds like a good place."

Marion let herself sink slowly into the maroon armchair. She watched him carefully, as though he would vanish right then and there if she as much as blinked.

"Advertise my room right away," he said seriously. "I want to make sure you get somebody decent in there."

She just looked at him. She thought perhaps there was something on her face for him to see, but had no idea what it might be.

After a while he came close and leaned down to kiss her forehead. "Good night, Marion."

She sat holding her drink after he'd left. The glass was cold and it made her hand feel cold, and soon her hand was as cold as the glass and she didn't feel it anymore.

She had to feed Spot. There was a thought, finally; and another one: I still have to make my bed.

She put the glass on the coffee table, centering it there, and stood, pressing her cold hands against the worn arms of the chair. For a few minutes she walked slowly around the sitting room, rubbing her arms, looking at the floor. Through the window she saw that it was almost dark.

She wanted to scold herself into activity, take herself in hand. Obviously I'm upset, she thought, that's what it is, I'm just upset. I'm just not used to having people tell me they're leaving, that's all, she thought. At least this time I'm saved the exasperation of telling him to go.

She sat down and observed her shaky hands with amazement, holding them out to see this phenomenon more closely.

Spot dragged himself up from the rug in front of the television set and ambled over to her. He rested his head on her thigh, and she bent to put her cheek against the top of his head. The fur was thick and silky but she could feel the bony ridge of his skull. His breath was warm through her robe. She enjoyed it when he played, and when he sometimes seemed to laugh at things, but most of all she loved his quiet dignity, and was able to accept compassion from him.

"You want your dinner, don't you," said Marion, and took courage from the calm in her voice.

She was mixing dry and wet food together in his big blue plastic bowl when the phone rang. There was no need for her to answer it. Her life was her own, as private as she wished it to be, and there was no reason why she should allow intruders into it. But it was important not to let emotion preoccupy her. To ignore emotion, as much as she could, was essential, and so she answered her telephone, and spoke to Leona.

"I think you should come over here," said Leona, "and talk to Emily."

Marion let the counter support her. She said nothing.

"I think there's something wrong with her," said Leona. "I just met her on the street. Jesus. I thought somebody had attacked her, or something. She looked terrible."

Marion noticed that she was full of achings, all over her body. Her head hurt, and the muscles in her legs and upper arms, and her back, too. She thought she must be getting sick.

"Marion? Are you there?"

"I'm here," said Marion.

"I tried to get her to come to my apartment," said Leona. "But she wouldn't. She insisted there was nothing wrong. But Jesus, Marion, she looked awful. I don't know what to do."

Marion contemplated walking out to her car, getting in it, driving to Emily's apartment building, parking, going into the lobby, waiting for the elevator, traveling up to the fourteenth floor, walking down the hall, ringing Emily's bell. It would take a long time to do all that.

I have to feed Spot, she thought. And change my bed. And take some aspirin, and some vitamin C, or something.

She told herself these things sternly, in an attempt to extinguish the savage anger building within her.

"Thank you for letting me know, Leona," she said. "I'll take care of it."

"If you'd like to drop in here," said Leona, suddenly hesitant, "after you've seen her, I'll give you a drink, and we can have a talk."

Marion smiled to herself, and her anger grew larger. "I'll take care of it, Leona," she said gently, and hung up.

She gave herself no time to think first but dialed Emily's number immediately and was relieved when Emily answered, sounding perfectly all right.

"Leona said you aren't looking well, Emily."

"Oh, goodness, I'm fine," said Emily with a shrill laugh. "She startled me, that's all, pounding down the sidewalk toward me. She was jogging, I think. I couldn't make out who she was, at first. Couldn't imagine who would be leaping along the sidewalk toward me like that."

"You're sure you're all right."

"Oh, absolutely," said Emily heartily. "I'm completely all right."

"Then I won't keep you."

"I'm glad you called, Marion. It's—it's nice to be worried about sometimes."

Marion watched Spot, who was still standing near her, his tail wagging hopefully, waiting for his dinner.

"Is it?" she said to Emily. Her anger was fading. She felt distant and mildly amazed. "Good night, Emily."

She went back to mixing dog food. Her aches had subsided somewhat but she would go to bed early anyway, with aspirin and scotch. Tomorrow she would be fit as a fiddle again. And on Friday she would go to Bruce's party, as she had planned, and nobody would be able to tell a thing from her face.

CHAPTER 19

On Friday evening Marion rocketed her small station wagon down the gravel road leading to Bruce's house, great banks of billowing dust behind her, and in the back seat Spot lumbered from one side of the car to the other, panting from heat and excitement, drooling on the windows which she had to keep closed because of the dust. Marion was singing out loud, with great pleasure, songs from musical comedies. She was belting out *Oklahoma!* when she turned into Bruce's driveway.

"You've brought your dog," said Bruce's son as Marion clipped the leash to Spot's collar.

She looked out the window and saw the boy standing there, a smile splashed all over his face. Marion got out of the car and Spot climbed out after her and stood panting, looking around, his long thick tail sweeping back and forth.

"Did he throw up in your car?" said Garry.

"No," said Marion. She could hear laughter and loud talk from behind the house.

"Can I look after him for you? Would he like a drink of water?"

"Yes, you can get him a pail of water if you like," she said, and the boy ran to the back door.

The party was gathered on the wide, open deck that stretched across the back of the house. On a long picnic table were the remains of salads and platters of chicken and roast beef, and pitchers of iced tea, ice cubes melted in them long ago. There was a big tub filled with more melting ice and cans of beer. Littering the deck were bodies, and paper plates holding the remnants of a summertime dinner, and beer cans and plastic glasses. It was only four days before the longest day of the year, and shafts of sunlight streamed from the tops of the mountains across the foothills and the distant city and into Bruce's backyard, where his friends sprawled in an early summer daze. They were dressed casually, in shorts or jeans and T-shirts or sleeveless dresses.

Marion, advancing upon them from the corner of the house, smiled as they noticed her and turned to watch her approach. She wore a long black dress with long sleeves and a low neck, its skirt split up one side almost to her thigh, and next to her walked her great gentle black dog, Spot.

"Jesus," said Vern, staring, and he scrambled up from his lolling position at the feet of Silka Witowsky.

"Marion, that's a gorgeous dress," said Norma, hurrying to the edge of the deck, "but it's going to get ruined out here if you're not careful. Sit in a chair—here, Bruce, get up, let her sit down."

"It's a very old dress, Norma, and I wouldn't care a bit if it did get ruined," said Marion. "I just felt like wearing it, and besides, it's black, and Spot's hairs don't show on it." She sat in the chair Bruce had vacated and turned to Garry, who had appeared with a metal pail so full that the water slopped over its sides. "Here, child—it's Garry, isn't it?" She held out the leash. "Take him far enough away that he doesn't slobber on people. May I please have a drink?" she said politely to Bruce, who went off into the house, knowing that Marion didn't like beer.

Leona hauled herself up from where she was sitting on the edge of the deck, and went over to Marion. "I don't think you should wear things like that without giving people some warning," she said. "How are you, anyway? And how's Emily?" she added quietly.

"Emily's just fine, I called her right after I talked to you. And I myself am positively blooming, my dear, full of health and good cheer." She took a glass of scotch from Bruce.

"Where's Bermas?" said Vern, hovering. "Didn't you bring your tenant?"

"I haven't the faintest idea where he is," said Marion. "I'm not a taxi service."

"Take it easy with the scotch," said Bruce. "Looks to me like you've had enough already. How about I get you some food?"

"Do you have any popcorn?" said Marion. "No? Then I think I'll stay with this, thank you."

"I'm not surprised he didn't come," said Vern. "He's not very sociable, your tenant."

Marion looked thoughtfully out toward the mountains.

"He gave his notice yesterday, Marion," said Leona. "Did you know?"

"Yes," said Marion. "I'll have to put an ad in. Eventually."

"Maybe I'll apply," said Vern, grinning.

"Jesus, Palmer," said Leona, "bugger off, will you?"

"He's not the only one who's quit," said Bridget Walmsley, her glasses glinting in the long low sunlight.

"Yes, Christ, can you believe it, Marion?" said Leona. "Gloria-Rose Merriwether quit. Can you believe that?"

"I should think," said Marion, "that it would come as a relief to all of you."

"We should tell Emily," said Leona. "In case she wants to apply for her job."

"She's running away," said Bridget, grinning. "Gloria-Rose. That's what she said. 'I'm running away,' she told me in the ladies' room. 'To Egypt.'"

"It's not far enough," said Bruce.

"Why Egypt?" said Norma.

"What's she going to do in Egypt?" said Leona.

Bridget threw her arms out wide. "She's running away with that guy in her apartment building. The one who's allergic to money."

"Christ," said Bruce.

"But why Egypt?" said Norma, patient.

"I can't see any point at all," said Marion, whirling ice in her empty glass, "in going any farther away than San Francisco."

"The guy who's allergic to money, he works for some oil company," said Bridget vaguely, and turned away to get another beer.

Out on the lawn Garry was throwing sticks for Spot, who chased them amiably enough, and even picked them up in his mouth, but couldn't be persuaded to retrieve them.

"Oh dear," said Marion, sighing, looking into the sun. "I feel quite aggressive this evening, Leona." She wished for physical violence, but knew she would flee if it occurred, because like Leona she flinched and weakened at the sight of blood. She felt her restlessness in hands that ceaselessly turned her glass, and legs that crossed themselves, uncrossed, and crossed again, as the skirt of her black dress fell farther and farther from her thigh.

"Listen, Leona," said Bridget, rejoining them. "I wanted to ask you. Do you think I could get out of Lifestyles? Onto a beat, or general assignment, or something?"

"Jesus, don't ask me," said Leona. "Go talk to Ziggy. I don't make those kinds of decisions."

"I thought maybe you could put in a good word for me."

"Count your blessings, dear," said Marion. "I remember when it was Family Living, and we had to write about golden wedding anniversaries."

"And before that it was the Women's Page," said Bruce. He was lying on a canvas chaise longue with his hands behind his head. "Charlie Keyes was editor." He looked over at Marion, grinning. "Remember Charlie Keyes? He hated being on the Women's Page. He's the one got the name changed to Family Living. One of those damn school tours came past the door one day. Jesus. It comes clackety-clacking down the hall. Keyes is in there half pissed, as usual, with his feet up on the desk and the tour lady calls out, 'Now in here is the women's department,' and Keyes hollers, 'It's Family fucking Living!' "

They sighed, and shifted in their chairs, and smiled.

"I love newspaper stories," said Silka Witowsky. Vern was absorbed in stroking the bare skin above her right ankle. As she spoke she seemed to become aware of this. Her foot twitched, and she raised it, crossing her legs. Vern began to stroke her other leg as Marion watched.

"There was a guy at the *Sun,* in Vancouver," said Leona, wandering over to the edge of the deck. "A long time ago, when I worked there in the summers, while I was going to the University of B.C." She sat, letting her legs dangle, facing the mountains. "This guy told me that his first reporting job was up in Kamloops. One day he had to go to the funeral home—God knows why. Anyway, he walked in there and found a female corpse sitting up in her coffin, and when he opened the door her hair started blowing in the breeze." She looked over her shoulder at Silka, and grinned.

"My goodness," said Silka uncertainly. At her feet, Vern studied her skin, and sighed.

"Christ," said Bruce, staring up at the darkening sky.

"I'm going to get myself another drink," said Marion.

"I'll get it," said Bruce. He got up and took her glass.

Garry had been telling Spot to sit, and stay. When he was obeyed, which was frequently, Garry would look up at his mother and smile. Now he left the dog sitting on the lawn and climbed the steps to the deck. "Can I give him some scraps?" he said to Marion. Spot, having sat for what seemed long enough, got up and headed for the stairs.

"Yeah, Marion," said Vern. "Dogs like parties, too. Why leave him out?"

"He's going to knock somebody over," said Marion, as Spot clambered up the steps and joined them on the deck.

"Hell, nobody's standing up anyway," said Bruce, handing her a fresh drink. He lay back down on the chaise. "Just don't let him lick me, that's all. If there's anything I can't stand it's being licked by a dog."

Spot trundled over to Marion and put his head in her lap.

"Jeeze, look at that," said Vern. "That's a lucky dog."

"Here, Spot," said Garry, collecting leftovers on a paper plate. "C'mon and have a bite to eat." He put the plate down in an unoccupied corner of the deck and bent over, his hands on his knees. "C'mere, Spot. Come."

Spot lifted his head, looked up at Marion, turned, and made his way over to Garry, who patted him while he ate.

"Marion, come for a walk with me," said Leona.

They went along the deck and down the steps and across the lawn, where they stopped at a barbed wire fence and looked at the mountains, black now against an indigo sky. A full moon stood above them and stars had begun to penetrate the gathering dark. Marion leaned carefully against a fence post and sipped from her glass, her back to the mountains, moonlight on her face.

"I think Bruce is going to apply for Ziggy's job after all," said Leona. She took a swig from her bottle of beer.

"Good," said Marion.

"He'll probably get it."

"Good."

Leona was silent for a moment. "Did you know they'd offered it to Peter?" she said.

"I heard the rumor."

Leona nodded. "It was true. They did. But he's turned it down."

"Thank God," said Marion, watching Spot, who was still on the deck, and appeared to be looking for her.

Leona went up to the fence and grasped the wire between the barbs. "I saw him, you know. When I was out there in April."

"No," said Marion. She turned to look at Leona's profile. "No, I didn't know that."

"I went to bed with him."

Marion smiled. "Then it wasn't a completely wasted trip after all. I've never been able to understand your fondness for that place."

"Partly," said Leona dryly, glancing at her, "it's because my parents live out there."

Marion shrugged, and looked back toward the deck. "Such a dreary city," she said absently. "All that rain."

"Jesus, Marion," said Leona. "I told you. I *saw* the man. This *affected* me, Marion. I was hoping very much that he'd take the goddamn job here. And Wednesday I got this letter saying he's not going to. I'm *upset*, Marion, goddamn it."

"Then you're a fool." Marion turned quickly, to face her. "He wouldn't have been here a month, not a week, probably, before he'd have had his hands all over someone else. You can't take that, Leona, you know you can't." She waved toward the deck. "Find somebody else, for heaven's sake. They're all the same in bed, more or less. And if they aren't, you can teach them." She looked away, and drank some of her scotch.

Leona studied her closely. "Marion. Did he ever have his hands all over you?"

Marion smiled at her slowly. "Of course not. I can't stand the man. You know that." Leona's face in the moonlight had lost its tan, and her eyes were large round shadows. She stood straight, holding her beer, her body so taut that Marion could almost hear it hum. "What on earth do you think I am?" said Marion. "I don't have any trouble finding them, Leona. I certainly have no need to take anybody else's."

"Never? Have you *never* gone to bed with somebody else's guy?"

Marion sighed. "Only if it didn't matter." She turned back to the house, and the deck, where Norma had brought out coal oil lanterns and placed them on either end of the picnic table. Spot was making his way carefully down the steps to the lawn. "Bruce, for instance. That didn't matter."

"Bruce?" said Leona incredulously. "Bruce? When the hell was this?"

"Ages ago, positively ages. Norma was angry with him for drinking again, and he came to me for comfort, and one thing led to another. It didn't go on for very long," she said, almost soothingly, still watching Norma, who was lighting the lanterns.

Leona burst out laughing.

"I can't say," said Marion coldly, "that I see what's so amusing."

Leona leaned against the fence post, still laughing.

Spot had reached the grass, and broke into a lope, aiming for Marion. Leona straightened up and wiped her eyes. Marion put her glass on the top of the fence post, preparing for the impact of Spot's greeting, but when he reached them he didn't barrel into Marion but began running in large circles.

"Well I've had it with all this crap," said Leona, suddenly grim.

"What crap?" said Marion.

Leona waved the empty bottle toward the sky. "All crap. Men. Sex. Life. Questions. I'm sick to bloody death of questions."

"Hey!" someone called from the deck. A male figure stood there, looking out toward them, his face in darkness. For a moment Marion thought it was David. Her nipples swelled against her black dress, and she took a step toward the house, and felt the slit in her dress open.

"It's Vern," said Leona. She put her arm around Marion's waist as they walked.

Marion sighed. "I'm on the prowl tonight, Leona. He may have to do." Vern waved vigorously, and she lifted a languid arm in reply, and let it drop around Leona's shoulders.

"Jesus Christ, I'd hope you could do better than that. Where's your tenant when you need him?"

Marion stopped, and disengaged herself. "Exactly what's that supposed to mean?"

Leona just grinned at her, looking, thought Marion, like a self-satisfied fox.

"It's academic now, anyway," Marion muttered. She stared up at the sky. "I have decided, Leona, to become slightly more predatory in my middle age." Spot tore off after a rabbit, possibly imagined. They began walking again. "I'm going to become less demure. More—predatory. I'm going to let the real me happen more often."

Leona stopped. "Oh God, Marion. Don't go and change on me, for God's sake."

"Change?" Marion wanted to smile. She put her arm around Leona's shoulder. "People don't change." They moved on. Spot hurled himself out of the darkness and scrambled up on to the deck, out of breath and pleased with himself. "It's only a change in emphasis I'm talking about," said Marion. "That's all."

She stumbled slightly on the steps, and felt Leona's small hand firm on her back, steadying her.

CHAPTER 20

On the last Monday in June, Marion drove home from her father's house with a box containing some china (a Royal Doulton service for eight with only three pieces missing, one of them a gravy boat she had dropped on the kitchen floor when she was thirteen), another box with her mother's fur coat in it, and, on the seat beside her, a leather jewel case. She hadn't wanted to take any of these things.

"Stop thrusting things at me," she had said to her father.

"But I want you to have something to remember her by," he had said.

"Good heavens, Dad," said Marion, pushing almost violently away from the dining room table where they were sitting, "if it's so important to you, ask me what I want, don't keep thrusting things at me, just ask me if there's anything I want."

"Is there?" he said.

So the back of her station wagon also held the painting that looked like a wheat field, wrapped carefully in an old blanket, and Marion thought that taking the other things off her father's hands had been a small price to pay.

When she turned onto her street she saw Emily's car parked outside her house. She's come to thank me for the roses, thought Marion, and then her front door opened and Clara ran out onto the porch, waving to her agitatedly.

Marion pulled in carefully behind the yellow Volkswagen, turned off her car's engine, and with both hands on the wheel looked out across the street, where a man mowing his lawn kept glancing curiously over at her house. It was a sunny day, pleasantly warm, and the sun would shine for a couple more hours. Marion saw that the balcony doors from

Clara's room were open; the long white curtains licked out to taste the breeze. Beneath David's window geraniums were growing, a red row of them in the box he had filled with dirt last spring.

Clara on the porch kept waving. As Marion looked at her, she grasped the iron railing and started down the steps. Marion got out of the car and walked toward her. She was extremely calm.

"Oh, Marion, thank God, it's so horrible." Her small brown eyes filled and overflowed. "Come in, come in, these nosy people. It was her eyes, Marion, oh, it was so horrible," she said, grabbing Marion's hand and pulling her into the house.

Spot hadn't come to the door to greet her. "Where's my dog?" said Marion.

"In the yard I put him for now, oh, Marion, so horrible it is." She leaned close, and Marion moved slightly away.

"You'd better tell me what you're talking about, Clara, because I am not understanding you at all. That's my aunt's car out there. Where is she?"

"She got hurt, an accident it was, he didn't mean it, the dog. He bumped her, that's all, made her fall down those stairs."

"What stairs? What are you talking about?"

"To your basement, those stairs."

Marion went quickly down the hall to the kitchen. The basement door was closed.

"Where is she?" said Marion loudly above the hard, fast beating of her heart.

"In the hospital, Marion, I called for an ambulance. She hit her head —there was blood—oh, Marion." She was squeezing her hands, and her eyes continued patiently to feed the streams that flowed down her face. "I heard it, oh, I heard it. First I didn't know she was here. Then I heard yelling—screaming, it was."

Marion opened the door and turned on the light at the top of the steps. Most of the railing was gone, scattered like pieces of kindling over the basement floor.

"I heard the sounds she made," said Clara, "and the thump-thump-thump—it was terrible, terrible."

Spot was scratching urgently at the back door.

"What did my dog have to do with all this?"

"She say to me, lying there, 'It's not his fault.' " Clara clutched at her dirndl skirt, concentrating. "She say to me, she's coming up the stairs fast, and tries to push through the door, but that crazy dog, he's in the way."

Marion spoke coldly and clearly. "My dog is not crazy."

"It's just the way I talk," said Clara. "I know he's a good dog. I know it."

"She spoke to you," said Marion, controlling herself. "Then she must be all right."

Clara hesitated. "On a stretcher, they took her. She broke something, I think."

Marion closed the basement door. "What was she doing down there, anyway? What on earth was she doing in my basement?"

Clara shrugged, embarrassed. "Something chased her, she say."

Marion stared at her.

"I don't know," said Clara.

Marion went to the hall door and held it open. "Thank you, Clara. I appreciate very much what you've done. I know Emily does, too."

Clara stopped in the hall, and turned. "She's at the Foothills. They took her to the nearest one."

"Thank you, Clara." Marion shut the door.

Spot's scratching had become more agitated. She let him in. He butted his head gently against her thigh. She rubbed his head, behind his ears, and got down on the floor to hug him. With her hands on either side of his head she looked into his eyes. He whimpered, and lifted a heavy paw to put it on her knee. She gave him his dinner, but he didn't eat it.

Marion sat in the maroon chair. She thought about the boxes in her car and the painting wrapped in a blanket. Her instincts told her to get up and rush to her car and drive quickly to the hospital, or at least to go to the phone and call. But she couldn't seem to move. She felt taut and strained. She tried to breathe slowly and deeply, to relax herself, but she continued to make shallow, shuddering sounds.

She sat there for a long time, looking at the floor, and whenever Spot came to her and rested his great head on her knee she put her arm around his neck and soothed him and told him that she loved him.

Gradually the light faded.

It was almost dark in the sitting room when the dog, a pool of black on the floor at her feet, lifted his head, listening. He got up and went to the door, his tail wagging. There was a knock. Spot wagged harder. The knock sounded again.

"Who is it?" said Marion.

"It's me. David."

Marion got up and turned on a lamp. She went to the door.

"Hi," said David. His skin was browned by the sun, dark against his white shirt. She heard the rustle of his light jacket as he pushed himself away from the wall against which he had been leaning.

"I thought you'd left," she said.

He looked at her quizzically. "Nope. Not till Thursday. Last day of the month." He bent toward her. "What's wrong? Are you sick?"

Marion retreated into the kitchen. "Sick," she said flatly. "No. I'm not sick."

"What is it, then? What's the matter?"

Marion breathed in, cautiously, and found that she could breathe deeply, and did. "Nothing is the matter. Everything is perfect. I love it."

David came into the kitchen and closed the door.

"Everything is just wonderful," said Marion. "I do enjoy it, the way people keep coming and going, going and coming, in and out of my life." She hugged her arms, as if she were cold. "You will discover," she said, "that Vancouver is a vastly overrated place." She leaned down to peer out through the window into the darkness of her backyard. "Emily seems to have gone off to the hospital. And my old mother, of course, is in her grave, bless her small black heart." Still hugging herself, she stood straight and turned to him. He was just inside her kitchen door, and Spot leaned against his leg. They were both looking at her, and she knew they could see the tears on her face, as clear as day.

David watched her for quite a while. "Actually," he said, "I was going to ask if I could stay on through the long weekend. The traffic's probably going to be pretty bad. I'd really prefer to leave next Monday, when everybody's back at work. But I didn't want to impose on you." He went to her and sat her down in the maroon chair. "Do you want some coffee or anything?"

She said no. Spot plodded over and lay down heavily at her feet.

"So how about it?" said David. "Can I stay on over the weekend?"

Marion shook her hair away from her face. "I really don't care, since I haven't yet gotten around to renting your room. Unfortunately."

He smiled his radiant smile. "Good." He turned to leave, but stopped at the door to the hall. "By the way. I doubt very much that your mother had a black heart. See you later."

She opened her mouth to argue, but he was out the door before she could say anything.

Marion went to the sink and poured herself a glass of water. She fussed around the sitting room for a while, pulling the curtains closed and straightening newspapers and magazines into piles, but finally she gave up. She thrust him from her mind, succumbed to her instincts, and went to the phone to call the hospital.

She wasn't allowed to speak to Emily, but received courteous answers to her questions and was told she could visit the next day. She was exhausted when she hung up the phone. She slumped against the wall and had been staring down at the kitchen counter for several seconds before she realized that she was looking at an unfamiliar object. It was a small leather-bound book.

Marion picked it up and flicked through it. She knew it must be Emily's, and expected to see rows of figures, or grocery shopping lists, or names and telephone numbers. But the phrases which shot into her face from its pages were so arresting, so puzzling, that she was certain they couldn't have been written by her aunt. Bewildered, she turned to the flyleaf, and there, printed carefully, was Emily's name.

Marion went slowly to the sofa and sat down, and turned to the first page of Emily's notebook, and read it to the end.

EPILOG

CHAPTER 1

On the last Monday in June, Leona went in to see her managing editor. She closed the door after her as she entered his office, and Jack Hiller looked at her warily.

"I have a request," said Leona. He waved her to a chair. "I want to request a leave of absence. How do I go about it?"

"You're going about it right now," said Hiller. He leaned back and lit a cigarette.

"Well, good," said Leona. "What happens next?"

"I ask you a few questions, and I consider your replies, and in due course you get my decision."

"Let's get at it, then," said Leona, and grinned.

"Ah, a smile. I'm relieved. This is not, then, a compassionate leave you're requesting."

Leona pursed her lips, considering. "If that means somebody's died, no. But if you decide to grant my request, it will seem a very compassionate act indeed, to me."

"Mmmm," said Hiller. They were silent a moment, looking at each other over the top of his desk. Leona wondered how old he was. He had high school aged children, who lived with his ex-wife. He must miss them, she thought, and tears pricked the back of her eyelids, but she blinked them dead.

"I want to change my emphasis," she said huskily. "I want to travel for a while; see some places I've never seen before. Maybe it isn't a good enough reason."

He offered her a cigarette. Without thinking, she took it from him, and he stood to lean across his desk and light it for her.

"If it weren't a good enough reason," he said, "would you resign?" He sat down again, rested his elbows on the arms of his chair, and made a steeple of the fingers of his two hands.

"I don't know," said Leona. "I hadn't thought that far ahead." She looked at the row of windows across the room, then back at him. "I guess I would, yes. I don't want to, but I guess I would."

He swung his chair around until he was facing the windows. "I'm concerned that your recurring restlessness with the *Star* has finally become terminal." He turned to look at her again. "If that's the case, traveling isn't going to solve your problem. You would return to us perhaps more dissatisfied than when you left."

Leona put out her cigarette in his ashtray, a square marble one already half-filled with butts, although it was only ten in the morning. "I believe you smoke more than I used to," she said. She was quite relaxed now, knowing that she would, regretfully, quit her job if necessary.

He continued to study her, waiting, and even this didn't make her nervous.

"I have it in mind," said Leona, "to change my life. I want to have six months. I plan to go to England, and live in London, and travel from there. I don't want to see the whole world, just a few places, and mostly I want to go to London, because people have been living there for so many hundreds of years, and you can see the traces there of all those centuries." She shrugged and spread her hands. "I don't know why this is important to me, but it is."

Hiller nodded. "Go on, Ms. Hadden."

"And of course in London, they speak my language."

"Or a reasonable facsimile thereof."

He rocked slowly back and forth in his swivel chair, and then sat up and moved some papers around on his desk. "Have you undergone some sort of—trauma, Ms. Hadden?" He looked at her quickly. "I'm not attempting to pry into your personal life, understand. I am curious, however. Is this a sudden decision? An impulse of the moment? Or is it something you've been contemplating for a long time? If so, you're more enigmatic than I had thought."

"It's both," said Leona. "It's sudden, yes. But I've been contemplating it for a long time. I just wasn't sure what I was contemplating, until a little while ago." She hesitated. "And yes, I have undergone a trauma." She gave him a wry grin. "A couple of them, actually."

"Hmmm." He picked up a pencil and began doodling on something that looked like a letter. "It *is* your intention," he said, looking at her over his glasses, "to return to us."

"Oh yes. Of course. I want to be city editor." This time her grin was easily produced.

"Do you indeed," said Hiller. He put down the pencil and leaned back. "Do you indeed."

"Eventually, that is," said Leona. "I'm not quite ready yet. But I will be."

"I can't assure you that you'll be able to go back on the desk the moment you reappear. You might have to become a reporter again, for a while."

"I understand that."

He looked at her meditatively. "Let us say, then, that you will begin this half-year holiday on September first."

Leona stood up, and found that her legs were trembling. "Thank you," she said with formality, and walked toward his office door, focusing on the round brass handle.

"Enjoy yourself, Leona."

She turned to smile at him.

"And do come back. We shall miss you."

"I'll be back," said Leona. "You can count on it."

CHAPTER 2

The next morning Marion was lying in a chaise longue in her back-yard, on the small patch of lawn between the house and the vegetable garden, when David came through the gate at the side of the house.

"I was going to go out and get some things for my breakfast," he said. "Then I thought maybe I could scrounge breakfast from you."

"I never eat breakfast," said Marion, sheltered behind large sun-glasses.

"Neither do I." He wandered over to look at the garden. "I knocked on your door last night. Were you out?"

"No."

He sat cross-legged on the grass next to her chaise. "Clara told me about your aunt. I'm sorry."

Marion nodded slowly.

David looked over at Spot, lying panting on his side in the shade of the house. "I'll fix the railing before I go."

"There's no need. I can hire someone."

"You're giving me four free nights in my room, aren't you?" He stood up and held out his hands to her. "Come on inside. You're going to get burned. Come on. Let's have some coffee." He pulled her to her feet. She allowed him to do this, and to lead her indoors, Spot hurriedly following, because it was extremely hot outside, even though it wasn't yet noon.

"Why aren't you at work?"

"I'm on nights today and tomorrow," said David, making coffee. He was wearing shorts and a T-shirt that left his arms bare. He put cream and sugar on the table. "How long will she be in the hospital?"

"You're making yourself greatly at home, I must say," said Marion. She removed her sunglasses.

He frowned into the fridge. "Don't you have any fruit? For God's sake, Marion. Not even an orange?"

"She'll be in there for two weeks."

He sat opposite her at the table. "What a shitty thing to happen," he said gently. "She's a very nice woman, your aunt."

There was real sympathy in his voice. Marion knew it was meant for Emily, but it spilled over onto her, as well. She did not enjoy the sensation it produced in her, of tumbling, of relinquishment.

"Now," said David, as he poured the coffee, "we have to have a conversation."

"I'm sure I don't know why," said Marion. She did not enjoy, either, the pleasure she took in the sight of his bare arms.

"I want you to come with me to Vancouver. Take a holiday. Help me get settled."

"I couldn't possibly," she said quickly.

"Why not?"

"Why should I, for heaven's sake?" Marion noticed that her voice was shaking. "It's the stupidest idea I've heard in months. Years, in fact."

"We'll take Spot with us. I hear there's a beach there where they let dogs run free. He'll love it."

She stood up. "It isn't possible." She took the cream and sugar to the kitchen counter. "Don't be ridiculous." She went to the window. "Oh, it's fine for some people. You run off to Vancouver; Leona called, now she's running off to England; that sort of thing is fine for some people, just picking up and running off whenever they feel like it." She turned and looked out at the garden. "You planted all those things, didn't you, fine and dandy, then you up and leave, who's supposed to look after them now, would you care to tell me that?" She whirled around. "Why do you insist on pretending that things are simple, uncomplicated? Life is *not* simple. Life is *very* complicated, *extremely* complicated."

He got up from the table and as he approached her, the hairs on his arms gleamed copper in the sunlight. He wasn't much taller than she. There were a few freckles on his face.

"Poor Marion." He smiled at her, and brushed her cheek with his finger.

"There's nothing permanent between you and me," she said. "We agreed on that."

He stood very close to her. She wanted to put her hands flat against his chest.

"Ask me for something, Marion. Why don't you ever ask me for anything?"

"You've done lots of things for me," she said to his dark blue T-shirt, "since you've been here."

"But you didn't ask me to do them. I volunteered." He didn't embrace her, but leaned closer, and she felt his lips on her forehead, tasting the sweat on her skin. It was a very warm day. "Ask me for something," he said. "Anything."

She thought about Emily's notebook, filled with blood and confusion and fear and loneliness.

"Please put your arms around me," said Marion, "and hold onto me. Just for a minute."

CHAPTER 3

There was a lot of pain, but she was comforted by drugs, by the sun pouring through the window, by the presence of others in her hospital room, and by a peculiar clarity of mind. Floating in successive moments and hours of strength, she was content to concentrate on healing herself.

It hurt to move. It hurt to try to think. Emily watched the sunshine, and saw through the window blue sky and the tops of trees. She listened to desultory conversations among the women who occupied the other three beds in the room. She lay still, and looked, and listened, and imagined bones knitting and bruised skull healing and a damaged mind attempting to restore itself: it was time, she thought, that her imagination did something useful for her.

It was still morning when Grace, with an armful of yellow irises, appeared hesitantly around the half-open door. Emily turned her head and smiled. Even that hurt, she discovered.

Grace hurried in. She put the irises on the end of the bed and took

Emily's hand. "Marion just told me. I wish she'd called last night. I would have come right away. I would have stayed while they fixed your hip. I would have been here when you woke up."

"It's all right, Grace." To Emily, her own voice sounded harsh and rusty.

Grace pulled a chair next to the bed and sat down. "Do you feel like reading, yet? Can I bring you some books?"

"Not yet." Grace was wearing an obviously expensive summer dress, and her hair was combed, but she had left her house without putting on any makeup. Her eyes looked smaller than usual. She looked older. "Oh God," said Emily, reaching out a hand. "I'm sorry, Grace."

Grace took Emily's hand in both of hers. "Later, when you're better, you can explain to me why on earth you're apologizing for having broken your hip and cracked your skull." She leaned down to kiss Emily's cheek, and her bandaged head. Then she sat back.

Emily closed her eyes. She could hear Grace breathing. Through her eyelids she saw the brightness of the sunshine. It must be very hot outside today, she thought. The nurse would probably let down the blinds after lunch, so the patients could sleep. Hospitals had very strict routines.

Eventually she opened her eyes and looked at Grace, who was smiling at her.

"What's so funny?" said Emily.

"This is not a smile of amusement," said Grace. "It's a smile of pleasure. I was thinking how glad I am that you didn't kill yourself, falling down those damn stairs."

Emily felt tears trickle from the corners of her eyes. Grace pulled a tissue from the box on the bedside table and wiped them away.

"How about television?" Grace looked up at the set suspended above the end of the bed. "Can you watch it, without making your head hurt more?"

"I haven't tried. Maybe later. I don't feel like doing anything, yet, except just to lie here."

"When you want things," said Grace, "you must tell me. Books, flowers, a pretty nightgown—anything."

"I don't want to go back to my apartment." Emily hadn't planned to say it. She hadn't even known it was in her mind.

Grace nodded, as though it were perfectly understandable. "I'll fix up my spare room for you. Stay with me for a while, when you get out of here. You'll have to have physiotherapy anyway. I'll drive you." She sounded calm and matter-of-fact. "There'll be lots of time to decide things, Emily." She squeezed Emily's hand. "And I'll be there to help you all you want. Or as little as you want."

After a while she kissed Emily again, and stood up. "You look tired. I'll be back this afternoon."

Emily drowsed for a while, aware of pain and sunshine and murmuring voices and safety. She had no dreams, but now and then looked restlessly at flashes of memory.

When finally she opened her eyes, Marion was there, looking down at her intently.

"I have this perfectly good room in my house, Aunt Emily," said Marion, "and after this weekend there will be nobody in it. You'll love it there, I know you will." Her voice rang out warm and strong.

Emily struggled to sit up but couldn't. Marion knelt by the bed. How lovely she is, thought Emily; how beautiful she is.

"Marion," she said with difficulty. "Thank you for the roses. For my birthday."

Marion nodded. "I knew that's why you'd come to my house." Emily tried to speak, but Marion went on. "You can expect a flurry of visitors. I've called Dad, and all the aunts."

"Grace has already come." Emily pointed to the flowers, which someone had put in a vase while she slept.

"You're going to be fine," said Marion confidently. "Just fine, Emily."

She talked for several minutes, then, about inconsequential things. She talked about the hot weather, and a column she had written, and a new chair she had decided to buy, and a party she had recently been to. Emily, listening and watching her face, wasn't surprised. It was the way Marion dealt with things. She felt herself weakening. Maybe Marion was right.

But when her niece prepared to leave, Emily spoke up as she had planned, despite humiliation and a throbbing head. "My notebook, Marion." The words fell like alien things, transforming the familiar into something threatening. But Emily had expected this. "You must have found it," she said.

Marion looked at her blankly. For a moment Emily thought she wasn't going to answer.

Then, slowly, Marion reached into her purse and pulled out the notebook.

Emily took it from her. Her throat was thick; swollen. "Thank you."

"I was going to throw it away," said Marion. "In the kitchen garbage. With the coffee grounds, and the bread crusts." She tried to say it lightly.

"You read it, then." Emily felt weak and nauseous. She was surprised at how small the notebook seemed, in the protective grip of her hands. She looked up. Marion's face was flushed. "I would have, too," said Emily. "It's all right." She sighed. "I can't live in your house, Marion. I'm going to Grace."

"Grace?" Marion sounded stricken. "Why?"

Emily laughed shakily. "Oh, Marion." Her hands were sticky on the leather binding of the notebook. "I'll feel more comfortable there, that's all."

"But I'll worry, Aunt Emily." Marion kept her voice low. "I can't stand this. I'll worry about you."

Emily put the notebook on the bedside table. "You can't be responsible for me. I'm my own responsibility." She looked up at Marion. "I'm not stupid, Marion. I know what was happening to me."

"What if it happens again?"

"I'll recognize it, this time." She felt a little calmer, now. "I can't live in your house. I'm sorry."

"I wish I hadn't read it," said Marion passionately. "I wish I'd never seen it."

"I know." Emily was waiting for a nurse to appear. Surely it must be time for lunch, or a pill, or something. "It's going to be a little harder for you to love me, now, isn't it?" She sounded almost amused.

Marion stooped next to the bed and looked closely at her aunt. Emily wondered what she thought she was trying to see. She lay still, as relaxed as possible, while Marion's clear green gaze searched her face.

Finally Marion sighed, and got to her feet. "I'm going now, Emily," she said. "But I'll be back soon."

She left, then, and Emily was grateful. She wanted to cry again, and it was important that Marion not see her tears.

Marion left the hospital quickly, and in the hot summer afternoon, as she got into her car, she saw her father drive into the parking lot. Olive sat next to him, and Polly was in the back. They parked without noticing her, and hurried off toward the hospital.

She opened all the windows and leaned back, letting the seat and the headrest support her. She closed her eyes. The sun's heat pressed against her body; she felt sweat trickle between her breasts, and ran her tongue along her upper lip.

Marion struggled against relief, and all of its reverberations.

I must be kinder to myself, she decided.

She thought about the beach in Vancouver, where dogs were allowed to run free.